THE CHARLTON STANDARD CATALOGUE

ROYAL DOULTON BUNNYKINS

FIRST EDITION

By

JEAN DALE

LOUISE IRVINE

W. K. CROSS
Publisher

The Charlton Press

TORONTO, ONTARIO ✶ BIRMINGHAM, MICHIGAN

Canadian Catalogue in Publication Data

The National Library of Canada has catalogued this publication as follows:

Main entry under title:

The Charlton standard catalogue of Royal Doulton bunnykins

Annual
1st ed.-
ISSN 1485-1008
ISBN 0-88968-210-0 (1999)

1. Porcelain animals - Catalogs.   2. Royal Doulton figurines - Catalogs.
3. Children's china (Porcelain) - Catalogs

NK4660.C515   738.8'2'029442   C98-900623-9

EDITORIAL

Editor	Jean Dale
Graphic technician	Davina Rowan
Graphic technician	Alan Ho

ACKNOWLEDGEMENTS

The Charlton Press wishes to thank those who have helped with the first edition of *The Charlton Standard Catalogue of Royal Doulton Bunnykins*.

The publisher would like to thank Louise Irvine for her work on this edition. Louise is an independent writer and lecturer on Royal Doulton's history and products and is not is anyway connected with the pricing in this guide.

Special Thanks

We would like to thank Richard Dennis of Richard Dennis Publications, Somerset, England, for graciously supplying images for this catalogue.

Joan Barwick, Caledon East, Ontario; Tony Kenney, England; Scott Reichenberg, North Smithfield, RI; Leah Selig, Merrylands, NSW, Australia; Jennifer Shockey, Brentwood, Tennessee; Stan Worrey / Sara Stone, Colonial House Antiques and Collectibles, Berea, Ohio;

Our thanks also go to the staff of Royal Doulton (UK) Limited, who have helped with additional information, especially Valerie Baynton, Lisa Hale, Julie McKeown, Maria Murtagh and Gill Walters; and Ian Howe, Royal Doulton Visitor Centre.

Contributors to the First Edition

The publisher would also like to thank the following individuals and companies who graciously supplied photographs or information or allowed us access to their collections for photographic purposes:

Ann Babychyck, Massachusetts; **Alistair Carstairs**, Thirsle, North Yorkshire, England; **K. Conley**, Pennsylvania; **William T. Cross**, William Cross Antiques and Collectibles, Burnaby, B.C.; **Lee and Dee Cunnigham**, Pennsylvania; **Nancy Daggett**, Eagle River, Arkansas; **Susan Evans**, Markham, Ontario; **Mary Farmer**, Minneapolis, Minnesota; **Mark Oliver**, Phillips, London, England; **Ed. Pascoe**, Pascoe & Co., Coral Gables, Florida; **Pat Sage**, Unionville, Ontario; **Nick Tzimas**, U.K.I. Ceramics, Woodbridge, Suffolk, England; **Peter and Marilyn Sweet**, Lymbridge, England

A SPECIAL NOTE TO COLLECTORS

We welcome and appreciate any comments or suggestions in regard to *The Charlton Standard Catalogue of Royal Doulton Bunnykins*. If any errors or omissions come to your attention, please write to us, or if you would like to participate in pricing or supply previously unavailable data or information, please contact Jean Dale at (416) 488-1418, or e-mail us at chpress@charltonpress.com.

**Printed in Canada
in the Province of Ontario**

The Charlton Press

**Editorial Office
2040 Yonge Street, Suite 208
Toronto, Canada. M4S 1Z9
Telephone (416) 488-1418 Fax: (416) 488-4656
Telephone 800-442-6064 Fax: 800-442-1542
www.charltonpress.com**

Early Bunnykins advertisement

HOW TO USE THIS GUIDE

THE PURPOSE

As with the other catalogues in Charlton's Royal Doulton reference and pricing library, this publication has been designed to serve two specific purposes: first, to furnish collectors with accurate and detailed listings that will provide the essential information needed to build a rich and rewarding collection; second, to provide collectors and dealers with an indication of the current market prices of Bunnykins figurines and tableware items.

The first edition of this price guide is the first attempt to link Bunnykins tableware designs to shapes and to prices. While all designs are more than likely known to collectors, the list of shapes on which they appear is still being compiled.

THE LISTINGS

The Charlton Standard Catalogue of Bunnykins is divided into four chapters, the first being devoted to Bunnykins tableware and the fourth, to modern Bunnykins figurines. It is within these two chapters that we will outline how the listings function.

The tableware chapter has the Bunnykins designs listed in alphabetical order, beginning with the *ABC Theme* and ending with *Xmas Menu*. Within the design layout is a shape/price table incorporating, on the left side of the table, a vertical listing of the different shapes on which the design appears. To the right of the shape column is the price column indicating a level at which collectors may expect to see that design/shape trade.

Within these columns are two sub-listings that must be understood to make the catalogue the useful tool that it is intended to be.

The Barbara Vernon designs carried her facsimile signature, unless, of course, the shape was too small and the signature was therefore dropped. These signatures were in continuous use until the early 1950s. As a result, a shape that was in production from 1934 to the mid-1950s will appear in the shape column as "with signature" and "without signature." The demand is much greater for shapes with the facsimile signature and this necessitates a two-tier pricing structure.

The second sub-listing is the copy printed in bold type, indicating a design that is current, on a shape that is current, and that is still being produced by Royal Doulton. The lines that are not bold indicate shapes that have been discontinued.

In the pricing tables of the tableware section, we have listed all the shapes that are known to exist with a specific design. There is a good possibility that more shapes exist, and these will be added to the design table in future editions as they become known.

The list of Bunnykins figurines is simple by comparison. Royal Doulton numbered the Bunnykins figurines in chronological order, as they were issued, starting with DB1 and carrying on to the present, which is above DB190.

STYLES AND VERSIONS

Tableware

All designs are named by the designer and, within any design, modifications may be needed so that the design may better fit the shape. As designs are changed or modified, it is necessary to bring our classifications to bear on Bunnykins tableware.

Styles: If the same design name is used at various times by different designers, the earlier issue then becomes Style One and the latter, Style Two.

Versions: The design may have one or more elements removed from the main design.

Variations: The design has all elements intact but minor modifications have been made to allow the design to better fit the shape.

Figurines

All listings include the modeller, where known, and the name of the animal figurine, designer, height, colour, dates of issue and discontinuation, varieties and series.

Styles: A change in style occurs when a design is altered or modified by a deliberate change that will result in a new design carrying the same name.

Versions: Versions are modifications in a major style element.

Variations: Variations are modifications in a minor style element. A change in colour is a variation.

SIGNATURES

A second word about the facsimile signature of Barbara Vernon is needed. Designs discontinued by 1952 should all carry the Barbara Vernon signature. However, there is the possibility that the signature was cut away from the transfer when the shape was too small to accommodate it, and the piece was issued without it.

While the absence of the signature affects the value of a piece, we consider that the value would be in the range of 75 percent of the catalogue price listed.

SHAPES

Some shapes will not carry a Bunnykins design. For example, the Stratford teacup will carry a design, while the Stratford saucer has a decoration of running rabbits around the edge. In our design/shape listing, we show only the item that carries the Bunnykins design — in this case, the Stratford teacup.

THE PRICING

One of the purposes of this catalogue is to give readers the most accurate, up-to-date retail prices for Royal Doulton Bunnykins in the United States, Canada, the United Kingdom and Australia.

To accomplish this, The Charlton Press continues to access an international pricing panel of experts who submit prices based on both dealer and collector retail-price activity, as well as current auction results in the U.S., Canada, and the U.K. These market prices are carefully averaged to reflect accurate valuations for figurines in each of these markets.

Current Bunnykins tableware/figurines are priced according to the manufacturer's suggested retail price in each of the market regions. Please be aware that price or promotional sales discounting is always possible and can result in lower prices than those listed.

One exception, however, occurs in the case of current figurines or recent limited editions issued in only one of the three markets. Since such items were priced by Royal Doulton only in the country in which they were to be sold, prices for the other markets are not shown.

A further word on pricing: as mentioned previously, this is a catalogue giving prices for items in the currency of a particular market (for example, U.S. dollars for the American market and sterling for the U.K. market). The bulk of the prices given herein are determined not by currency exchange calculations, but by actual market activity in the market concerned.

In some cases, the number of models produced is so small that market activity does not exist. There is no price activity on which to base a price. The price in this instance is purely between the buyer and the seller. We have therefore listed the last known auction price for the model. If the model were to be offered for sale at a future date, the price might be higher or lower than the auction price listed, depending on the demand for the model at that time.

When prices are italicized in the pricing tables, this means that the price is only an indication; prices are too volatile to establish a solid market price. Once again, the final price determination must be made between the buyer and the seller.

The prices published herein are for tableware items and figurines in mint condition. Collectors are cautioned that a repaired, restored or badly scratched piece may be worth as little as 25 percent of the value of the same piece in mint condition.

THE INTERNET AND PRICING

The Internet is changing the way that business is done in the collectable market. It links millions of collectors around the world to one another, allowing communication to flow freely among them. Chat rooms, antique and collector malls, internet auctions and producer web sites, all promote the new e-commerce.

Three major effects that e-commerce will have on the collectable market are:

1. Collectors will deal with collectors. They will also continue with their customer/dealer relationships, but the dealer's margin will come under pressure.

2. Information on new issues, new finds, and new varieties will spread faster, the bad news will spread even faster. Collectors' wants will be made known instantaneously to a wide universe of dealers and collectors.

3. Prices will be impacted on two fronts:

   (a) Price differentials will disappear between global market areas as collectors and delivery services teamup to stretch the purchasing power of the collectable dollar/pound.

   (b) As margins come under pressure, overheads being low in virtual operations, prices of the common to scarce collectable items will adjust downward to compensate. The rare and extremely rare items will move up as a result of their increased exposure.

Bunnykins for Grownups by Walter Hayward

Christmas Tree Ornament 1995 - Fun in the Snow

TABLE OF CONTENTS

INTRODUCTION
    Collecting Bunnykins Tableware   xi
        Barbara Vernon Designs   xi
        Walter Hayward Designs   xii
        Colin Twinn Designs   xiii
        Frank Endersby Designs   xiii
    Collecting Bunnykins Figurines   xv
        THE DB Range   xv
        Harry Sales Designs   xv
        Graham Tongue Designs   xvi
        Limited Edition Designs   xvi
        Resin Bunnykins Figurines   xvi
        The Success of the DB Range   xvi

ROYAL DOULTON COLLECTORS CLUB AND GUILD
    Royal Doulton International Collectors Club   xvii
    Royal Crown Derby Collectors Club   xvii
    Caithness Glass Paperweight Collectors Society   xvii
    Collectors Club Chapters   xvii
    Royal Doulton Visitors Centres   xviii

WHERE TO BUY   xix

FURTHER READING   xxi

PART ONE
    Bunnykins Tableware   1
        Backstamps   3
        Shape Guide   5
    Bunnykins Tableware Issues of 1934 to the present   11
    Bunnykins Breakfast Set, Issues of 1939 - 1945   179
    Bunnykins Banks, Issues of 1967 - 1991   183
    Bunnykins Teapots, Issues of 1994 - 1998   185
    Bunnykins China Teaset, Issues of 1998   189

PART TWO
    Bunnykins Figurines   193
        Backstamps   195
        Earthenware Issues of 1939 - 1940   197
        Earthenware Issues of 1972 to the present   199
        Resin Figurines 1996- 1997   263

INDICES
    Alphabetical Index to Bunnykins Tableware   274
    Numeical Index to Bunnykins Tableware   278
    Alphabetical index to Bunnykins Figurines   281
    Numerical index to Bunnykins Figurines   284

STERLING SILVER CHILD'S CUPS and PAP BOWLS

E.P.N.S. Child's Cup on page 42

No. 3415
Child's Cup in sterling silver.
Gilt lined. 2¾" x 2". May be
supplied plain or hand engraved.

No. 2083
Child's Cup in sterling silver.
Gilt lined. 2⅝" x 2¼". May be
supplied plain or hand engraved.

No. 2395
Child's Cup in sterling silver.
Gilt lined. 2½" x 2½". May be
supplied plain or hand engraved.

No. 2601
Child's Cup in sterling silver.
Gilt lined. 2⅝" x 2⅜". May be
supplied plain or hand engraved.

No. 3638
Sterling silver Child's Cup.
Gilt line. 2⅝" x 2¼".

No. 3056
Child's Cup in sterling silver.
Gilt lined. 2⅝" x 2½". May be
supplied plain or hand engraved.

No. 6800-1
Child's Baby Plate and Cup in china, with
sterling silver deposit rim and coloured
decoration. Diameter of Bowl, 7½";
Cup, 3" x 3⅜".

No. 3639
Sterling silver Child's Cup.
Gilt lined. 2½" x 2½".

No. 2951
Child's Pap Bowl in sterling silver,
with handle. Diameter 4½".

No. 3142
Child's Pap Bowl in sterling silver, extra
weight, with handle. Diameter 6".

ORDERS SUBJECT TO PRICE AT DATE OF SHIPMENT

Roden advertisement, 1955, showing a Bunnykins baby plate and Don mug with sterling silver rims.

INTRODUCTION

COLLECTING BUNNYKINS TABLEWARE

Generations of children around the world have been weaned with Bunnykins nursery ware as it has been in continuous production since 1934. Few could have imagined that their favourite baby plate would one day become collectable but that is the fate of many of the Bunnykins designs, particularly the early pieces featuring Barbara Vernon's signature.

Bunnykins in use by original customer!

Barbara Vernon Designs

Barbara Vernon was a young nun in an English convent school when she first imagined the exploits of the Bunnykins family to entertain the children in her class. Her father was the Manager of the Royal Doulton Pottery in Stoke-on-Trent and he recognised the potential of her rabbit drawings for a range of nursery ware. Sister Mary Barbara, as she was known in the convent, began to send her sketches to the factory where they were adapted for the lithographic printing process by one of the resident designers, Hubert Light. He also created the backstamp from the *Tug of War*

scene LF1 and designed the chain of running rabbits which has appeared around the rim of the Bunnykins pieces since their launch in 1934.

Rare Jam Pot with *Pulling on Trousers* (HW2) design

A surviving catalogue of 1937 shows that the range grew quickly to include two sizes of baby plate, a child's dinner plate, Don beakers and mugs, cereal and porridge bowls, a Jaffa fruit saucer, a jam pot, a Casino teapot, cup, saucer, sugar bowl and jugs in various sizes. These shapes were all made in a deep ivory glazed earthenware and decorated with colourful transfer prints. Barbara Vernon's bunnies were usually dressed in sky blue and cherry red and the background was coloured in subtle shades of brown and green.

More shapes had been added by 1940, notably an oval baby plate, a hot water plate with cover and a candle holder. Bunnykins collectors usually like to find an example of each shape featuring a Barbara Vernon design and the jam pot and candle holder, which were withdrawn in 1952, are amongst the hardest to find in the earthenware range.

Some of the early Bunnykins designs were also available

Rare sugar bowl with handles,
Lambeth Walk, Second Version (HW16) design

Candle holder with *Bedtime in Bunks* (SF3) design

Early china nursery ware, *Proposal* (HW11) left,
Pressing Trousers (HW14) centre, *Greetings* (HW7) right

Pressing Trousers HW14 which shows the bunny struggling to remove the creases with a garden roller! Sadly, Barbara Vernon only produced Bunnykins drawings for a few years because of her other commitments at the convent and so Walter Hayward, one of Royal Doulton's Art Directors, took over the range after the Second World War.

Walter Hayward Designs

Initially Walter Hayward adapted the remaining Barabara Vernon drawings for production but he soon began to create his own scenes although her facsimile signature continued to appear on the ware until the mid 1950s. However, Walter Hayward's work can usually be identified by the presence of some lively little mice that

Juggling Scene LF127

in a white bone china body. This finer body was only produced until the Second World War and, as not many bone china pieces survived the rough and tumble of nursery life, they are very rare today. One collector was fortunate enough to find an original boxed bone china breakfast set, complete with silver spoons, whilst another boasts a tea set in pristine condition.

The condition of Bunnykins nursery ware, whether it is bone china or earthenware, is very important for serious collectors who seek out pieces with the minimum of scratches. Sometimes it is very hard to find early baby plates which have not been scraped by enthusiastic eaters scooping up their porridge to enjoy the scene underneath. Collectors also like to find scenes incorporating Barbara Vernon's facsimile signature although sometimes this was cut off the transfer.

Many of Barbara Vernon's scenes had been withdrawn by 1952 and these are amongst the most desirable today. Collectors appreciate her simple designs and the charming subjects which evoke her era, for example one of her bunnies is being dosed with castor oil at *Medicine Time* SF1 and others dance the *Lambeth Walk* HW16. Her quiet sense of humour can also be enjoyed in scenes like *Frightening Spider* SF4 and

became his trademark. Generally his scenes are much busier than their predecessors and some reflect new topical themes such as the advent of television and space travel. Over the years, he was encouraged to add more and more bunnies, particularly by Doulton's agent in Australia which was one of the strongest markets for Bunnykins. Some of his most ambitious designs, such as *Juggling* LF127 and *Hoopla* LF129, were only available for three years and so these are two of the hardest Hayward designs to find today

The Bunnykins shapes remained much the same throughout the 1950s and 60s although some larger sizes of Casino teapots and jugs were added in 1952. They were all withdrawn in the late 1960s together with a wide range of scenes when the original earthenware body was replaced with a new ivory bone china. By the late 1970s, new shapes had been developed for the china body including the Hug-a-mug which replaced the original Don mug and a range of egg-shaped boxes. Unfortunately, the egg boxes were not made for long and they are now very collectable. Savings books and money balls followed in the early 1980s and these were used occasionally to commemorate special events, such as royal births and weddings.

In the early 1980s, Walter Hayward was commissioned to design a range of scenes celebrating birthdays, christenings and Christmas. He also helped the Bunnykins family celebrate their own birthday with special commemorative pieces to mark their Golden Jubilee in 1984. In addition, all

Early Bunnykins scenes, *Pillow Fight* SF7 centre
Kissing Under Mistletoe (with mistletoe) HW11R left
Kissing Under Mistletoe (without mistletoe) HW11R right

the nursery ware made during 1984 had the inscription Golden Jubilee Celebration added to the backstamp. Bunnykins birthday parties were held all over the world during 1984 and the resulting publicity attracted many new enthusiasts.

An anniversary weekend in Stoke-on-Trent was the catalyst for the largest Bunnykins collection in the UK which boasts examples of every scene and shape from 1934 to the present day. The first Bunnykins reference book was published at the end of 1984 and for the first time collectors could see the full extent of the range. Some scenes could only be illustrated from the pattern books and collectors all over the world began hunting for rarities like *Air Mail Delivery* LFa, *Carving the Chicken* LFc and *Dodgems* LF4.

No longer was Bunnykins intended exclusively for youngsters, Walter Hayward designed a set of Bunnykins for Grown Ups featuring bunnies with brief-cases dashing to work. These adult designs only remained in production from 1986 to 1988 so examples are very hard to find today. Walter Hayward's last Bunnykins design following his retirement was the plate to commemorate Australia's Bicentenary in 1988. Meanwhile, another artist was getting to know the Bunnykins family for a series of story books.

Colin Twinn

Colin Twinn Designs

In 1987, Colin Twinn was commissioned to produce a collection of Bunnykins books for the publishers, Frederick Warne, and many of his drawings were adapted for use on the nursery ware. As a successful illustrator of children's books, Twinn had considerable experience with anthropomorphic characters, particularly rabbits, and he created a new look for the Bunnykins family. Pastel colours predominate in his detailed scenes and his bunnies seem softer and fluffier than the originals. Whilst this approach worked well in the little picture books, the new Bunnykins nursery ware designs did not have sufficient impact on the china shop shelves. Established collectors felt that the Bunnykins characters had lost their identity and it would appear that general gift buyers were not enthused either as production of Colin Twinn designs had ceased by the early 1990s.

Dancing in the Moonlight CT91 and CT92
Bunnykins 60th Anniversary

Many of Colin Twinn's designs appeared on the new shapes which were developed in the late 1980s. An Albion style tea service was introduced in 1987 together with a Stratford tea cup and saucer which replaced the Casino shape. The traditional Don beaker was replaced by a straight sided Malvern beaker and a 10 ½" dinner plate was added to the range. Decorative accessories, such as a lamp and two picture plaques, were also available for a few years and these are now sought after by collectors.

Gradually, as Colin Twinn's designs began to disappear from the shops, new stocks of Barbara Vernon and Walter Hayward designs appeared. Around 50 patterns for hollow ware and flat ware had never been withdrawn and these were modified in line with new requirements for colour printing. A tuft of green grass on the left of the backstamp distinguishes the more recent Vernon/Hayward wares from earlier examples. A classic Barbara Vernon scene *Dancing in the Moonlight* was re-drawn for the 60th Anniversary of the Bunnykins range in 1994 and a set of commemorative ware was made for that year only. Royal Doulton's company in Australia commissioned their own exclusive anniversary scenes featuring an Aussie picnic complete with kangaroos and koalas and this was one of the last designs by Colin Twinn as a new artist had been found to continue the Bunnykins tradition, Frank Endersby.

Frank Endersby Designs

Frank Endersby is a freelance illustrator who works from his own studio in the idyllic Cotswolds region. During his career, he has worked in a busy graphic design studio and also with a children's book publisher so he has a wide experience of all aspects of design and illustration. He quickly assimilated the essential qualities of the original Bunnykins style and his scenes feature the strong outlines used for the original characters as well as their bright blue and red clothes. To date he has worked on 20 new sets of Bunnykins designs and each set incorporates three scenes, the larger for decorating plates and two smaller ones to use on the front and reverse of cups and other hollow ware. These scenes began to appear in the shops in 1995 but it was a couple of years before dedicated collectors had located all his designs. Early indications are that the new Frank Endersby designs are being very well received by gift buyers and collectors alike, so much so that the original Vernon/Hayward scenes have now been phased out of production.

A few new Bunnykins shapes have been introduced in recent years, such as the divided children's dish and the photograph frame, but the most exciting new concept is the annual Bunnykins Christmas plate made exclusively for members of the Royal Doulton International Collectors Club. These lively designs by Frank Endersby have a wealth of colourful detail, including some of Walter Hayward's cheeky mice and the running rabbits wearing Christmas hats! The limited distribution and short production period is guaranteed to make these very special Bunnykins pieces.

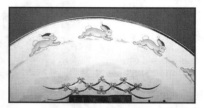

Running rabibits wearing
Christmas hats

Collection of Frank Endersby designs

Collecting Bunnykins Figures

Bunnykins figures made their debut in 1939 but the war soon halted production and the original six characters are extremely rare today. It is believed that they were modelled by Charles Noke, the Art Director who developed the HN range of Royal Doulton figures, as they resemble some of his early character animals. These large scale figures, which range in size from 3 to 7 inches, have little in common with Barbara Vernon's designs which might explain why they were never revived after the war.

Buntie Bunnykins Helping Mother (DB2) figurine
Baking (SF19) nurseryware plate

As well as these character figures, Noke also introduced a Bunny shaped breakfast set, featuring a teapot, cream jug, sugar bowl, sugar sifter and egg cup, but this suffered a similar fate in the war years. The idea of Bunny shaped ware to accompany the successful nursery ware was not revived until 1967 when a Bunny money bank was added to the range and this remained in production until 1981.

The DB Range

When Royal Doulton took over the Beswick factory in 1969, they acquired the modelling skills of Albert Hallam who worked on the Beatrix Potter range of figures. These little character animals were amongst Beswick's most

Artist Bunnykins DB13 with the *Portrait Painter* SF20
nurseryware plate

successful products and it was decided to create a similar collection of Bunnykins figures. The first nine figures were launched in 1972 with DB pattern numbers and they averaged four inches in height. All were inspired by Walter Hayward's nursery ware patterns, for example *The Artist* DB13 is derived from *The Portrait Painter* SF20. This approach continued until 1974 when there was a total of 15 characters in the range but a new look developed in the 1980s.

Harry Sales Designs

Harry Sales, the Design Manager of the Beswick factory, took over responsibility for the Bunnykins range in 1980. He believed that the rabbit characters should reflect the interests of contemporary children and his first figure of a guitar-playing rock star *Mr Bunnybeat Strumming* DB16 was followed by a space traveller *Astro Bunnykins Rocket Man* DB20. After seeing his colleagues response to these entertaining designs, it occurred to Harry that Bunnykins figures could also have an adult audience and he began to work on a collection of sporting subjects at the time of the Los Angeles Olympics in 1984. Adults began to purchase these as whimsical gifts, sharing Harry's sense of humour in subjects like *Freefall Bunnykins* DB41 whose pained expression suggested a not so perfect landing.

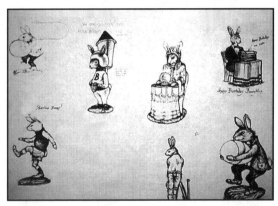

Harry Sales designs

This new direction coincided with the Bunnykins Golden Jubilee when nursery ware first began to be taken seriously by collectors. Before long, the figures were also included in the hunt and early discontinued models, such as *Mr Bunnykins Autumn Days* DB5 and *Daisy Bunnykins Spring Time* DB7 were sought at collectors fairs and markets. In 1987, the Royal Doulton International Collectors Club commissioned a figure exclusively for its members and *Collector Bunnykins* DB54 is now one of the most expensive figures on the secondary market.

Several special commissions were produced in the late 1980s and these now command premium prices. National subjects such as *Australian Bunnykins* DB58 were made to celebrate that country's bicentenary and new colourways of existing models were produced for sale at special events in the USA, notably *Mr and Mrs Bunnykins at the Easter Parade* DB51 and 52.

Graham Tongue Designs

When Harry Sales left Royal Doulton in 1986 to pursue a freelance career, Graham Tongue became the Beswick Studio Manager and he has been responsible for a number of Bunnykins figures, either as designer or modeller. His most popular figure is *Bedtime Bunnykins* DB55 which was made in four different colourways for special occasions. He also produced some figures inspired by Colin Twinn's nursery ware illustrations, for example *Lollipopman*

Cavalier Bunnykins DB179 figurine

Bunnykins DB65, but these were less successful and were withdrawn after a few years. Since his retirement in 1995, Graham has continued to model Bunnykins figures at his own studio and he created *Ballerina Bunnykins* DB176 and *Cavalier Bunnykins* DB179, a recent limited edition design.

Limited Edition Designs

The first limited edition Bunnykins figures were commissioned in 1990 for sale at a Doulton collectors fair in London. The *Oompah Band* was renamed the *Royal Doulton Collectors Band* for this occasion and the new blue colourway was so successful that other special editions swiftly followed. Denise Andrews, a freelance illustrator from Suffolk, was invited to produce special designs which were modelled by the team of resident artists at the Beswick

studio. Her footballing and cricketing characters augmented the earlier sporting range and her colourful *Clown* and *Jester Bunnykins* have entertained collectors all over the world. Over the years, limited edition sizes have grown from 250 to 3,500 but many new Bunnykins figures are over-subscribed as soon as they are launched. Collectors were bewitched by *Trick or Treat Bunnykins* DB162, which was issued in 1995 and was soon changing hands for many times its issue price. In 1996, Royal Doulton introduced their first Bunnykins Figure of the Year and collectors responded enthusiastically to this new initiative.

Resin Bunnykins Figures

In 1995, the Bunnykins characters became movie stars when an animated feature film was screened in North America and the UK. *Happy Birthday Bunnykins* was later distributed in video form and inspired a new collection of Bunnykins figures in a resin body. Resin is the name given to a cold cast sculptural material which retains intricate modelling detail more effectively than conventional fired clay bodies. The resin Bunnykins figures are smaller in scale than their ceramic cousins and are decorated primarily in pastel colours. During 1996 and 1997, twenty models were issued in the resin range, including two ambitious musical boxes and two photograph frames, but they did not appeal to collectors or gift buyers and were all withdrawn at the end of 1997. Fortunately the traditional ceramic figures continue to go from strength to strength.

The Success of the DB Range

After just 25 years in production, the DB figures are amongst the most collectable Royal Doulton products and Bunnykins fans are multiplying faster than rabbits. With this in mind, it is a good idea to buy the new Bunnykins figures as soon as they are issued. Royal Doulton have now allocated 200 DB numbers and, although a few intervening numbers have not been issued, committed collectors now have quite a challenge to find them all. Figures are now withdrawn regularly from the range, adding to the excitement of the chase so, in the words of the song, if you want to keep up you'll have to.. run rabbit... run rabbit... run.. run.. run!

Grouping of Bunnykins Figurines

ROYAL DOULTON COLLECTORS CLUB AND GUILD

Royal Doulton International Collectors Club

Founded in 1980, the Royal Doulton International Collectors Club provides an information service on all aspects of the company's products, past and present. A club magazine, *Gallery*, is published four times a year with information on new products and current events that will keep the collector up-to-date on the happenings in the world of Royal Doulton. Upon joining the club, each new member will receive a free gift and invitations to special events and exclusive offers throughout the year.

To join the Royal Doulton Collectors Club, please contact your local stockist, or contact the club directly at the address or telephone numbers below:

Royal Crown Derby Collectors Guild

The Royal Crown Derby Collectors Guild was established in 1994 to facilitate closer contact with Royal Crown Derby Collectors. Membership entitles the collector to a yearly subscription to the quarterly *Gallery* magazine, *Royal Crown Derby News*, membership gifts and free admission to the Royal Crown Derby Visitor Centre.

To join the Royal Crown Derby Collectors Guild, please contact the club at the address or telephone numbers below:

Minton House
London Road, Stoke-on-Trent
Staffordshire ST4 7QD, England

Telephone:
U.K.: (01782) 292127
U.S.A. and Canada: 1-800-747-3043 (toll free)
Australia: 011-800-142624 (toll free)
Fax: U.K.: (01782) 292099
Attn.: Maria Murtagh

Caithness Glass Paperweight Collectors Society
Caithness Glass International
Paperweight Collectors Society

Founded in 1997 by Colin Terris, the society is the clearing house for information on Caithness Glass Paperweights. Membership in the society entitles the collector to receive *Reflections*, the society's magazine, plus three newsletters and a personal tour of the paperweight studios in Perth, Scotland, if you are ever in the area. An annual International Convention is held in Scotland in October.

To join the Caithness Glass Paperweight Collectors Society, please contact the club at one of the addresses or telephone numbers below:

In the U.K. and International
Caithness Glass Paperweight Collectors Society
Caithness Glass Inc.
Inveralmond, Perth PH1 3TZ, Scotland
Tel.: (44) (0) 1738 637373
Fax: (44) (0) 1738 622494

In the U.S.A.
Caithness Glass Paperweight Collectors Society
Caithness Glass Inc.
141 Lanza Avenue, Building No. 12
Garfield, N.J. 07026, U.S.A.
Tel.: 973-340-3330
Fax: 973-340-9415

COLLECTOR CLUB CHAPTERS

Chapters of the RDICC have formed across North America and are worthy of consideration in those areas.

Detroit Chapter
Frank Americk, President
1771 Brody, Allen Park, MI 48101

Edmonton Chapter
Mildred's Collectibles
6813 104 Street, Edmonton, AB

New England Chapter
Charles Wood, President
Charles Briggs, Secretary
21 Walpole Street, Norwood, MA 02062
Tel.: (781) 784-8121

Northern California Chapter
Donald A. Blubaugh, President
P.O. Box 3665, Walnut Creek, CA 94598
Tel.: (925) 945-1687 Fax: (925) 938-6674
Blubaugh@usa.net

Northwest, Bob Haynes, Chapter
Alan Matthew, President
15202 93rd Place N.E., Bothell, WA 98011
Tel.: (425) 488-9604

Ohio Chapter
Reg Marvis, President
Dick Maschmeier, Treasurer
5556 Whitehaven Avenue
North Olmstead, OH 44070
Tel.: (216) 779-5554

Rochester Chapter
Judith L. Trost President
103 Garfield Street, Rochester, NY 14611
Tel.: (716) 436-3321

Western Pennsylvania Chapter
John Re, President
9589 Parkedge Drive, Allison Park, PA 15101
Tel.: (412) 366-0201 Fax: (412) 366-2558

ROYAL DOULTON VISITOR CENTRES

Royal Doulton Visitor Centre

Opened in the summer of 1996, the Royal Doulton Visitor Centre houses the largest collection of Royal Doulton figurines in the world. The centre also is home to the Minton Fine Art Studio, which specializes in hand painting and gilding. Demonstration areas offer the collector a first hand insight on how figurines are assembled and decorated. Also at the Visitor Centre is a cinema showing a 20 minute video on the history of Royal Doulton, plus a restaurant, and a retail shop offering both best quality ware and slight seconds.

Factory tours may be booked, Monday to Friday, at the Visitor Centre.

Nile Street, Burslem
Stoke-on-Trent, ST6 2AJ, England
Tel.: (01782) 292434
Fax: (01782) 292424
Attn.: Yvonne Wood

Royal Doulton John Beswick Studios

Tours of the John Beswick Factory and Museum are available Monday to Thursday by appointment only. Please book in advance.

Gold Street, Longton
Stoke-on-Trent, ST3 2JP, England
Tel.: (01782) 291213
Fax: (01782) 291279
Attn.: Joan Barker

Royal Crown Derby Visitor Centre

Opened in the spring of 1998, the Visitor Centre was created to provide an insight into the tradition, history and skills that go into making Royal Crown Derby collectables. The centre houses the largest collection of Royal Crown Derby seen anywhere in the world, a demonstration area for skilled Royal Crown Derby artists and crafts people, restaurants, and shops.

Factory tours may be booked Monday to Friday at the centre, with advance bookings suggested.

194 Osmaston Road
Derby, DE23 8JZ, England
Tel.: (01332) 712841
Fax: (01332) 712899
Attn.: Stella Birks

Caithness Glass Visitor Centre

The Visitor Centre is home to the largest public display of Caithness Glass paperweights. Over 1200 individual weights are on display. Also at the centre is a special viewing gallery for visitors to watch the glass making process.

Inveralmond
Perth, PH1 3TZ, Scotland
Tel.: (44) (0) 1738 637373
Fax: (44) (0) 1738 622494
Attn.

Factory Shops

Royal Doulton Visitor Centre
Nile Street, Burslem
Stoke-on-Trent, England
Tel.: (01782) 292451

Royal Doulton Group Factory Shop
Lawley Street, Longton, England
Stoke-on-Trent ST3 2PH
Tel.: (01782) 291172

Royal Doulton Factory Shop
Minton House, London Road
Stoke-on-Trent, ST4 7QD, England
Tel.: (01782) 292121

Royal Doulton Factory Shop
Leek New Road, Baddeley Green,
Stoke-on-Trent ST2 7HS, England
Tel.: (01782) 291700

Royal Doulton Factory Shop
Victoria Road, Fenton,
Stoke-on-Trent ST4 2PJ, England
Tel.: (01782) 291869

Beswick Factory Shop
Barford Street, Longton,
Stoke-on-Trent. ST3 2JP, England
Tel.: (01782) 291237

Web Site and E-mail Addresses

Site: www.royal-doulton.com
www.caithnessglass.co.uk
E-mail:
 Clubs: icc@royal-doulton.com
 Visitor Centre: Visitor@royal-doulton.com
 Consumer Enquiries:
  enquiries@royal-doulton.com
 Museum Curator: heritage@royal-doulton.com
 Lawleys by Post: lbp@royal-doulton.com

WHERE TO BUY

Discontinued Doulton collectables can be found in Antique shops, Markets, Auctions, Shows and Fairs. Specialist dealers in Royal Doulton collectables attend many of the events listed below.

For Auction happenings it is necessary to subscribe to Auction Houses that hold 20th Century or Doulton Auctions.

UNITED KINGDOM
Auction Houses

BBR Auctions
Elsecar Heritage Centre
Nr. Barnsley,
South Yorkshire, S74 8HJ, England
Tel.: (01226) 745156
Fax: (01226) 351561
Attn: Alan Blakeman

Bonhams
65-69 Lots Road, Chelsea,
London, SW10 0RN, England
Tel.: (0171) 393-3900
Fax: (0171) 393-3906
www.bonhams.com
Attn: Neil Grenyer

Christie's South Kensington
85 Old Brompton Road
London, SW7 3LD, England
Tel.: (0171) 581 7611
Fax: (0171) 321-3321
www.christies.com
Attn: Michael Jeffrey

Potteries Specialist Auctions
271 Waterloo Road, Cobridge
Stoke-on-Trent
Staffordshire, ST13 5AJ, England
Tel.: (01782) 286622
Fax: (01782) 213777
Attn: Steve Anderson

Louis Taylor
Britannia House
10 Town Road, Hanley,
Stoke-on-Trent, ST1 2QG
England
Tel.: (01782) 21411
Fax: (01782) 287874
Attn: Clive Hillier

Phillips
101 New Bond Street
London, W1Y 0AS, England
Tel.: (0171) 629-6602
Fax: (0171) 629-8876
www.phillips-auctions.com
Attn: Mark Oliver

Sotheby's
34-35 New Bond Street
London, W1A 2AA, England
Tel.: (0171) 293-5000
Fax: (0171) 293-5989
www.sothebys.com
Attn: Christina Donaldson

Sotheby's Sussex
Summers Place
Billingshurst, Sussex, RH14 9AF
England
Tel.: (01403) 833500
Fax: (01403) 833699

Thomson Roddick & Laurie
60 Whitesands
Dumfries, DG1 2RS
Scotland
Tel.: (01387) 255366
Fax: (01387) 266236
Attn: Sybelle Medcalf

Peter Wilson Auctioneers
Victoria Gallery, Market Street
Nantwich, Cheshire, CW5 5DG
England
Tel.: (01270) 623878
Fax: (01270) 610508
Attn: Stella Ashbrook or
Robert Stone

Antique Fairs

Doulton and Beswick Collectors Fair
National Motorcycle Museum, Meriden, Birmingham,
Usually March and August
For information on times and dates:
Doulton and Beswick Dealers Association
(0181) 303 3316

Doulton and Beswick Collectors Fair
The Queensway Hall Civic Centre, Dunstable,
Bedfordshire. Usually in October.
For information on times and location:
UK Fairs Ltd. 10 Wilford Bridge Spur,
Melton,Woodbridge, Suffolk, IP12 1 RJ
901394) 386663

20th Century Fairs
266 Glossop Road, Sheffield S10 2HS, England
Usually the last week in May or the first week in June.
For information on times and dates:
Tel.: (0114) 275-0333
Fax: (0114) 275-4443

International Antique & Collectors Fair
Newark, Nottinghamshire
Usually six fairs annually.
For information on times and dates:
International Antique & Collectors Fair Ltd.
P.O. Box 100, Newark, Nottinghamshire, NG2 1DJ
(01636) 702326

West London Wade Beswick & Doulton Fair
Brunel University, Kingston Lane,
Uxbridge, Middlesex
For information on times and dates:
B & D Fairs, P.O. Box 273, Uxbridge,
Middlesex, UB9 4LP
(01895) 834694 or 834357

Yesterdays Doulton Fair
Usually November.
For information on times and location:
Doulton and Beswick Dealers Association
Tel.: (0181) 303-3316

London Markets

Alfie's Antique Market
13-25 Church Street, London
Tuesday - Saturday

Camden Passage Market
London
Wednesday and Saturday

New Caledonia Market
Bermondsey Square, London
Friday morning

Portobello Road Market
Portobello Road, London
Saturday

UNITED STATES
Auction Houses

Christie's East
219 East 67th Street
New York, NY 10021
(212) 606-0400
www.christies.com
Attn: Timothy Luke

Sotheby's Arcade Auctions
1334 York Avenue
New York, NY 10021
(212) 606-7000
www.sothebys.com
Attn: Andrew Cheney

Collectable Shows

Atlantique City
New Atlantic City Convention Centre
Atlantic City, NJ
Usually March and October
For information on times and dates:
Brimfield and Associates
P.O. Box 1800, Ocean City, NJ 08226
(609) 926-1800
www.atlantiquecity.com

Florida Doulton Convention & Sale
Sheraton Hotel
1825 Griffin Road
Dania, Florida
Usually mid-January
For information on times and dates:
Pascoe and Company, 101 Almeria Avenue,
Coral Gables, Florida 33134. (305) 44503229
Charles Dombeck, 29720 Rich Walk Court
Davie, Florida 33328. (954) 452-9174

O'Hare National Antiques Show & Sale
Rosemont Convention Centre,
Chicago, IL.
Usually April, August and November
For information on times and dates:
Manor House Shows Inc.
P.O. Box 7320, Fort Lauderdale, Florida 33338
(954) 563-6747

Royal Doulton Convention & Sale
John S. Knight Convention Centre
77 E. Mill Street, Akron, Ohio 44308
Usually August.
For information on times and dates:
Colonial House Productions
182 Front Street, Berea, Ohio 44017
(800) 344-9299

CANADA
Auction Houses

Maynards
415 West 2nd Avenue, Vancouver, BC V5Y 1E3
Tel.: (604) 876-1311

Ritchie's
288 King Street East, Toronto, Ontario. M5A 1K4
Tel.: (416) 364-1864   Fax: (416) 364-0704
Attn: Caroline Kaiser

Collectable Shows

Canadian Art & Collectibles Show & Sale
Kitchener Memorial Auditorium, Kitchener, Ontario.
Usually early May.
For information on times and location:
George or Jackie Benninger
P.O. Box 130, Durham. Ont. N0G 1R0. (519) 369-6950

Canadian Doulton & Collectable Fair
Toronto, Ontario.
Usually early September.
For information on times and location:
George or Jackie Benninger
P.O. Box 130, Durham, Ont. N0G 1R0. (519) 369-6950

FURTHER READING

Storybook Figurines

The Charlton Standard Catalogue of Royal Doulton Beswick Storybook Figurines by Jean Dale
Cartoon Classics and other Character Figures by Louise Irvine
Royal Doulton Bunnykins Figures by Louise Irvine
Bunnykins Collectors Book by Louise Irvine
Beatrix Potter Figures and Giftware edited by Louise Irvine
The Beswick Price Guide by Harvey May

Animals, Figures and Character Jugs

Royal Doulton Figures by Desmond Eyles, Louise Irvine and Valerie Baynton
The Charlton Standard Catalogue of Beswick Animals by Diane & John Callow
    and Marilyn & Peter Sweet
The Charlton Standard Catalogue of Royal Doulton Animals by Jean Dale
The Charlton Standard Catalogue of Royal Doulton Beswick Figurines by Jean Dale
The Charlton Standard Catalogue of Royal Doulton Beswick Jugs by Jean Dale
Collecting Character and Toby Jugs by Jocelyn Lukins
Collecting Doulton Animals by Jocelyn Lukins
Doulton Flambé Animals by Jocelyn Lukins
The Character Jug Collectors Handbook by Kevin Pearson
The Doulton Figure Collectors Handbook by Kevin Pearson

General

The Charlton Standard Catalogue of Beswick Pottery by Diane and John Callow
Discovering Royal Doulton by Michael Doulton
The Doulton Story by Paul Atterbury and Louise Irvine
Royal Doulton Series Ware by Louise Irvine (Vols. 1-5)
Limited Edition Loving Cups by Louise Irvine and Richard Dennis
Doulton for the Collector by Jocelyn Lukins
Doulton Kingsware Flasks by Jocelyn Lukins
Doulton Burslem Advertising Wares by Jocelyn Lukins
Doulton Lambeth Advertising Wares by Jocelyn Lukins
The Doulton Lambeth Wares by Desmond Eyles
The Doulton Burslem Wares by Desmond Eyles
Hannah Barlow by Peter Rose
George Tinworth by Peter Rose
Sir Henry Doulton Biography by Edmund Gosse
Phillip's Collectors Guide by Catherine Braithwaite
Royal Doulton by Jennifer Queree
John Beswick: A World of Imagination. Catalogue reprint (1950-1996)
Royal Doulton by Julie McKeown

Magazines and Newsletters

Rabbitting On (Bunnykins Newsletter) Contact Leah Selig: 2 Harper Street, Merrylands 2160
    New South Wales, Australia. Tel./Fax 61 2 9637 2410 (International), 02 637 2410 (Australia)
Collect It! Contact subscription department at: P.O. Box 3658, Bracknell, Berkshire RG12 7XZ
    Telephone: (1344) 868280 or e-mail: collectit@dialpipex.com
Collecting Doulton Magazine, Contact Doug Pinchin, P.O. Box 310, Richmond, Surrey TW9 1FS, England
Doulton News, published by Thorndon Antiques & Fine China Ltd., edited by David Harcourt
    P.O. Box 12-076 (109 Molesworth Street), Wellington, New Zealand
Beswick Quarterly (Beswick Newsletter) Contact Laura J. Rock-Smith: 10 Holmes Court, Sayville
    N.Y. 11782-2408, U.S.A. Tel./Fax (516) 589-9027

THE COLLECTOR'S CHECKLIST OF SHAPES

The following provides the collector with a starting point to developing a checklist of designs vs. shapes. As the Barbara Vernon facsimile signature plays an important role in Bunnykins tableware we have also enclosed that information in the listing.

For continuity in the listing, we have noted where a signature was not included in the design.

On checking your collection you may find we have not included a particular design/shape with or without a signature. Why not bring this information to our attention? Please contact:

The Charlton Press at (416) 488-1418 or (800) 442-6042, you can fax us at (416) 488-4656 or (800) -442-1542

ALBION
Cream jug
¼ pint — 1987 - 1991
without signature
Jug
½ pint — 1988 - 1991
without signature

1 pint — 1988 - 1991
without signature
Sugar bowl
¼ pint — 1897 - 1991
without signature
Teapot
1 pint — 1987 - 1991
without signature
BABY PLATE
Small
oval, 8¼" — 1940 - 1952
with signature
without signature

round, 6", first issue — 1937 - 1978
with signature
without signature

round, 6", second issue — 1978 - 1988
without signature

round, 6", third issue — 1988 to the present
without signature
Large
oval, 8½" — 1940 - 1968
with signature
without signature

round, 7½" — 1937 - 1969
with signature
without signature
BEAKER PAD — 1940 - 1968
with signature
without signature
BREAD AND BUTTER PLATE
WITH HANDLES — 1940 - 1968
with signature
without signature
CAKE STAND — 1987 - 1991
without signature
CANDLE HOLDER — 1940 - 1952
with signature
without signature

CASINO
Jug
42s, ¾ pint —1937 - 1968
with signature
without signature

36s, 1 pint — 1937 - 1968
with signature
without signature

30s, 1½ pint — 1937 - 1968
with signature
without signature

24s, 2 pint — 1952 - 1968
with signature
without signature
Saucer — 1937 - 1989
with signature
without signature
Sugar
36s, 1 pint — 1937 - 1968
with signature
without signature

30s, 1 ½ pint — 1937 - 1968
with signature
without signature
Teacup
First issue — 1937 - 1968
with signature
without signature

Modifies — 1968 - 1989
without signature
Teapot
36s, 1 pint — 1937 - 1968
with signature
without signature

30s, 1 ½ pint — 1952 - 1968
with signature
without signature

24s, 2 pint — 1952 - 1967
with signature
without signature
CEREAL / OATMEAL BOWL — 1937 to the present
with signature
without signature
CLOCK — 1983 to the present
without signature

CUP / MUG LARGE — 1937 - c.1945
    with signature

DON
  Beaker — 1937 - 1989
    with signature
    without signature

  Beaker, one handle — 1940 - 1989
    with signature
    without signature

  Mug, one handle
    First issue — 1937 - 1968
      with signature
      without signature

    Modified — 1968 - 1983
      without signature

  Mug, two handles — 1940 - 1983
    with signature
    without signature

EGG BOX
  Small, 3" — 1979 - 1981
    without signature

  Medium, 3 ¾" — 1979 - 1981
    without signature

  Large, 4¾" — 1979 - 1981
    without signature

EGG CUP
  Style One, footless — 1937 - 1968
    with signature
    without signature

  Style Two, footed — 1940 - 1968
    with signature
    without signature

  Style Three, footless modified —
  1968 to the present
    without signature

EGG SAUCER — 1991 - 1996
    without signature

HOT WATER PLATE WITH COVER
  Plate
    First Issue, one stopper — 1940 - 1959
      with signature
      without signature

    Modified, two stoppers — 1959 - 1969
      with signature
      without signature

  Cover — 1940 - 1969
    with signature
    without signature

HUG-A-MUG
  One handle — 1979 to the present
    without signature

  Two handles — 1979 to the present
    without signature

JAFFA FRUIT SAUCER
  Wavy rim — 1937 - c.1950
    with signature
    without signature

  Plain rim — c.1950 to the present
    with signature
    without signature

JAM POT — 1937 - 1952
    with signature
    without signature

LAMP — 1985 - 1991
    without signature

MALVERN BEAKER — 1989 - 1997
    without signature

MONEY BALL — 1982 to the present
    without signature

NIGHT LIGHT (fine china) — 1937 - c.1945
    with signature

PICTURE PLAQUE
  Small, 6½" — 1991 - 1993
    without signature

  Large, 7¼" — 1991 - 1993
    without signature

PLATE
  6½" — 1937 to the present
    with signature
    with signature

  7½" — 1937 - 1968
    with signature
    without signature

  8" — 1968 to the present
    without signature

  8½" — 1937 - 1969
    with signature
    without signature

  10½" — 1987 to the present
    without signature

PORRIDGE PLATE — 1937 - 1960
    with signature
    without signature

SAVINGS BOOK — 1982 to the present
    without signature

STRATFORD
  Beaker — 1983 - 1993
    without signature

  Saucer — 1987 - 1997
    without signature

  Teacup — 1987 - 1997
    without signature

SUGAR BOWL WITH HANDLES — c.1950
    with signature
    without signature

PART ONE
BUNNYKINS TABLEWARE

BUNNYKINS TABLEWARE
Issues of 1934 to the present

BUNNYKINS BREAKFAST SET
Issues of 1939 - 1945

BUNNYKINS BANKS
Issues of 1967 - 1991

BUNNYKINS TEAPOTS
Issues of 1994 - 1998

Post Box reverse featuring *Holding Hat and Coat*, EC4
From the Royal Doulton Archives

BUNNYKINS TABLEWARE BACKSTAMPS

BKT-1. 1934 - 1937

1a. Lion, Crown, Made in England
1b. Lion, Crown, Made in England, Bunnykins

BKT-2. 1937 - c.1940

2a. Lion, crown, Made in England superimposed above *Tug of War* group. First issue of *Tug of War* logo, notice the lion is monochrome
2b. As above with date code (1927 + number = date of manufacture)

BKT-3. 1937 - 1953

3a. *Tug of War* group with modified lion, crown and Made in England mark to compliment the group. The lion is now coloured and the MADE IN ENGLAND is printed in green. The green print is found only on BKT-3.
3b. As above, but with additional A mark for kiln identification

3c. As 3a, but with 'A', lion, crown, and Made in England mark
3d. As 3c, but now with date code

BKT-4. 1940s

4. Monochrome *Tug of War* group

BKT-5. 1954 - 1958

5. *Tug of War* group with modified lion, crown, Made in England above the word Bunnykins. Now within a circle of registration numbers and trade mark numbers

BKT-6. 1959 - 1967

6. *Tug of War* group, modified lion, crown and Made in England. BUNNYKINS above the words ® REGD TRADE MARK

BKT-7. 1968 - 1971

7. *Tug of War* group, modified lion, crown and Made in England. ENGLISH FINE BONE CHINA above BUNNYKINS ® REGD TRADE MARK

BKT-8. 1972 - 1975

8. *Tug of War* group, modified lion, crown and Made in England, English Fine Bone China; Bunnykins ®, © 1936 Royal Doulton

BKT-9. 1976 - 1984

9. *Tug of War* group, modified lion, crown and Made in England, English Fine Bone China; now with copyright on two lines; © Royal Doulton Tableware Ltd 1936

BKT-10. 1984

10. *Tug of War* group, modified lion, crown and Made in England, English Fine Bone China; with the date 19___84 and all above the words Golden Jubilee Celebration

BKT-11. 1985 - 1987

11. *Tug of War* group, modified lion, crown and Made in England, English Fine Bone China; now with the last line changed to © 1936 Royal Doulton (U.K.)

BK-12. 1988 to the present

12. *Tug of War* group, modified lion, crown and Made in England, English Fine Bone China; now with the last line changed to © 1988 Royal Doulton

BKT-SPECIAL

Over the years special backstamps were used incorporating the *Tug of War* logo with other special design elements such as the logo for the Australian Bicentenary or a wreath of holly leaves for the Christmas plate. We have classified this style of backstamp as 'special.'

SHAPE GUIDE

This guide includes the standard Bunnykins shapes, their sizes and production dates. Originally Bunnykins was produced in either a deep ivory earthenware or a fine white bone china. The white china body was discontinued during the Second World War so examples are very hard to find today. A list of white china shapes from an early catalogue is included here.

In 1968, an ivory bone china body replaced the original earthenware and many early shapes were withdrawn. Those that remained were remodelled for the new body. Today, the majority of Bunnykins nurseryware is made in ivory bone china, the exceptions being the money ball and savings books which are made in a white earthenware body.

Some shapes were modelled specifically for the Bunnykins range, for example the candle holder. Others were adapted from existing tableware ranges. The Casino tea wares, for instance, were originally designed for a striking art deco pattern of that name and the Jaffa fruit saucer takes its name from a fruit set which was produced with various patterns in the 1930s.

The early Casino teapots and jugs were sold in several different sizes that are described as 24s, 30s, 36s and 42s and usually this number is incised on the base. This method of sizing was an industry standard and referred to the number of pieces which could be fitted on to a potter's board as he took them from the wheel. Thus the largest size is 24 as only that number of pieces could be accommodated on the potter's board compared to 42 smaller pieces. The capacity in pints is also given for reference. Collectors will find some slight differences in capacity and size because of potting variations, such as

clay thickness and kiln shrinkage. There were also slight modifications to handles and spouts in the early years.

The baby plates have also been altered over the years and the shape records indicate that the oval design was remodelled in 1947 and the round ones were reduced in weight by 5 ounces, also in 1947.

From time to time, shapes have been developed for the Bunnykins range and then not produced. The model books record that a framed stand for Bunnykins subjects was modelled in 1940 but not approved. This is probably the stand featuring *Going Shopping* (SF10) which has recently turned up in a private collection in the U.S.A. More recently, in the early 1980s, a money box in the form of a post box was modelled but it did not go into production for some reason. Two examples have been recorded, one in the Royal Doulton archives and another in a private collection, see the back cover for an illustration of the post box.

As with the original earthenware range, Bunnykins fine white china shapes were also used for other patterns, for instance the Rex mug can be found with several different nurseryware designs. As yet, not all the fine white china shapes have appeared in the market-place so information is limited. It is believed that the majority of them were exported to the U.S.A. and Canada during the Second World War as this is where examples tend to be found.y earthenware or a fine white bone china. The white china body was discontinued during the Second World War so examples are very hard to find today. A list of white china shapes from an early catalogue is included at the end of this guide.

Stand featuring *Going Shopping* SF10

PLATES AND SAUCERS

Oatmeal / cereal bowl
1937 to the present

Porridge plate
1937 - 1960

Jaffa fruit saucer
wavy rim, 1937 - c.1950
plain rim, c.1950 to the present

SUGAR BOWLS

STRATFORD BEAKER

Sugar bowl with handles
c.1950

Casino sugar bowl
Large, 1½ pint, 30s,
1937 - 1968
Medium, 1 pint, 36s
1937 - 1968

Albion sugar bowl
¼ pint
1987 - 1991

1983 - 1993

CANDLE HOLDER

TEACHING CLOCKS

PICTURE PLAQUES

1940 - 1952

Small second hand   Long second hand
1983 to the present

Small, 6½", 1991 - 1993
Large, 7¼", 1991 - 1993

NIGHT LIGHT
FINE CHINA

1937 - c.1945

MONEY BALL   JAM POT   SAVINGS BOOK   CAKE STAND

LAMP

1982 to the present   1937 - 1952   1982 to the present

BEAKER (PAD) COVER

1940 - 1968

1987 - 1991

1985 - 1991

PLATES

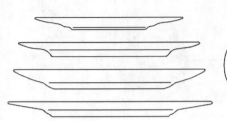

Plate in five sizes
6½", 1937 to the present
7½", 1937 - 1968
8", 1968 to the present
8½", 1937 - 1969
10½", 1987 to the present

Bread and butter plate
with handles
1940 - 1968

TEA CUPS AND SAUCERS

Casino 1937 - 1989
modified 1968

Stratford 1987 - 1997

JUGS

Casino jug in four sizes
¾ pint, 42s, 1937 - 1968
1 pint, 36s, 1937 - 1968
1½ pint, 30s, 1937 - 1968
2 pint, 24s, 1937 - 1968

Albion jug in three sizes
¼ pint, 1987 - 1991
½ pint, 1988 - 1991
1 pint, 1988 - 1991

DON BEAKERS

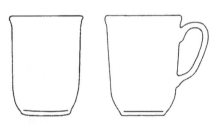

Don beaker, 1937 - 1989
Don beaker with handle, 1940 - 1989
Early Don beakers have running rabbits
border inside inside the rim, later outside

EGG SAUCER, CUPS, AND BOXES

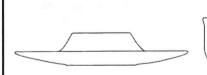

Egg saucer
one size, 1991 - 1996

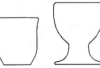

Egg cup, three styles
Footless, 1937 - 1968
Footed, 1940-1968
Semi-footed, 1968 to the present

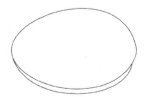

Egg boxes in three sizes
Large, 4¾", 1979 - 1981
Medium, 3¾", 1979 - 1981
Small, 3", 1979 - 1981

BABY PLATES

Round baby plate, small 6"
1937 to the present
modified in 1978 and 1988

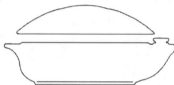

Oval baby plate, two sizes
Small 8¼", 1940 - 1952
Large 8½", 1940 - 1968

Round baby plate, large
7½", 1937 - 1969

HOT WATER PLATES

Hot Water Plate with Cover
One stopper, 1940 - 1959; Two stopper, 1959 - 1969

TEAPOTS

Albion teapot
1 pint size
1987 - 1991

Casino teapot
1 pint size, 36s, 1937 - 1968
1½ pint size, 30s, 1952 - 1968
2 pint size, 24s, 1952 - 1967

DON MUGS

One handle, 1937 - 1983
modified in 1968

Two handles, 1940 - 1983

HUG-A-MUGS

One handle, 1979 to the present

Two handles, 1979 to the present

MALVERN BEAKER

1989 - 1997

LARGE CUP / MUG

1937 - c.1945

FINE WHITE CHINA

The following is a list of shapes that were included in a price list of 1937.

- Beaker
    large
    small
    with one handle
- Beaker pad
- Bread and butter plate
- Carlton Jug
    24s (1 ¼pint)
    30s (1 pint)
    36s (¾ pint)
    42s (½ pint)

- Cecil bowl UBC
- Egg cup
- Night light
- Oatmeal saucer
- Phillips bowl
    30s
    36s
    48s
- Plate
    4 inches
    5 inches
    6 inches
    7 inches

- Porridge plate
- Prince
    Cream jug
        30s (½ pint)
    Teapot
        30s (1 ½ pint)
        42s (1 pint)
- Rex Mug
    large
    small
- Teacup and saucer

Rex Mug in fine china
Front design *Family at Breakfast* (HW12)

Rex Mug in fine china
Reverse design *Kissing Under the Mistletoe*
Second Version, Without mistletoe (HW11R)

Shallow bowl in fine china
Medicine Time (SF1)

Fine china teacups
Footballer (HW13R), *Leapfrog* (HW12R), *Cycling* (HW15R), *Cuddling Under a Mushroom* (HW4),
Kissing Under the Mistletoe, First Version— With Mistletoe (HW11R), *Proposal* (HW11)

BUNNYKINS TABLEWARE
Issues of 1934 to the present

Royal Doulton
Bunnykins Nurseryware Collection

Nursery Clock

3-Piece Child's Set
(8" Plate, Cereal Bowl
& Mug)

Saving Book

2-Piece Baby Set
(Baby Plate & Two
Handled Mug)

Christening Mug

2-Piece Nursery Set
(Baby Plate &
Feeding Spoon)

Divider Dish

Hug-A-Mug
(Two Handled)

Money Ball

ABC THEME
Colin Twinn

ABCDEF Scene

Design No.: CT94 ABCDEF Scene
Designer: Colin Twinn
Issued: 1994 to the present

Shape	U.S. $	Can. $	U.K. £	Aust. $
Baby plate, round, small	40.00	46.00	12.00	49.00
Plate, 8"	30.00	35.00	9.00	39.00

ABCDEF Scene (CT94)

ABC Scene (CT95)

ABC Scene / A Scene

Design No.: Front — CT95 ABC Scene
Reverse — CT96 A Scene
Designer: Colin Twinn
Issued: 1994 to the present

Shape	U.S. $	Can. $	U.K. £	Aust. $
Hug-a-mug, one handle	30.00	33.00	9.00	39.00
Money ball	35.00	40.00	13.00	45.00

Note: Boxed set containing a plate and a hug-a-mug, one handle, U.S. $39.95, £18.00.

A Scene (CT96)

Aerobics

Jogging

Aerobics / Jogging

A boxed Bunnykins for Grown Ups set containing a cereal bowl and hug-a-mug with one handle with the *Aerobics/Jogging* design, a 6" plate with the *Aeroplane* design, an 8" plate with the *Breakfast Time* design and a cereal bowl with the *Tennis* design was distributed mainly in the U.S.A.

Design: Front — Aerobics
             Reverse — Jogging
Designer: Walter Hayward
Issued: 1986 - 1988
Series: Bunnykins for Grown Ups

Shape	U.S. $	Can. $	U.K. £	Aust. $
Cereal bowl	40.00	60.00	25.00	60.00
Hug-a-mug, one handle	30.00	50.00	15.00	50.00
Complete set (M.I.B.)	200.00	300.00	100.00	300.00

Note: See also *Aeroplane* below, *Breakfast Time* page 30 and *Tennis* page 161.

Aeroplane

A boxed Bunnykins for Grown Ups set containing a cereal bowl and hug-a-mug with one handle with the *Aerobics/Jogging* design, a 6" plate with the *Aeroplane* design, an 8" plate with the *Breakfast Time* design and a cereal bowl in the *Tennis* design was distributed mainly in the U.S.A.

Design: Aeroplane
Designer: Walter Hayward
Issued: 1986 - 1988
Series: Bunnykins for Grown Ups

Shape	U.S. $	Can. $	U.K. £	Aust. $
Plate, 6"	40.00	50.00	20.00	50.00
Complete set (M.I.B.)	200.00	300.00	100.00	300.00

Note: See also *Aerobics/Jogging* above, *Breakfast Time* page 30 and *Tennis* page 161.

Aeroplane

Afternoon Tea / Serving Tea

Design No.:	Front — HW116 Afternoon Tea
	Reverse — HW116R Serving Tea
Designer:	Walter Hayward
Issued:	1959 - by 1998
Combined with:	*Ice Cream on the Beach*, HW136R
	Playing with Dolls and Prams, HW115
	Sheltering Under an Umbrella, EC3
	Sledging, Style One, HW141
	Trying on Hats, HW28R

Afternoon Tea (HW116)

Shape	U.S. $	Can. $	U.K. £	Aust. $
Albion cream jug	50.00	75.00	25.00	80.00
Albion jug, ½ pint	50.00	100.00	35.00	100.00
Albion jug, 1 pint	75.00	150.00	50.00	150.00
Albion sugar bowl	40.00	60.00	25.00	55.00
Albion teapot	50.00	100.00	30.00	125.00
Casino jug, 36s	125.00	175.00	75.00	175.00
Casino jug, 42s	150.00	200.00	85.00	175.00
Casino saucer	20.00	30.00	10.00	35.00
Casino sugar bowl, 30s	150.00	225.00	95.00	250.00
Casino sugar bowl, 36s	200.00	300.00	125.00	325.00
Casino teacup	40.00	60.00	15.00	55.00
Casino teapot, 30s	275.00	400.00	125.00	425.00
Divided dish	45.00	65.00	30.00	65.00
Don beaker	45.00	65.00	20.00	65.00
Don beaker, one handle	55.00	75.00	25.00	75.00
Don mug, one handle	40.00	60.00	10.00	60.00
Don mug, two handles	45.00	65.00	12.00	65.00
Egg box				
small	275.00	375.00	100.00	400.00
medium	325.00	475.00	150.00	500.00
large	400.00	575.00	200.00	600.00
Hug-a-mug, one handle	20.00	30.00	8.00	35.00
Hug-a-mug, two handles	25.00	35.00	10.00	40.00
Jaffa fruit saucer (plain)	20.00	30.00	10.00	30.00
Lamp	175.00	250.00	75.00	275.00
Lid of hot water plate	100.00	150.00	60.00	175.00
Malvern beaker	30.00	45.00	15.00	50.00
Money ball	25.00	35.00	12.00	40.00
Picture plaque, small	40.00	60.00	25.00	65.00
Plate, 6½"	20.00	30.00	10.00	30.00
Savings book	35.00	40.00	14.00	45.00
Stratford teacup	30.00	45.00	15.00	45.00

Serving Tea (HW116R)

Airmail Delivery (LFa)

Airmail Delivery

Design No.: LFa
Designer: Barbara Vernon
Issued: By 1937 - by 1952

Shape	U.S. $	Can. $	U.K. £	Aust. $
Baby plate, round, large	650.00	750.00	450.00	800.00
Bread/butter plate, handles	600.00	700.00	400.00	725.00
Porridge bowl	600.00	700.00	400.00	725.00
Plate, 8 ½"	600.00	700.00	400.00	725.00

Note: This design should appear with the Barbara Vernon facsimile signature.

Apple Picking (SF25)

Apple Picking

Design No.: SF25
Designer: Walter Hayward
Issued: 1954 - by 1998

Shape	U.S. $	Can. $	U.K. £	Aust. $
Baby plate, round, small				
with signature	50.00	75.00	35.00	75.00
without signature	20.00	30.00	12.00	30.00
Cake stand	150.00	200.00	65.00	200.00
Casino saucer				
with signature	30.00	35.00	15.00	35.00
without signature	10.00	10.00	5.00	10.00
Cereal / oatmeal bowl				
with signature	50.00	75.00	35.00	75.00
without signature	25.00	30.00	15.00	30.00
Hot water plate				
with signature	125.00	200.00	85.00	200.00
without signature	100.00	150.00	75.00	150.00
Plate, 6 ½"				
with signature	90.00	135.00	50.00	135.00
without signature	20.00	30.00	10.00	25.00
Plate, 7 ½"				
with signature	100.00	150.00	60.00	150.00
without signature	20.00	30.00	10.00	30.00
Plate, 8"	20.00	30.00	10.00	30.00
Plate, 8", 'Special Events'	100.00	100.00	50.00	100.00

'Special Events Tour 1990'

Note: An 8" plate was issued for the U.S. 'Special Events Tour 1990.' The year 1990 was incorporated under the design. The reverse is inscribed 'To' and 'From' to be completed by customer, and 'Special Events Tour 1990.'

Art Class

Design No.: LF107
Designer: Walter Hayward
Issued: 1959 - 1970

Shape	U.S. $	Can. $	U.K. £	Aust. $
Baby plate, oval, large	100.00	150.00	75.00	165.00
Baby plate, round, large	150.00	200.00	95.00	195.00
Porridge bowl	125.00	165.00	85.00	175.00
Plate, 8 ½"	100.00	20000	75.00	195.00

Art Class (LF107)

Artist

Design No.: HW1
Designer: Barbara Vernon
Issued: By 1937 - by 1952
Combined with: *Dunce*, HW1R
Pulling on Trousers, HW2

Shape	U.S. $	Can. $	U.K. £	Aust. $
Baby plate, round, small				
with signature	100.00	150.00	60.00	150.00
without signature	75.00	100.00	45.00	100.00
Casino jug, 42s				
with signature	200.00	300.00	150.00	300.00
without signature	125.00	175.00	75.00	165.00
Casino saucer				
with signature	75.00	100.00	45.00	100.00
without signature	50.00	75.00	35.00	75.00
Casino sugar bowl, 30s				
with signature	150.00	225.00	85.00	250.00
without signature	100.00	150.00	65.00	175.00
Casino teacup				
with signature	100.00	150.00	60.00	150.00
without signature	75.00	100.00	45.00	100.00
Don beaker				
with signature	115.00	165.00	70.00	150.00
without signature	65.00	100.00	40.00	100.00
Don beaker, one handle				
with signature	115.00	165.00	70.00	150.00
without signature	65.00	100.00	40.00	100.00
Don mug, one handle				
with signature	100.00	150.00	60.00	175.00
without signature	75.00	115.00	45.00	115.00
Don mug, two handles				
with signature	125.00	175.00	75.00	175.00
without signature	100.00	150.00	60.00	150.00
Jam pot	850.00	1,275.00	500.00	1,300.00
Plate, 6 ½"				
with signature	100.00	150.00	60.00	150.00
without signature	50.00	75.00	30.00	75.00
Plate, fine china	100.00	150.00	60.00	150.00
Teacup, fine china		Very rare		

Artist (HW1)

Asleep in the Open Air (HW10)

Asleep in the Open Air

Design No.: HW10
Designer: Barbara Vernon
Issued: By 1937 - by 1967
Combined with: *Bathtime*, Style One, SF18
Convalescing, SF5
Leapfrog, HW12R
Washing in the Open Air, HW10R

Shape	U.S. $	Can. $	U.K. £	Aust. $
Casino jug, 30s				
with signature	175.00	250.00	125.00	250.00
without signature	150.00	200.00	80.00	200.00
Casino jug, 36s				
with signature	150.00	225.00	90.00	225.00
without signature	135.00	200.00	80.00	200.00
Casino jug, 42s				
with signature	135.00	200.00	85.00	200.00
without signature	125.00	175.00	70.00	175.00
Casino saucer				
with signature	35.00	50.00	25.00	50.00
without signature	25.00	40.00	15.00	40.00
Casino sugar bowl, 30s				
with signature	200.00	300.00	125.00	325.00
without signature	150.00	225.00	85.00	225.00
Casino sugar bowl, 36s				
with signature	200.00	300.00	125.00	325.00
without signature	150.00	225.00	85.00	225.00
Casino teacup				
with signature	65.00	95.00	40.00	100.00
without signature	35.00	45.00	20.00	50.00
Casino teapot, 24s				
with signature	300.00	450.00	175.00	575.00
without signature	250.00	400.00	150.00	525.00
Casino teapot, 30s				
with signature	375.00	575.00	225.00	650.00
without signature	300.00	450.00	175.00	575.00
Casino teapot, 36s				
with signature	375.00	575.00	225.00	650.00
without signature	300.00	450.00	175.00	575.00
Don beaker				
with signature	75.00	100.00	45.00	100.00
without signature	50.00	75.00	30.00	80.00
Don beaker, one handle				
with signature	75.00	100.00	45.00	100.00
without signature	50.00	80.00	30.00	80.00
Don mug, one handle				
with signature	100.00	150.00	60.00	150.00
without signature	75.00	100.00	45.00	100.00
Don mug, two handles				
with signature	75.00	100.00	45.00	100.00
without signature	50.00	75.00	30.00	75.00
Jaffa fruit saucer				
plain rim	50.00	75.00	30.00	75.00
wavy rim	125.00	175.00	75.00	175.00
Plate, 6½"				
with signature	65.00	100.00	40.00	100.00
without signature	50.00	75.00	30.00	75.00

AUSTRALIANA BUNNYKINS
Colin Twinn

Picnic with Kangaroo and Koala
First Variation, Large Size

The 1994 plates have a leaf border with the inscription 'Bunnykins 60th Anniversary 1994.'

Design No.: Front — CT84 Picnic With Kangaroo And Koala
Reverse — CT85 Commemorative Leaf Border
Designer: Colin Twinn
Issued: 1994 - 1994
Backstamp: 'Bunnykins 60th Anniversary Australiana Bunnykins. Produced exclusively for Royal Doulton Australia.'

Shape	U.S. $	Can. $	U.K. £	Aust. $
Plate, 8"	40.00	50.00	20.00	50.00

Picnic with Kangaroo and Koala
First Variation (CT84)

Picnic with Kangaroo and Koala
Second Variation (CT86)

Picnic with Kangaroo and Koala
Second Variation, Small Size

Design No.: CT86 Picnic with Kangaroo and Koala
Designer: Colin Twinn
Issued: 1994 - 1994
Backstamp: 'Australiana Bunnykins. Produced exclusively for Royal Doulton Australia.'

Shape	U.S. $	Can. $	U.K. £	Aust. $
Baby plate, round, small	35.00	50.00	20.00	45.00
Cereal / oatmeal bowl	25.00	40.00	15.00	35.00

ENGLISH FINE BONE CHINA
"BUNNYKINS" ®
© 1936 ROYAL DOULTON

**Australiana Bunnykins
Produced exclusively
for Royal Doulton
Australia.**

Backstamp (CT86)

Front — Picnic Scene (CT87)

Picnic Scene / Bunny with Cake Plate

The backstamp on this teacup and saucer does not refer to the 60th Anniversary celebrations.

Design No.: Front — CT87 Picnic scene
Reverse — CT88 Bunny with cake plate
Designer: Colin Twinn
Issued: 1994 - 1994

Shape	U.S. $	Can. $	U.K. £	Aust. $
Stratford teacup	40.00	50.00	25.00	50.00

Reverse — Bunny with Cake Plate (CT88)

Front — Picnic Scene with Hamper (CT89)

Picnic Scene with Hamper / Father Asleep

Design No.: Front — CT89 Picnic scene with hamper
Reverse — CT90 Father asleep
Designer: Colin Twinn
Issued: 1994 - 1994
Backstamp: 'Australiana Bunnykins. Produced exclusively for Royal Doulton Australia.'

Shape	U.S. $	Can. $	U.K. £	Aust. $
Hug-a-mug, one handle	40.00	40.00	20.00	35.00
Money ball	40.00	50.00	20.00	50.00

Reverse — Father Asleep (CT90)

Baking

Design No.: SF19
Designer: Walter Hayward after Barbara Vernon
Issued: By 1952 - by 1998

Shape	U.S. $	Can. $	U.K. £	Aust. $
Baby plate, round, large				
with signature	90.00	150.00	45.00	175.00
without signature	35.00	50.00	25.00	50.00
Baby plate, round, small				
with signature	50.00	75.00	35.00	75.00
without signature	20.00	30.00	12.00	30.00
Casino jug, 30s				
with signature	125.00	175.00	75.00	175.00
without signature	100.00	150.00	60.00	150.00
Casino saucer				
with signature	35.00	50.00	15.00	50.00
without signature	10.00	15.00	5.00	15.00
Casino teapot				
with signature	275.00	525.00	175.00	550.00
without signature	225.00	350.00	140.00	375.00
Cereal / oatmeal bowl				
with signature	50.00	75.00	25.00	75.00
without signature	25.00	35.00	10.00	35.00
Hot water plate				
with signature	125.00	200.00	85.00	200.00
without signature	100.00	150.00	65.00	150.00
Jaffa fruit saucer				
plain rim	20.00	30.00	10.00	30.00
wavy rim				
with signature	95.00	150.00	40.00	150.00
without signature	50.00	75.00	20.00	75.00
Plate, 6 ½"				
with signature	90.00	135.00	50.00	135.00
without signature	20.00	25.00	10.00	25.00
Plate, 8"	20.00	30.00	10.00	30.00
Plate, 8½"				
with signature	65.00	125.00	30.00	150.00
without signature	25.00	30.00	10.00	30.00

Baking (SF19)

BAKING THEME
Frank Endersby

Baking Cakes with Mother (7)

Baking Cakes with Mother

Design No.: 7 Baking Cakes with Mother
Designer: Frank Endersby
Issued: 1995 to the present

Shape	U.S. $	Can. $	U.K. £	Aust. $
Baby plate, round, small	**40.00**	**46.00**	**12.00**	**49.00**
Cereal / oatmeal bowl	**25.00**	**33.00**	**9.00**	**39.00**
Jaffa fruit saucer	**25.00**	**30.00**	**9.00**	**35.00**
Plate, 6 ½"	**25.00**	**25.00**	**7.00**	**27.00**
Plate, 8"	30.00	35.00	9.00	39.00

Taking Cake From Oven (8)

Taking Cake from Oven / Decorating the Cake

Design No.: Front — 8 Taking Cake from Oven
Reverse — 9 Decorating the Cake
Designer: Frank Endersby
Issued: 1995 to the present

Shape	U.S. $	Can. $	U.K. £	Aust. $
Hug-a-mug, one handle	**30.00**	**33.00**	**9.00**	**39.00**
Hug-a-mug, two handles	**33.00**	**39.00**	**10.00**	**45.00**
Money ball	**35.00**	**40.00**	**13.00**	**45.00**
Stratford teacup	25.00	30.00	10.00	30.00

Note: Bold type in the listing tables indicate a current design on a current shape.

Decorating the Cake (9)

Bath Night

Design No.: LF7
Designer: Barbara Vernon
Issued: By 1940 - by 1952

Shape	U.S. $	Can. $	U.K. £	Aust. $
Baby plate, oval, small				
with signature	100.00	150.00	60.00	160.00
without signature	75.00	100.00	45.00	100.00
Baby plate, round, large				
with signature	150.00	225.00	100.00	225.00
without signature	125.00	175.00	75.00	150.00
Bread / butter plate, handles				
with signature	225.00	350.00	150.00	350.00
without signature	175.00	250.00	125.00	250.00
Cereal / oatmeal bowl				
with signature	85.00	135.00	65.00	135.00
without signature	25.00	35.00	10.00	35.00
Plate, 8 ½"				
with signature	100.00	150.00	65.00	150.00
without signature	85.00	135.00	60.00	135.00
Porridge bowl				
with signature	150.00	200.00	85.00	200.00
without signature	100.00	135.00	65.00	150.00

Bath Night (LF7)

Bathtime, Style One

Design No.: SF18
Designer: Walter Hayward after Barbara Vernon
Issued: By 1952 - 1994
Combined With: *Asleep in the Open Air*, HW10

Shape	U.S. $	Can. $	U.K. £	Aust. $
Baby plate, round, small				
with signature	50.00	75.00	35.00	75.00
without signature	25.00	50.00	15.00	50.00
Cake stand	150.00	200.00	65.00	200.00
Casino jug, 30s				
with signature	125.00	175.00	75.00	175.00
without signature	100.00	150.00	60.00	150.00
Casino saucer				
with signature	35.00	50.00	15.00	50.00
without signature	10.00	10.00	5.00	10.00
Cereal / oatmeal bowl				
with signature	90.00	135.00	60.00	135.00
without signature	25.00	40.00	15.00	40.00
Hot water plate				
with signature	125.00	175.00	85.00	175.00
without signature	100.00	150.00	75.00	150.00
Plate, 6 ½"				
with signature	100.00	135.00	60.00	135.00
without signature	20.00	30.00	10.00	30.00
Plate, 7 ½"				
with signature	115.00	150.00	70.00	150.00
without signature	20.00	30.00	10.00	30.00
Plate, 8 ½"				
with signature	125.00	165.00	80.00	165.00
without signature	20.00	30.00	10.00	30.00

Bathtime, Style One (SF18)

BATHTIME THEME
Colin Twinn

Bathtime, Style Two (CT21)

Bathtime
Style Two, First Variation

Design No.: CT21 Bathtime
Designer: Colin Twinn
Issued: 1991 - 1993

Shape	U.S. $	Can. $	U.K. £	Aust. $
Albion jug, 1 pint	75.00	150.00	50.00	150.00
Albion teapot	50.00	100.00	30.00	125.00
Baby plate, round, small	50.00	65.00	30.00	65.00
Cereal / oatmeal bowl	90.00	135.00	65.00	135.00
Picture plaque, large	50.00	75.00	30.00	80.00

Bathtime Scene, Style Two (CT24)

Bathtime Scene
Style Two, Second Variation /
Bunnies in the Bath, First Version

Design No.: Front — CT24 Bathtime Scene
Reverse — CT25 Bunnies in the Bath, First Version
Designer: Colin Twinn
Issued: 1991 - 1993
Combined with: *Bunnies in Bath,* Second Version, CT34
Bunny on Trike, CT23
School Gates, Second Variation, CT22

Shape	U.S. $	Can. $	U.K. £	Aust. $
Albion cream jug	50.00	75.00	35.00	80.00
Albion teapot	50.00	100.00	30.00	125.00
Hug-a-mug, one handle	20.00	30.00	8.00	30.00
Lamp	200.00	300.00	100.00	275.00
Malvern beaker	50.00	7500	20.00	75.00
Malvern mug	60.00	8500	25.00	85.00
Money ball	30.00	50.00	20.00	50.00
Stratford straight beaker	30.00	45.00	15.00	50.00
Stratford teacup	25.00	30.00	10.00	30.00

Note: *Bunnies in the Bath* (CT34) is combined with *Bathtime Scene* (CT24) on a Stratford straight beaker.

Bunnies in the Bath, First Version (CT25)

Bunnies in the Bath
Second Version

Design No.:   CT34
Designer: Colin Twinn
Issued: 1991 - 1993
Combined with: *Bathtime Scene*, Style Two, Second Variation, (CT24)
                Bunny with Mirror, CT35
                Pushing the Wheelbarrow, CT3

Shape	U.S. $	Can. $	U.K. £	Aust. $
Albion sugar bowl	40.00	60.00	25.00	55.00
Albion teapot	50.00	100.00	30.00	125.00
Egg cup				
Style Three	10.00	15.00	5.00	15.00
Savings book	35.00	40.00	15.00	45.00
Stratford straight beaker	30.00	45.00	15.00	50.00

Bunnies in the Bath, Second Version (CT34)

BATHTIME THEME
Frank Endersby

Bathtime
Style Three

Design No.: 22 Bathtime
Designer: Frank Endersby
Issued: 1995 to the present

Shape	U.S. $	Can. $	U.K. £	Aust. $
Baby plate, round, small	40.00	46.00	12.00	49.00
Plate, 6 ½"	25.00	25.00	7.00	27.00
Plate, 8"	30.00	35.00	9.00	39.00

Bathtime, Style Three (22)

Blowing and Bursting Bubbles (23)

Blowing and Bursting Bubbles /
Blowing Bubbles and Sailing Boats

Design No.: Front — 23 Blowing and Bursting Bubbles
             Reverse — 24 Blowing Bubbles and Sailing Boat
Designer: Frank Endersby
Issued: 1996 to the present

Shape	U.S. $	Can. $	U.K. £	Aust. $
Hug-a-mug, one handle	30.00	33.00	9.00	39.00
Hug-a-mug, two handles	33.00	39.00	10.00	45.00
Stratford teacup	25.00	30.00	10.00	30.00

Blowing Bubbles and Sailing Boats (24)

BEDTIME THEME
Frank Endersby

Bedtime in Bunks, Style Two (13)

Bedtime in Bunks, Style Two

Design No.: 13 Bedtime in Bunks
Designer: Frank Endersby
Issued: 1995 to the present

Shape	U.S. $	Can. $	U.K. £	Aust. $
Baby plate, round, small	40.00	46.00	12.00	49.00
Cereal / oatmeal bowl	25.00	33.00	9.00	39.00
Plate, 6 ½"	25.00	25.00	7.00	27.00
Plate, 8"	30.00	35.00	9.00	39.00

Pillow Fight, Style Two (14)

Pillow Fight, Style Two / Playing and Reading

Design No.: Front — 14 Pillow Fight
Reverse — 15 Playing and Reading
Designer: Frank Endersby
Issued: 1995 to the present

Shape	U.S. $	Can. $	U.K. £	Aust. $
Hug-a-mug, one handle	30.00	33.00	9.00	39.00
Hug-a-mug, two handles	33.00	39.00	10.00	45.00
Stratford teacup	25.00	30.00	10.00	30.00

Playing and Reading (15)

Bedtime in Bunks, Style One

Design No.: SF3
Designer: Barbara Vernon
Issued: By 1937 - by 1952

Shape	U.S. $	Can. $	U.K. £	Aust. $
Candle holder	1,500.00	2,500.00	500.00	2,500.00
Hot water plate	150.00	200.00	95.00	200.00
Plate, 7 ½"	150.00	200.00	95.00	200.00
Plate, 8 ½"	150.00	200.00	95.00	200.00

Note: This design should appear with the Barbara Vernon facsimile signature.

Bedtime in Bunks, Style One (SF3)

Bedtime Story (SF130)

Bedtime Story

Design No.: SF130
Designer: Walter Hayward
Issued: 1967 - 1994

Shape	U.S. $	Can. $	U.K. £	Aust. $
Baby plate, round, small	35.00	50.00	25.00	50.00
Cake stand	125.00	175.00	65.00	200.00
Casino saucer	10.00	15.00	5.00	15.00
Casino teapot, 24s	275.00	525.00	175.00	550.00
Cereal / oatmeal bowl	25.00	35.00	15.00	35.00
Hot water plate	100.00	150.00	65.00	150.00
Jaffa fruit saucer (plain)	45.00	60.00	25.00	60.00
Plate, 6 ½"	20.00	30.00	10.00	30.00
Plate, 8"	25.00	35.00	15.00	40.00

Bedtime with Dollies (EC125)

Bedtime with Dollies

Design No.:	EC125
Designer:	Walter Hayward
Issued:	1959 - 1992
Combined with:	*Cricketer*, HW22R
	Drummer, EC2
	Drummer and Bugler, EC126
	Holding Hat and Coat, EC4
	Playing with Cup and Spoon, EC6
	Playing with Doll and Pram, EC123
	Raising Hat, Style Two, EC7
	Reading, EC122
	Sheltering Under an Umbrella, EC3
	Trying on Knitting, HW119R
	Unravelling the Knitting, HW119
	Wheelbarrow Race, Style One, HW22

Shape	U.S. $	Can. $	U.K. £	Aust. $
Albion sugar bowl	40.00	60.00	25.00	55.00
Beaker cover	75.00	100.00	35.00	100.00
Casino sugar bowl, 36s	40.00	60.00	25.00	65.00
Egg cup				
Style One	35.00	60.00	25.00	65.00
Style Two	60.00	100.00	30.00	125.00
Style Three	10.00	15.00	5.00	15.00
Lid of hot water plate	100.00	150.00	75.00	150.00

Beware of the Bull

Design No.:	LF108
Designer:	Walter Hayward
Issued:	1959 - 1970

Shape	U.S. $	Can. $	U.K. £	Aust. $
Baby plate, oval, small	75.00	100.00	50.00	100.00
Baby plate, round, large	150.00	200.00	85.00	200.00
Plate, 8"	125.00	175.00	75.00	175.00
Plate, 8 ½"	125.00	175.00	75.00	175.00
Porridge bowl	150.00	200.00	80.00	200.00

Beware of the Bull (LF108)

Bonfire

Design No.: LF128
Designer: Walter Hayward
Issued: 1967 - 1970

Shape	U.S. $	Can. $	U.K. £	Aust. $
Baby plate, round, large	300.00	500.00	200.00	500.00
Plate, 8"	250.00	400.00	150.00	425.00

Bonfire (LF128)

Breakfast Time

Breakfast Time

A boxed Bunnykins for Grown Ups set containing a cereal bowl and hug-a-mug with one handle with the *Aerobics/Jogging* design, a 6" plate with the *Aeroplane* design, an 8" plate with the *Breakfast Time* design and a cereal bowl in the *Tennis* design was distributed mainly in the U.S.A.

Design: Breakfast Time
Designer: Walter Hayward
Issued: 1986 - 1988
Series: Bunnykins for Grown Ups

Shape	U.S. $	Can. $	U.K. £	Aust. $
Plate, 8"	40.00	50.00	25.00	50.00
Complete set (M.I.B.)	200.00	300.00	125.00	300.00

Note: See also *Aerobics/Jogging* and *Aeroplane* page 14 and *Tennis* page 161.

Building Sand Castles (HW138)

Sailing Boats (HW138R)

Building Sand Castles / Sailing Boats

Design No.:	Front — HW138 Building Sand Castles
	Reverse — HW138R Sailing Boats
Designer:	Walter Hayward
Issued:	1967 - by 1998
Combined with:	*Playing with Doll and Pram*, EC123
	Roller Skating Arm in Arm, HW137R
	Roller Skating Race, HW137

Shape	U.S. $	Can. $	U.K. £	Aust. $
Albion cream jug	50.00	75.00	25.00	80.00
Albion jug, ½ pint	50.00	100.00	35.00	100.00
Albion teapot	50.00	100.00	30.00	125.00
Don beaker	45.00	65.00	20.00	65.00
Don beaker, one handle	55.00	75.00	25.00	75.00
Don mug, one handle	40.00	60.00	10.00	60.00
Don mug, two handles	45.00	65.00	12.00	65.00
Hug-a-mug, one handle	20.00	30.00	8.00	35.00
Hug-a-mug, two handles	25.00	35.00	10.00	40.00
Lamp	175.00	250.00	75.00	275.00
Lid of hot water plate	100.00	150.00	60.00	175.00
Malvern beaker	30.00	45.00	15.00	50.00
Money ball	25.00	35.00	12.00	40.00
Picture plaque, small	40.00	60.00	25.00	65.00
Stratford straight beaker	30.00	45.00	15.00	50.00
Stratford teacup	30.00	45.00	15.00	45.00

Bunnykins Build a Snowman (PN198)

Bunnykins Build a Snowman

Design No.: PN198
Designer: Frank Endersby
Issued: 1998 - 1998
Series: RDICC Plate of the Year, Number 2

Shape	U.S. $	Can. $	U.K. £	Aust. $
Plate, 8"	45.00	60.00	30.00	60.00

Bunnykins Celebrate Australia's Bicentenary 1788-1988

Design No.: None
Designer: Walter Hayward
Issued: 1987 - 1988
Backstamp: 'The Australian Bicentenary 1788-1988'

Shape	U.S. $	Can. $	U.K. £	Aust. $
Plate, 8"	75.00	95.00	35.00	100.00

Bunnykins Celebrate Australia's Bicentenary
1788-1988

BUNNYKINS CELEBRATE THEIR GOLDEN JUBILEE
Walter Hayward / Barbara Vernon

Birthday Cake

Design No.: SF140 — Birthday Cake
Designer: Walter Hayward
Issued: 1984 - 1984
Backstamp: Golden Jubilee Celebration

Shape	U.S. $	Can. $	U.K. £	Aust. $
Baby plate, round, small				
with inscription	85.00	100.00	50.00	100.00
without inscription	60.00	85.00	35.00	85.00
Cereal bowl				
with inscription	85.00	100.00	50.00	100.00
without inscription	60.00	85.00	35.00	85.00
Plate, 8"				
with inscription	85.00	100.00	50.00	100.00
without inscription	60.00	75.00	35.00	75.00

Note: The inscription was removed from the design after the Jubilee and the design was sold on baby plates, cereal bowls and the 8" plate.

Birthday Cake (SF140)

Chicken Pulling a Cart (SF141)

Chicken Pulling a Cart

This scene was first issued in 1940 and discontinued by 1952. It was reissued in 1984 to commemorate the fiftieth anniversary of Bunnykins and was issued in two variations, with and without the inscription.

Design No.: SF141 — Chicken Pulling a Cart
Designer: After a design by Barbara Vernon (SF8)
Issued: 1984 - 1984
Backstamp: Golden Jubilee Celebration.

Shape	U.S. $	Can. $	U.K. £	Aust. $
Plate, 8"				
with inscription	125.00	175.00	70.00	175.00
without inscription	100.00	150.00	55.00	150.00

Note: See *Chicken Pulling a Cart* page 44.

BUNNYKINS CELEBRATE YOUR CHRISTENING
Walter Hayward

Bunnykins Celebrate Your Christening
First Version (SF139)

Style One, First Version

Design No.: SF139 Bunnykins celebrate your Christening
Designer: Walter Hayward
Issued: 1984 - 1989

Shape	U.S. $	Can. $	U.K. £	Aust. $
Plate, 8"	50.00	75.00	30.00	75.00

Bunnykins Celebrate Your Christening
Second Version (HW142)

Style One, Second Version

Design No.: Front — HW142 Bunnykins celebrate your Christening
             Reverse — HW142R Christening inscription
Designer: Walter Hayward
Issued: 1984 - 1990

Shape	U.S. $	Can. $	U.K. £	Aust. $
Hug-a-mug, one handle	40.00	60.00	25.00	65.00
Hug-a-mug, two handles	40.00	60.00	25.00	65.00
Money ball	40.00	60.00	25.00	60.00
Savings book	40.00	60.00	25.00	60.00

Christening Inscription (HW142R)

BUNNYKINS CELEBRATE YOUR CHRISTENING
Colin Twinn

Style Two, First Variation, Large Size

Design No.: Front — CT38 Bunnykins celebrate your Christening
Reverse no. one — without rhyme
Reverse no. two — CT 65 with rhyme
Designer: Colin Twinn
Issued: 1990 - 1993
Rhyme: 'Today, as your family welcomes you
To bless who you are and all you will do
The Bunnykins join in your bright celebration
And bring you a message of jubilation
For, on this day, we all wish for you
A lifetime of love and much happiness too.'

Shape	U.S. $	Can. $	U.K. £	Aust. $
Plate, 8"	50.00	75.00	30.00	65.00

Bunnykins Celebrate Your Christening (CT38)

Bunnykins Celebrate Your Christening (CT41)

Christening rhyme (CT65)

Style Two, SecondVariation, Small Size

Design No.: Front — CT41 Bunnykins celebrate your Christening
Reverse — CT42 Christening inscription
Designer: Colin Twinn
Issued: 1991 - 1993

Shape	U.S. $	Can. $	U.K. £	Aust. $
Hug-a-mug, one handle	40.00	60.00	25.00	65.00
Hug-a-mug, two handles	45.00	65.00	25.00	70.00
Money ball	35.00	50.00	25.00	55.00

Christening Inscription (CT42)

Baby in Crib with Father Looking On (CT76)

Style Three, First Variation
Baby in Crib with Father Looking On

Design No.: Front — CT76 Baby in crib with father looking on
Reverse — CT77 Rhyme
Designer: Colin Twinn
Issued: 1993 to the present
Rhyme: 'Today, as your family welcomes you
To bless who you are and all you will do
The Bunnykins join in your bright celebration
And bring you a message of jubilation
For, on this your day, we all wish for you
A lifetime of love and much happiness too.'

Shape	U.S. $	Can. $	U.K. £	Aust. $
Plate, 8"	30.00	35.00	11.00	39.00

Baby in Crib (CT78)

Style Three, Second Variation
Baby in Crib

Design No.: Front — CT78 Baby in Crib
Reverse — CT79 Christening inscription
Designer: Colin Twinn
Issued: 1993 to the present

Shape	U.S. $	Can. $	U.K. £	Aust. $
Hug-a-mug, one handle	30.00	33.00	9.00	39.00
Hug-a-mug, two handles	33.00	39.00	10.00	45.00
Money ball	35.00	40.00	13.00	45.00

Note: Bold type in the listing tables indicate a current design on a current shape.

Christening Inscription (CT79)

BUNNYKINS COLLECTORS CLUB, AUSTRALIA

Member of Bunnykins Club
Bunnykins Bunnies are Children Like You

These plates, with the Member of Bunnykins Club inscription, were made exclusively for the Bunnykins club members in Australia. Other designs with this inscription may exist.

Design No.: SF18 — Bathtime, Style One
SF112 — Television Time
SF113 — Camp Site
SF130 — Bedtime Story
SF131 — Home Decorating
SF132 — Space Rocket Launch
SF133 — Flying Kites
SF134 — Toppling the Fruit Cart
SF135 — Family in the Garden
Issued: 1979 - 1985

Shape	Design	U.S. $	Can. $	U.K. £	Aust. $
Plate, 6 ½"	Various	200.00	300.00	150.00	225.00

Member of Bunnykins Club/Television Time (SF112)

Bunnykins Help Santa (PN 175)

Bunnykins Help Santa

Design No.: PN175
Designer: Frank Endersby
Issued: 1997 - 1997
Series: RDICC Plate of the Year (No 1)
Backstamp: RDICC plus Bunnykins and Frank Endersby facsimile signature

Shape	U.S. $	Can. $	U.K. £	Aust. $
Plate, 8"	45.00	60.00	30.00	60.00

BUNNYKINS 60TH ANNIVERSARY

Dancing in the Moonlight, First Variation (CT91)

Dancing in the Moonlight
Second Version, First Variation, Large Size

Design No.: Front — CT91 Dancing in the Moonlight
Designer: Justin Clarke based on a design by Barbara Vernon
Issued: 1994 - 1994
Backstamp: Dancing in the Moonlight Bunnykins 60th Anniversary

Shape	U.S. $	Can. $	U.K.£	Aust. $
Baby plate, round, small	50.00	60.00	25.00	60.00
Plate, 8"	40.00	60.00	20.00	60.00

Note: See also *Dancing in the Moonlight*, Style One, page 56.

Dancing in the Moonlight, Second Variation (CT92)

Dancing in the Moonlight
Second Version, Second Variation, Small Size

Design No.: Front — CT92 Dancing in the Moonlight
             Reverse — CT93 Bunnykins 60th Anniversary inscription
Designer: Justin Clarke based on a design by Barbara Vernon
Issued: 1994 - 1994

Shape	U.S. $	Can. $	U.K.£	Aust. $
Hug-a-mug, one handle	40.00	50.00	15.00	50.00
Money ball	35.00	50.00	20.00	50.00

Bunnykins 60th Anniversary Inscription (CT93)

BUNNYKINS TEACHING CLOCKS
Walter Hayward, Colin Twinn, Frank Endersby

Bunnykins Teaching Clock, Long Second Hand
Classroom Scene, Style One

Design No.: Front — SF138 Classroom scene
            Rev. — Inscription
Designer: Walter Hayward
Issued: 1983 - 1990
Rhyme: 'Learning can be hours of fun
            For Bunnykins and everyone
            To tell the time we learn today
            As we see the clock tick minutes away.'

Shape	U.S. $	Can. $	U.K. £	Aust. $
Teaching clock	100.00	125.00	40.00	125.00

Bunnykins teaching clock, long second hand
Classroom Scene (SF138)

Bunnykins teaching clock, short second hand
Classroom Scene (CT36)

Bunnykins Teaching Clock, Short Second Hand
Classroom Scene, Style Two, First Version

Design No.: Front — CT36 Classroom scene
Designer: Colin Twinn
Issued: 1991 - 1993
Rhyme: 'Learning can be hours of fun
            For Bunnykins and everyone
            To tell the time we learn today
            As we see the clock tick minutes away."

Shape	U.S. $	Can. $	U.K. £	Aust. $
Teaching clock	100.00	1215.00	65.00	125.00

Note: For information on other shapes with this design see page 47.

Bunnykins teaching clock, short second hand
Four individual scenes

Bunnykins Teaching Clock, Short Second Hand
Four Individual Scenes

Design No.: None — Four individual scenes
Designer: Frank Endersby
Issued: 1996 to the present

Shape	U.S. $	Can. $	U.K. £	Aust. $
Teaching clock	90.00	100.00	30.00	120.00

Camp Site

Design No.: SF113 Camp Site
Designer: Walter Hayward
Issued: 1959 - by 1998

Shape	U.S. $	Can. $	U.K. £	Aust. $
Baby plate, round, small	20.00	30.00	12.00	30.00
Cake stand	150.00	200.00	75.00	200.00
Casino saucer	10.00	10.00	5.00	10.00
Cereal / oatmeal bowl	25.00	40.00	15.00	40.00
Jaffa fruit saucer (plain)	20.00	30.00	10.00	30.00
Hot water plate	100.00	150.00	75.00	150.00
Plate, 6 ½"	20.00	30.00	10.00	30.00
Plate, 7 ½"	20.00	30.00	10.00	30.00
Plate, 8"	20.00	30.00	10.00	30.00

Camp Site (SF113)

CAMPING THEME
Frank Endersby

Camping (34)

Camping

Design No.: 34 Camping
Designer: Frank Endersby
Issued: 1996 to the present

Shape	U.S. $	Can. $	U.K. £	Aust. $
Baby plate, round, small	40.00	46.00	12.00	49.00
Cereal / oatmeal bowl	25.00	33.00	9.00	39.00
Plate, 6 ½"	25.00	25.00	7.00	27.00
Plate, 8"	30.00	35.00	9.00	39.00

Campfire (35)

Campfire / Asleep in a Sleeping Bag

Design No.: Front — 35 Campfire
Reverse — 36 Asleep in a Sleeping Bag
Designer: Frank Endersby
Issued: 1996 to the present

Shape	U.S. $	Can. $	U.K. £	Aust. $
Hug-a-mug, one handle	30.00	33.00	9.00	39.00
Hug-a-mug, two handles	33.00	39.00	10.00	45.00
Stratford teacup	25.00	30.00	10.00	30.00

Asleep in a Sleeping Bag (36)

Carol Singer Bunnykins
Christmas Tree Ornament

Design No.: Front — CT70
             Reverse — CT71
Designer: Colin Twinn
Issued: 1992 - 1992
Series: Christmas Tree Ornaments

Shape	U.S. $	Can. $	U.K. £	Aust. $
Christmas tree ornament	25.00	40.00	15.00	50.00

Note: For other Christmas ornaments in this series see pages 45, 83, 144 and 166.

Carol Singer Bunnykins (CT70)

Christmas 1992 (CT71)

Carving the Chicken

Design No.: LFc
Designer: Barbara Vernon
Issued: By 1937 - by 1952

Shape	U.S. $	Can. $	U.K. £	Aust. $
Bread / butter plate, handles	200.00	300.00	150.00	250.00
Plate, 8 ½"	200.00	300.00	150.00	275.00
Porridge bowl	200.00	300.00	150.00	275.00

Note: These designs should appear with the Barbara Vernon facsimile signature.

Carving the Chicken (LFc)

Chicken Pulling a Cart (SF8)

Chicken Pulling a Cart

Design No.: SF8
Designer: Barbara Vernon
Issued: By 1940 - by 1952

Shape	U.S. $	Can. $	U.K. £	Aust. $
Baby plate, round, small				
with signature	100.00	150.00	60.00	150.00
without signature	50.00	75.00	30.00	75.00
Casino jug, 36s				
with signature	150.00	225.00	90.00	225.00
without signature	135.00	200.00	80.00	200.00
Casino saucer				
with signature	75.00	100.00	45.00	100.00
without signature	50.00	75.00	35.00	75.00
Casino sugar bowl, 30s				
with signature	150.00	225.00	85.00	250.00
without signature	100.00	150.00	65.00	175.00
Cereal / oatmeal bowl				
with signature	75.00	125.00	50.00	125.00
without signature	50.00	75.00	30.00	75.00
Jaffa fruit saucer				
plain rim	150.00	225.00	100.00	250.00
wavy rim	75.00	125.00	50.00	125.00
Hot water plate				
with signature	125.00	200.00	85.00	200.00
without signature	100.00	150.00	75.00	150.00
Plate, 6 ½"				
with signature	65.00	100.00	45.00	100.00
without signature	50.00	75.00	30.00	75.00
Plate, 7 ½"				
with signature	75.00	125.00	55.00	125.00
without signature	50.00	75.00	30.00	75.00
Plate, 8½"				
with signature	85.00	150.00	65.00	150.00
without signature	75.00	125.00	60.00	125.00
Saucer, fine china		Very rare		

Note: This scene was re-issued on an 8" plate in 1984 with the Bunnykins Golden Jubilee backstamp, see page 33.

Christmas Morn
Christmas Tree Ornament

This Christmas tree ornament has a rabbit-shaped rim. It was commissioned by Royal Doulton U.S.A. and made in the U.S.A.

Design No.: None
Designer: Frank Endersby
Issued: 1996 - 1996
Backstamp: 'Christmas Morn' Christmas 1996 Royal Doulton 'Bunnykins' ® © 1996 Royal Doulton made in U.S.A.
Series: Christmas Tree Ornaments

Shape	U.S. $	Can. $	U.K. £	Aust. $
Christmas tree ornament	30.00	50.00	20.00	50.00

Note: For other Christmas ornaments in this series see pages 43, 83, 144 and 166.

Christmas Morn

Christmas Party (LF9)

Christmas Party

Design No.: LF9
Designer: Barbara Vernon
Issued: By 1940 - 1967

Shape	U.S. $	Can. $	U.K. £	Aust. $
Baby plate, oval, large				
with signature	125.00	200.00	100.00	200.00
without signature	100.00	150.00	75.00	150.00
Baby plate, round, large				
with signature	125.00	175.00	100.00	200.00
without signature	100.00	150.00	75.00	150.00
Bread / butter plate, handles				
with signature	200.00	275.00	175.00	300.00
without signture	150.00	225.00	100.00	250.00
Plate, 8 ½"				
with signature	85.00	135.00	60.00	135.00
without signature	75.00	125.00	50.00	125.00
Porridge bowl				
with signature	135.00	175.00	85.00	175.00
without signature	90.00	145.00	75.00	150.00

Christmas Tree (LF16)

Christmas Tree

Design No.: LF16
Designer: Walter Hayward
Issued: 1954 - 1967

Shape	U.S. $	Can. $	U.K. £	Aust. $
Baby plate, oval, large				
with signature	225.00	325.00	135.00	300.00
without signature	125.00	200.00	80.00	225.00
Baby plate, round, large				
with signature	250.00	350.00	150.00	300.00
without signature	125.00	200.00	80.00	225.00
Bread / butter plate, handles				
with signature	200.00	275.00	175.00	300.00
without signature	150.00	225.00	100.00	250.00
Plate, 8½"				
with signature	125.00	175.00	85.00	180.00
without signature	90.00	125.00	60.00	135.00
Porridge bowl				
with signature	150.00	200.00	85.00	200.00
without signature	100.00	145.00	75.00	150.00

Classroom Scene
Style Two, First Version

Design No.: CT36
Designer: Colin Twinn
Issued: 1991 - 1993

Shape	U.S. $	Can. $	U.K. £	Aust. $
Albion jug, 1 pint	100.00	150.00	60.00	150.00
Plate, 6"	25.00	40.00	15.00	40.00
Plate, 8"	30.00	45.00	20.00	50.00

Note: For information on the Bunnykins Teaching Clock with this design see page 39.

For illlustration of
this design see
Bunnykins Teaching Clock,
page 39.

Classroom, Style Two (CT16)

Classroom Scene
Style Two, Second Version

Design No.: CT16 Classroom
Designer: Colin Twinn
Issued: 1990 - 1993
Combined with: *Picking Daisies,* CT4

Shape	U.S. $	Can. $	U.K. £	Aust. $
Albion cream jug	75.00	115.00	45.00	125.00
Albion jug, ½ pint	50.00	75.00	30.00	75.00
Albion jug, 1 pint	100.00	150.00	60.00	150.00
Albion teapot	65.00	100.00	45.00	120.00
Baby plate, round, small	25.00	30.00	15.00	35.00
Cake stand	175.00	250.00	100.00	275.00
Jaffa fruit saucer (plain)	30.00	45.00	20.00	50.00
Stratford straight beaker	25.00	40.00	15.00	45.00

COMMEMORATIVE WARE

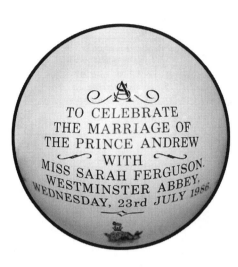

Marriage of the Prince Andrew
with Miss Sarah Ferguson

To Celebrate the Marriage of the Prince Andrew with Miss Sarah Ferguson Westminster Abbey, Wednesday, 23rd July 1986

The following is a list of designs known to appear on these shapes., more may exist.

Design No.: HW27, HW29, HW29R, HW115, HW115R
HW116, HW119, HW119R, HW120,
HW136, HW136R, HW139, HW139R

Issued: 1986

Shape	U.S. $	Can. $	U.K. £	Aust. $
Hug-a-mug, one handle	90.00	135.00	45.00	150.00
Money ball	75.00	110.00	45.00	125.00

To Celebrate the Birth of the First Child of T.R.H. the Prince and Princess of Wales 1982

The following is a list of designs known to appear on these shapes., more may exist.

Design No.: HW17, HW17R, HW22, HW22R, HW 23, HW23R
HW26, HW26R, HW27R, HW137, HW137R
EC1, EC4, EC121, EC126

Issued: 1982

Shape	U.S. $	Can. $	U.K. £	Aust. $
Hug-a-mug, one handle	75.00	110.00	40.00	125.00
Hug-a-mug, two handles	90.00	135.00	60.00	150.00
Savings book	80.00	110.00	50.00	125.00

Birth of the First Child of
T.R.H. The Prince & Princess of Wales 1982

To T.R.H. the Prince and Princess of Wales
A Second Child 1984 in Joyful Celebration

The following is a list of designs known to appear on these shapes., more may exist.

Design No.:   HW 22R, HW23R, HW27, HW27R
Issued: 1984

Shape	U.S. $	Can. $	U.K. £	Aust. $
Hug-a-mug, one handle	40.00	70.00	25.00	75.00
Savings book	90.00	145.00	50.00	225.00

To T.R.H. The Prince and Princess of Wales
A Second Child 1984

Conducting the Orchestra (LF5)

Conducting the Orchestra

The large, round baby plate was also available with a sterling silver rim, see 1955 Roden catalogue page viii.

Design No.: LF5
Designer: Barbara Vernon
Issued: By 1940 - by 1952
Combined with: *Frightening Spider*, SF4

Shape	U.S. $	Can. $	U.K. £	Aust. $
Baby plate, oval, large				
with signature	225.00	325.00	135.00	350.00
without signature	125.00	200.00	80.00	225.00
Baby plate, round, large				
with signature	250.00	350.00	150.00	350.00
without signature	125.00	200.00	80.00	225.00
Bread / butter plate, handles				
with signature	200.00	275.00	175.00	300.00
without signature	150.00	225.00	100.00	250.00
Casino jug, 24s				
with signature	225.00	350.00	150.00	350.00
without signature	175.00	250.00	125.00	250.00
Hot water plate				
with signature	175.00	275.00	110.00	275.00
without signature	125.00	200.00	85.00	200.00
Plate, 8 ½"				
with signature	175.00	275.00	100.00	275.00
without signature	125.00	200.00	75.00	200.00
Porridge bowl				
with signature	150.00	200.00	90.00	200.00
without signature	100.00	145.00	75.00	150.00

Convalescing

Design No.: SF5
Designer: Barbara Vernon
Issued: By 1940 - by 1952
Combined with: *Asleep in the Open Air* , HW10
                 Soldiers Marching to the Music, HW18
                 Washing in the Open Air, HW10R

Shape	U.S. $	Can. $	U.K. £	Aust. $
Baby plate, round, small	175.00	100.00	60.00	115.00
Bread / butter plate, handles	200.00	275.00	175.00	300.00
Casino saucer	75.00	100.00	45.00	100.00
Casino teapot, 24s	300.00	450.00	175.00	575.00
Cereal / oatmeal bowl	100.00	150.00	65.00	165.00
Jaffa fruit saucer				
plain rim	150.00	225.00	100.00	250.00
wavy rim	75.00	125.00	50.00	125.00
Hot water plate	175.00	275.00	100.00	275.00
Plate, 6 ½"	75.00	100.00	45.00	100.00
Plate, 7 ½"	100.00	150.00	60.00	150.00

Convalescing (SF5)

Note: The above shapes should all appear with the Barbara Vernon facsimile signature.

Cowboys and Indians / Cowboy on Rocking Horse

Design No.:   Front — HW140 Cowboys and Indians
                 Reverse — HW140R Cowboy on Rocking Horse
Designer: Walter Hayward
Issued: 1967 - by 1998
Combined with: *Hobby Horse*, Style Two, EC121

Shape	U.S. $	Can. $	U.K. £	Aust. $
Albion cream jug	50.00	75.00	25.00	80.00
Albion teapot	50.00	100.00	30.00	125.00
Casino teacup	40.00	60.00	15.00	55.00
Divided dish	45.00	65.00	30.00	65.00
Don beaker	45.00	65.00	20.00	65.00
Don beaker, one handle	55.00	75.00	25.00	75.00
Don mug, one handle	40.00	60.00	10.00	60.00
Don mug, two handles	45.00	65.00	12.00	65.00
Egg box				
small	275.00	375.00	100.00	400.00
medium	325.00	475.00	150.00	500.00
large	400.00	575.00	200.00	600.00
Hug-a-mug, one handle	20.00	30.00	8.00	35.00
Hug-a-mug, two handles	25.00	35.00	10.00	40.00
Lamp	175.00	250.00	75.00	275.00
Lid of hot water plate	100.00	150.00	60.00	175.00
Malvern beaker	30.00	45.00	15.00	50.00
Money ball	25.00	35.00	12.00	40.00
Picture plaque, small	40.00	60.00	25.00	65.00
Savings book	35.00	40.00	14.00	45.00
Stratford teacup	30.00	45.00	15.00	45.00

Cowboys and Indians (HW140)

Cowboy on Rocking Horse (HW140R)

Cricket Game (LF12)

Cricket Game

Design No.: LF12
Designer: Walter Hayward after Barbara Vernon
Issued: 1952 - 1967

Shape	U.S. $	Can. $	U.K. £	Aust. $
Baby plate, oval, large				
with signature	225.00	325.00	135.00	350.00
without signature	125.00	200.00	80.00	225.00
Baby plate, round, large				
with signature	250.00	350.00	150.00	350.00
without signature	125.00	200.00	80.00	225.00
Bread / butter plate, handles				
with signature	200.00	275.00	175.00	300.00
without signature	150.00	225.00	100.00	250.00
Plate, 8 ½"				
with signature	175.00	275.00	100.00	275.00
without signature	125.00	200.00	75.00	200.00
Porridge bowl				
with signature	150.00	200.00	85.00	225.00
without signature	100.00	150.00	65.00	150.00

Cuddling under a Mushroom

Design No.: HW4
Designer: Barbara Vernon
Issued: By 1937 - by 1952
Combined with: *Footballer*, HW13R
                 Golfer, HW4R
                 Netting a Cricket, HW6

Shape	U.S. $	Can. $	U.K. £	Aust. $
Casino sugar bowl, 30s				
with signature	150.00	225.00	85.00	250.00
without signature	100.00	150.00	65.00	175.00
Casino teacup				
with signature	65.00	95.00	40.00	95.00
without signature	50.00	75.00	30.00	75.00
Don beaker				
with signature	125.00	175.00	75.00	175.00
without signature	75.00	125.00	45.00	125.00
Don beaker, one handle				
with signature	100.00	150.00	60.00	150.00
without signature	65.00	100.00	40.00	100.00
Don mug, one handle				
with signature	100.00	150.00	60.00	150.00
without signature	75.00	125.00	45.00	125.00
Don mug, two handles				
with signature	75.00	95.00	45.00	95.00
without signature	50.00	75.00	30.00	75.00
Lid of hot water plate				
with signature	85.00	125.00	50.00	125.00
without signature	75.00	100.00	45.00	100.00
Teacup, fine china		Very rare		

Cuddling under a Mushroom (HW4)

Cycling

Design No.:   HW15R
Designer: Barbara Vernon
Issued: By 1937 - by 1967
Combined with: *Family at Breakfast,* HW12
                   Family Going Out on Washing Day, HW8
                   Family with Pram, Style One, HW15
                   Feeding the Baby, HW13
                   Golfer, HW4R
                   Kissing Under Mistletoe, HW11R
                   Pressing Trousers, HW14
                   Proposal, HW11

Cycling (HW15R)

Shape	U.S. $	Can. $	U.K. £	Aust. $
Casino sugar bowl				
with signature	150.00	225.00	85.00	250.00
without signature	100.00	150.00	75.00	175.00
Casino teacup				
with signature	125.00	175.00	75.00	175.00
without signature	75.00	125.00	45.00	125.00
Casino teapot, 30s				
with signature	375.00	575.00	225.00	650.00
without signature	300.00	450.00	175.00	575.00
Don beaker, one handle				
with signature	100.00	150.00	60.00	150.00
without signature	65.00	100.00	40.00	100.00
Don mug, one handle				
with signature	115.00	150.00	60.00	150.00
without signature	75.00	125.00	45.00	125.00
Don mug, two handles				
with signature	75.00	100.00	45.00	95.00
without signature	50.00	75.00	30.00	75.00
Rex mug, fine china		Extremely rare		
Teacup, fine china		Very rare		

Note: The Rex mug combines Cycling (HW15R) with Proposal (HW11).

CYCLING THEME
Frank Endersby

Cycle Ride

Cycle Ride (46)

Design No.: 46 Cycle Ride
Designer: Frank Endersby
Issued: 1995 to the present

Shape	U.S. $	Can. $	U.K. £	Aust. $
Baby plate, round, small	40.00	46.00	12.00	49.00
Jaffa fruit saucer	25.00	33.00	9.00	35.00
Plate, 6 ½"	25.00	25.00	7.00	27.00
Plate, 8"	30.00	35.00	9.00	39.00

Resting (47)

Resting / Cleaning Bike

Design No.: Front — 47 Resting
Reverse — 48 Cleaning bike
Designer: Frank Endersby
Issued: 1995 to the present

Shape	U.S. $	Can. $	U.K. £	Aust. $
Hug-a-mug, one handle	30.00	33.00	9.00	39.00
Hug-a-mug, two handles	33.00	39.00	10.00	45.00

Note: Bold type in the listing tables indicate a current design on a current shape.

Cleaning Bike (48)

Daisy Chains / Smelling Flowers

Daisy Chains (HW25)   Smelling Flowers (HW25R)

Design No.:	Front — HW25 Daisy Chains
	Reverse — HW25R Smelling Flowers
Designer:	Walter Hayward

Issued:	1954 - by 1998
Combined with:	*Hikers*, EC124
	Playing with Cup and Spoon, EC6

Shape	U.S. $	Can. $	U.K. £	Aust. $
Albion cream jug	50.00	75.00	25.00	80.00
Albion jug, ½ pint	50.00	100.00	35.00	100.00
Albion jug, 1 pint	75.00	150.00	50.00	150.00
Albion teapot	50.00	100.00	30.00	125.00
Casino jug, 36s				
with signature	125.00	175.00	75.00	175.00
without signature	100.00	150.00	60.00	150.00
Casino jug, 42s				
with signature	100.00	150.00	60.00	150.00
without signature	85.00	125.00	50.00	125.00
Casino saucer				
with signature	35.00	50.00	15.00	50.00
without signature	10.00	15.00	5.00	15.00
Casino teacup				
with signature	85.00	125.00	50.00	125.00
without signature	40.00	60.00	15.00	70.00
Casino teapot, 30s				
with signature	375.00	575.00	225.00	650.00
without signature	275.00	400.00	125.00	425.00
Don beaker				
with signature	60.00	90.00	55.00	95.00
without signature	35.00	50.00	35.00	60.00
Don beaker, one handle				
with signature	50.00	80.00	50.00	9500
without signature	40.00	60.00	30.00	65.00
Don mug, one handle				
with signature	50.00	80.00	50.00	95.00
without signature	40.00	60.00	30.00	65.00

Shape	U.S. $	Can. $	U.K. £	Aust. $
Don mug, two handles				
with signature	50.00	80.00	50.00	95.00
without signature	40.00	60.00	30.00	65.00
Egg box				
small	250.00	350.00	150.00	375.00
medium	325.00	475.00	200.00	500.00
large	400.00	575.00	250.00	600.00
Hug-a-mug, one handle	20.00	30.00	8.00	35.00
Hug-a-mug, two handles				
Regular issue	25.00	35.00	10.00	40.00
'Special Events'	50.00	75.00	30.00	100.00
Jaffa fruit saucer (plain)	20.00	35.00	10.00	35.00
Lamp	150.00	250.00	75.00	225.00
Lid of hot water plate				
with signature	85.00	125.00	50.00	150.00
without signature	75.00	100.00	45.00	100.00
Malvern beaker	30.00	45.00	15.00	50.00
Money ball	25.00	35.00	12.00	40.00
Picture plaque, small	40.00	65.00	25.00	75.00
Plate, 6½"				
with signature	50.00	75.00	30.00	85.00
without signature	20.00	25.00	7.00	25.00
Savings book	30.00	40.00	15.00	50.00
Stratford straight beaker	30.00	45.00	15.00	75.00
Stratford teacup	30.00	45.00	15.00	50.00

Note: A hug-a-mug (two handles) was issued for the U.S. Special Event Tour in 1993. The front illustrates *Daisy Chains* (HW25), and the back *Hikers* (EC124) with the words '*US Special Events Tour 1993*'.

Dancing in the Moonlight, Style One (LFb)

Dancing in the Moonlight
First Version

Design No.:   LFb
Designer: Barbara Vernon
Issued: 1937 - by 1952

Shape	U.S. $	Can. $	U.K.£	Aust. $
Baby plate, round, large				
with signature	250.00	350.00	150.00	350.00
without signature	125.00	200.00	80.00	225.00
Bread / butter plate, handles				
with signature	200.00	275.00	175.00	300.00
without signature	150.00	225.00	100.00	250.00
Porridge bowl				
with signature	150.00	200.00	85.00	200.00
without signature	100.00	145.00	75.00	150.00
Plate, 8 ½"				
with signature	175.00	275.00	100.00	275.00
without signature	125.00	200.00	75.00	250.00

Note: See also Bunnykins 60th Anniversary page 38.

Dancing Round the Barrel Organ / Skipping Game

Design No.: Front — HW139 Dancing Round the Barrel Organ
Reverse — HW139R Skipping Game
Designer: Walter Hayward
Issued: 1967 - by 1998

Shape	U.S. $	Can. $	U.K. £	Aust. $
Albion cream jug	50.00	75.00	25.00	80.00
Albion jug, ½ pint	50.00	100.00	35.00	100.00
Albion jug, 1 pint	75.00	150.00	50.00	150.00
Albion teapot	50.00	100.00	30.00	125.00
Casino jug, 36s	125.00	125.00	75.00	175.00
Casino saucer	20.00	30.00	10.00	30.00
Casino teacup	40.00	60.00	20.00	60.00
Don beaker	45.00	65.00	20.00	65.00
Don beaker, one handle	55.00	75.00	25.00	75.00
Don mug, one handle	40.00	60.00	10.00	60.00
Don mug, two handles	45.00	65.00	12.00	65.00
Egg box				
small	250.00	375.00	100.00	400.00
medium	325.00	475.00	150.00	500.00
large	400.00	575.00	200.00	600.00
Hug-a-mug, one handle	20.00	30.00	8.00	35.00
Hug-a-mug, two handles	25.00	35.00	10.00	40.00
Jaffa fruit saucer (plain)	20.00	30.00	10.00	30.00
Lamp	175.00	250.00	75.00	275.00
Malvern beaker	30.00	45.00	15.00	50.00
Money ball	25.00	35.00	12.00	40.00
Picture plaque, small	40.00	60.00	25.00	65.00
Plate, 6½"	20.00	30.00	10.00	30.00
Savings book				
regular issue	35.00	40.00	14.00	45.00
'Special Events 1994'	75.00	100.00	45.00	125.00
Stratford straight beaker	30.00	45.00	15.00	50.00
Stratford teacup	30.00	45.00	15.00	45.00

Dancing Round the Barrel Organ (HW139)

Skipping Game (HW139R)

Note: A savings book was issued for the U.S. Special Events Tour 1994. The front features *Skipping Game* (HW139R) and the reverse is inscribed 'To' and 'From' for the customer to complete and 'US Special Events Tour 1994.'

DINNERTIME THEME
Frank Endersby

Preparing Dinner (43)

Preparing Dinner

Design No.:   43 — Preparing Dinner
Designer: Frank Endersby
Issued: 1995 to the present

Shape	U.S. $	Can. $	U.K.£	Aust. $
Baby plate, round, small	40.00	46.00	12.00	49.00
Jaffa fruit saucer	25.00	30.00	9.00	35.00
Plate, 6 ½"	25.00	25.00	7.00	27.00
Plate, 8"	30.00	35.00	9.00	3.00

Serving Dinner (44)

Serving Dinner / Carrying Plates

Design No.:   Front — 44 Serving Dinner
              Reverse — 45 Carrying plates
Designer: Frank Endersby
Issued: 1995 to the present

Shape	U.S. $	Can. $	U.K.£	Aust. $
Hug-a-mug, one handle	30.00	33.00	9.00	35.00
Hug-a-mug, two handles	33.00	39.00	10.00	45.00
Stratford teacup	25.00	30.00	10.00	30.00

Carrying Plates (45)

Disturbing Sleeping Father / Pea Shooter

Design No.:	Front — HW118 Disturbing Sleeping Father	
	Reverse — HW118R Pea Shooter	
Designer:	Walter Hayward	
Issued:	1959 - by 1998	
Combined with:	*Dancing with Doll*, HW115R	

Disturbing Sleeping Father (HW118)

Shape	U.S. $	Can. $	U.K. £	Aust. $
Albion cream jug	50.00	75.00	25.00	80.00
Albion jug, ½ pint	50.00	100.00	35.00	100.00
Albion jug, 1 pint	75.00	150.00	50.00	150.00
Albion teapot	50.00	100.00	30.00	125.00
Casino jug, 36s	150.00	200.00	85.00	175.00
Casino jug, 42s	125.00	175.00	75.00	150.00
Casino saucer	25.00	30.00	10.00	35.00
Casino teacup	40.00	60.00	15.00	55.00
Divided dish	45.00	65.00	30.00	65.00
Don beaker, one handle	45.00	65.00	20.00	65.00
Don beaker, two handles	55.00	75.00	25.00	75.00
Don mug, one handle	40.00	60.00	10.00	60.00
Don mug, two handles	45.00	65.00	12.00	65.00
Egg box				
small	250.00	375.00	100.00	400.00
medium	325.00	475.00	150.00	500.00
large	400.00	575.00	200.00	600.00
Hug-a-mug, one handle	20.00	30.00	8.00	35.00
Hug-a-mug, two handles	25.00	35.00	10.00	40.00
Jaffa fruit saucer (plain)	20.00	30.00	10.00	30.00
Lamp	175.00	250.00	75.00	275.00
Lid of hot water plate	100.00	150.00	60.00	175.00
Malvern beaker	30.00	45.00	15.00	50.00
Money ball	25.00	35.00	12.00	40.00
Picture plaque, small	40.00	60.00	25.00	65.00
Plate, 6½"	20.00	30.00	10.00	30.00
Stratford straight beaker	30.00	45.00	15.00	50.00
Stratford teacup	30.00	45.00	15.00	45.00

Pea Shooter (HW118R)

Dodgem Cars (LF4)

Dodgem Cars

Design No.: LF4
Designer: Barbara Vernon
Issued: By 1940 - by 1952

Shape	U.S. $	Can. $	U.K. £	Aust. $
Baby plate, oval, large				
with signature	250.00	350.00	150.00	350.00
without signature	150.00	225.00	90.00	250.00
Baby plate, round, large				
with signature	250.00	350.00	150.00	350.00
without signature	150.00	225.00	90.00	250.00
Bread / butter plate, handles				
with signature	200.00	275.00	175.00	300.00
without signature	150.00	225.00	100.00	250.00
Cereal / oatmeal bowl				
with signature	125.00	175.00	75.00	175.00
without signature	75.00	110.00	45.00	125.00
Plate, 8 ½"				
with signature	225.00	350.00	150.00	350.00
without signature	125.00	200.00	75.00	200.00
Porridge bowl				
with signature	225.00	325.00	150.00	350.00
without signature	125.00	200.00	80.00	200.00

Dog Carriage

Design No.: LFe
Designer: Barbara Vernon
Issued: By 1937 - by 1952

Shape	U.S. $	Can. $	U.K. £	Aust. $
Baby plate, oval, large				
with signature	275.00	375.00	175.00	375.00
without signature	175.00	275.00	100.00	275.00
Baby plate, round, large				
with signature	250.00	350.00	150.00	350.00
without signature	125.00	200.00	85.00	225.00
Bread / butter plate, handles				
with signature	250.00	375.00	200.00	350.00
without signature	150.00	225.00	100.00	250.00
Cereal / oatmeal bowl				
with signature	150.00	225.00	100.00	225.00
without signature	100.00	150.00	65.00	150.00
Plate, 8 ½"				
with signature	225.00	350.00	150.00	350.00
without signature	125.00	200.00	75.00	200.00
Porridge bowl				
with signature	225.00	325.00	150.00	350.00
without signature	125.00	200.00	80.00	200.00

Dog Carriage (LFe)

The Doll's House / Playing with Doll and Teddy

Design No.:	Front — HW120 The Doll's House
	Reverse — HW120R Playing with Doll and Teddy
Designer:	Walter Hayward
Issued:	1959 - by 1998
Combined with:	*Hikers*, EC124
	Reading, EC122

Shape	U.S. $	Can. $	U.K. £	Aust. $
Albion cream jug	50.00	75.00	25.00	80.00
Albion teapot	50.00	100.00	30.00	125.00
Cake stand	150.00	200.00	65.00	200.00
Casino saucer	20.00	30.00	10.00	35.00
Casino teacup	40.00	60.00	15.00	55.00
Divided dish	45.00	65.00	30.00	65.00
Don beaker	45.00	65.00	20.00	65.00
Don beaker, one handle	50.00	75.00	25.00	65.00
Don mug, one handle	40.00	60.00	10.00	60.00
Don mug, two handles	35.00	60.00	12.00	60.00
Egg box				
small	250.00	375.00	100.00	400.00
medium	325.00	475.00	150.00	500.00
large	400.00	575.00	200.00	600.00
Hug-a-mug, one handle	20.00	30.00	8.00	45.00
Hug-a-mug, two handles	25.00	35.00	10.00	50.00
Jaffa fruit saucer (plain)	20.00	30.00	10.00	30.00
Lamp	175.00	250.00	75.00	275.00
Lid of hot water plate	100.00	150.00	60.00	150.00
Malvern beaker	40.00	45.00	15.00	50.00
Money ball	25.00	35.00	12.00	40.00
Picture plaque, small	40.00	60.00	25.00	65.00
Plate, 6½"	20.00	25.00	7.00	25.00
Savings book	35.00	40.00	15.00	45.00
Stratford straight beaker	30.00	45.00	15.00	50.00
Stratford teacup	30.00	45.00	15.00	45.00

Note: *Reading* (EC122) is combined with *The Doll's House* (HW120) on a money ball.

The Doll's House (HW120)

Playing with Doll and Teddy (HW120R)

Dress Making / Bugler with Toy Donkey

Dress Making (HW26) is combined with Toast for Tea Today (SF23) and Windy Day (HW27) on the casino teapot (24s).

Dress Making (HW26)

Bugler with Toy Donkey (HW26R)

Design No.:	Front — HW26 Dress Making
	Reverse — HW26R Bugler with Toy Donkey
Designer:	Walter Hayward
Issued:	1954 - by 1998

Combined with:	*Serving Tea*, HW116R
	Sleeping in a Rocking Chair, EC126
	Toast for Tea Today, SF23
	Windy Day, HW27

Shape	U.S. $	Can. $	U.K. £	Aust. $
Albion cream jug	50.00	75.00	30.00	75.00
Albion jug, ½ pint	50.00	75.00	30.00	75.00
Albion jug, 1 pint	75.00	100.00	50.00	125.00
Albion teapot	50.00	75.00	30.00	75.00
Casino jug, 30s				
with signature	150.00	225.00	90.00	225.00
without signature	125.00	175.00	80.00	175.00
Casino jug, 36s				
with signature	125.00	175.00	85.00	175.00
without signature	100.00	150.00	60.00	150.00
Casino jug, 42s				
with signature	100.00	150.00	60.00	150.00
without signature	75.00	100.00	45.00	100.00
Casino saucer				
with signature	35.00	50.00	20.00	60.00
without signature	10.00	15.00	5.00	15.00
Casino teacup				
with signature	50.00	75.00	30.00	75.00
without signature	25.00	35.00	15.00	45.00
Casino teapot, 24s				
with signature	300.00	450.00	175.00	550.00
without signature	275.00	400.00	150.00	500.00
Casino teapot, 30s				
with signature	275.00	450.00	175.00	500.00
without signature	250.00	375.00	150.00	400.00
Don beaker				
with signature	50.00	75.00	30.00	85.00
without signature	35.00	50.00	20.00	60.00

Shape	U.S. $	Can. $	U.K. £	Aust. $
Don beaker, one handle				
with signature	50.00	75.00	30.00	75.00
without signature	35.00	50.00	25.00	60.00
Don mug, one handle				
with signature	50.00	75.00	30.00	75.00
without signature	35.00	50.00	20.00	60.00
Don mug, two handles				
with signature	50.00	75.00	30.00	75.00
without signature	35.00	50.00	20.00	60.00
Egg box				
small	250.00	350.00	100.00	400.00
medium	325.00	475.00	150.00	500.00
large	400.00	575.00	200.00	600.00
Jaffa fruit saucer (plain)				
with signature	75.00	100.00	60.00	100.00
without signature	25.00	35.00	15.00	40.00
Hug-a-mug, one handle	25.00	35.00	10.00	45.00
Hug-a-mug, two handles	25.00	35.00	10.00	50.00
Lamp	150.00	225.00	100.00	225.00
Lid of hot water plate				
with signature	125.00	175.00	75.00	150.00
without signature	100.00	150.00	60.00	150.00
Malvern beaker	40.00	60.00	25.00	65.00
Money ball	25.00	35.00	12.00	40.00
Picture plaque, small	40.00	60.00	20.00	65.00
Savings book	30.00	45.00	15.00	50.00
Stratford straight beaker	30.00	45.00	15.00	50.00
Stratford teacup	30.00	45.00	15.00	50.00

Dressing Up
First Version

Design No.: SF22
Designer: Walter Hayward
Issued: 1954 - by 1998

Shape	U.S. $	Can. $	U.K. £	Aust. $
Albion jug, 1 pint	75.00	150.00	50.00	150.00
Baby plate, round, small				
with signature	50.00	75.00	35.00	75.00
without signature	20.00	30.00	12.00	30.00
Cake stand	150.00	200.00	65.00	200.00
Casino jug, 30s				
with signature	125.00	175.00	75.00	175.00
without signature	100.00	150.00	60.00	150.00
Casino saucer				
with signature	35.00	50.00	15.00	50.00
without signature	10.00	15.00	5.00	15.00
Casino teapot				
with signature	275.00	525.00	175.00	550.00
without signature	225.00	350.00	140.00	375.00
Cereal / oatmeal bowl				
with signature	50.00	75.00	25.00	75.00
without signature	25.00	35.00	10.00	35.00
Jaffa fruit saucer (plain)	20.00	30.00	10.00	30.00
Hot water plate				
with signature	125.00	200.00	85.00	200.00
without signature	100.00	150.00	65.00	150.00
Plate, 6 ½"				
with signature	50.00	75.00	30.00	75.00
without signature	20.00	25.00	7.00	25.00
Plate, 8"	20.00	30.00	10.00	30.00

Dressing Up, First Version (SF22)

Dressing Up
Second Version

This design incorporates scenes from SF22 and EC4.

Design No.: None
Designer: Monica Ford based on designs by Walter Hayward
Issued: 1987 - 1993

Shape	U.S. $	Can. $	U.K. £	Aust. $
Plate, 10 ½"	75.00	100.00	50.00	100.00

Dressing Up, Second Version

Drummer (EC2)

Drummer

Design No.:	EC2
Designer:	Barbara Vernon
Issued:	1937 to the present
Combined with:	*Bedtime with Dollies*, EC125
	Cricketer, HW22R
	Drummer and Bugler, EC126
	Hikers, EC124
	Holding Hat and Coat, EC4
	Playing with Cup and Spoon, EC6
	Playing with Doll and Pram, EC123
	Raising Hat, Style Two, EC7
	Sheltering Under an Umbrella, EC3
	Sleeping in a Rocking Chair, EC1
	Trumpeter, EC5
	Wheelbarrow Race, Style One, HW22

Shape	U.S. $	Can. $	U.K. £	Aust. $
Albion sugar bowl	40.00	60.00	25.00	60.00
Beaker cover				
with signature	100.00	150.00	60.00	150.00
without signature	75.00	95.00	35.00	100.00
Casino sugar bowl				
with signature	175.00	.00	.00	.00
without signature	40.00	60.00	25.00	65.00
Egg cup				
Style One	35.00	60.00	25.00	65.00
Style Two	60.00	100.00	35.00	125.00
Style Three	**10.00**	**15.00**	**5.00**	**15.00**

Drummer and Bugler

Design No.:	EC126
Designer:	Walter Hayward
Issued:	1959 to the present
Combined with:	*Bedtime with Dollies*, EC125
	Drummer, EC2
	Hat Shop, HW28
	Hikers, EC124
	Hobby Horse, Style Two, EC121
	Playing with Cup and Spoon, EC6
	Playing with Doll and Pram, EC123
	Reading, EC122
	Trumpeter, EC5
	Trying on Hats, HW28R

Shape	U.S. $	Can. $	U.K. £	Aust. $
Albion sugar bowl	40.00	60.00	25.00	60.00
Beaker cover	100.00	150.00	60.00	150.00
Egg cup				
Style One	35.00	60.00	25.00	60.00
Style Two	60.00	100.00	35.00	125.00
Style Three	**10.00**	**15.00**	**5.00**	**15.00**
Lid of hot water plate	100.00	150.00	60.00	175.00

Drummer and Bugler (EC126)

Note: *Drummer and Bugler* (EC126) was combined with *Hat Shop*
(HW28) and *Trying on Hats* (HW28R) on the lid of the hot water plate.

Duet, The

Design No.: LF13
Designer: Walter Hayward after Barbara Vernon
Issued: By 1952 - 1970

Shape	U.S. $	Can. $	U.K.£	Aust. $
Baby plate, oval, large				
with signature	250.00	350.00	150.00	375.00
without signature	100.00	150.00	65.00	175.00
Baby plate, round, large				
with signature	200.00	300.00	125.00	325.00
without signature	100.00	150.00	65.00	175.00
Bread / butter plate, handles				
with signature	250.00	375.00	150.00	375.00
without signature	150.00	250.00	100.00	250.00
Cereal / oatmeal bowl				
with signature	95.00	150.00	65.00	150.00
without signature	75.00	100.00	45.00	125.00
Hot water plate				
with signature	150.00	225.00	100.00	225.00
without signature	125.00	200.00	75.00	200.00
Porridge bowl				
with signature	150.00	225.00	85.00	250.00
without signature	100.00	150.00	50.00	150.00
Plate, 8"	50.00	75.00	35.00	80.00
Plate, 8 ½"				
with signature	125.00	175.00	75.00	175.00
without signature	100.00	150.00	60.00	150.00

The Duet (LF13)

Dunce (HW1R)

Dunce

Design No.:	HW1R
Designer:	Barbara Vernon
Issued:	By 1937 - by 1952
Combined with:	*Artist*, HW1
	Embracing at a Window, HW5
	Greetings, HW7
	Netting a Cricket, HW6
	Pressing Trousers, HW14
	Proposal, HW11

Shape	U.S. $	Can. $	U.K. £	Aust. $
Casino jug, 42s				
with signature	135.00	200.00	85.00	200.00
without signature	100.00	150.00	65.00	150.00
Casino sugar bowl, 30s				
with signature	150.00	225.00	85.00	250.00
without signature	100.00	150.00	65.00	175.00
Casino sugar bowl, 36s				
with signature	200.00	300.00	125.00	325.00
without signature	150.00	225.00	85.00	225.00
Casino teacup				
with signature	125.00	175.00	75.00	175.00
without signature	75.00	125.00	45.00	125.00
Casino teapot, 36s				
with signature	375.00	575.00	225.00	650.00
without signature	300.00	450.00	175.00	575.00
Don beaker				
with signature	150.00	200.00	85.00	200.00
without signature	90.00	140.00	65.00	125.00
Don beaker, one handle				
with signature	160.00	225.00	90.00	200.00
without signature	100.00	150.00	65.00	150.00
Don mug, one handle				
with signature	150.00	200.00	90.00	200.00
without signature	100.00	150.00	60.00	150.00
Don mug, two handles				
with signature	150.00	200.00	50.00	200.00
without signature	100.00	150.00	60.00	150.00
Lid of hot water plate				
with signature	85.00	125.00	50.00	125.00
without signature	75.00	100.00	45.00	100.00

Embracing at a Window

Design No.: HW5
Designer: Barbara Vernon
Issued: By 1937 - by 1952
Combined with: *Dunce*, HW1R
Fixing Braces, HW3
Leapfrog, HW12R
Top Hat, HW14R

Shape	U.S. $	Can. $	U.K. £	Aust. $
Casino saucer	75.00	125.00	45.00	125.00
Casino teacup	115.00	165.00	75.00	175.00
Casino teapot, 30s	375.00	575.00	225.00	650.00
Don beaker	135.00	185.00	80.00	175.00
Don beaker, one handle	135.00	185.00	80.00	175.00
Don mug, one handle	125.00	175.00	75.00	165.00
Don mug, two handles	135.00	185.00	80.00	175.00
Jaffa fruit saucer	125.00	175.00	75.00	165.00
Plate, 6½"	95.00	150.00	60.00	150.00

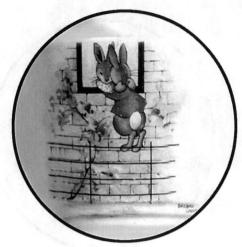

Embracing at a Window (HW5)

Note: This design should appear with the Barbara Vernon facsimile
signature.

Engine Pulling a Carriage / To the Station

Engine Pulling a Carriage (HW17)

To the Station (HW17R)

Design No.:	Front — HW17 Engine Pulling a Carriage			
	Reverse — HW17R To the Station			
Designer:	Walter Hayward after Barbara Vernon			

Issued:	By 1952 - by 1998	
Combined with:	*Raising Hat*, Style Two, EC7	
	Snowball Fight, HW141R	

Shape	U.S. $	Can. $	U.K. £	Aust. $
Albion cream jug	50.00	75.00	30.00	80.00
Albion jug, ½ pint	50.00	100.00	30.00	100.00
Albion teapot	50.00	100.00	30.00	125.00
Casino jug, 36s				
with signature	125.00	175.00	85.00	175.00
without signature	100.00	150.00	60.00	150.00
Casino jug, 42s				
with signature	100.00	150.00	60.00	150.00
without signature	75.00	100.00	45.00	100.00
Casino saucer				
with signature	35.00	50.00	20.00	60.00
without signature	10.00	15.00	5.00	15.00
Casino sugar bowl, 36s				
with signature	150.00	225.00	85.00	150.00
without signature	100.00	150.00	65.00	100.00
Casino teacup				
with signature	50.00	75.00	30.00	75.00
without signature	25.00	35.00	15.00	50.00
Casino teapot, 24s				
with signature	325.00	500.00	200.00	550.00
without signature	250.00	375.00	150.00	400.00
Casino teapot, 30s				
with signature	250.00	350.00	150.00	400.00
without signature	200.00	300.00	125.00	350.00
Don beaker				
with signature	50.00	75.00	35.00	75.00
without signature	35.00	50.00	20.00	60.00
Don beaker, one handle				
with signature	50.00	75.00	30.00	75.00

Shape	U.S. $	Can. $	U.K. £	Aust. $
Don beaker, one handle (cont.)				
without signature	35.00	50.00	20.00	50.00
Don mug, one handle				
with signature	50.00	75.00	30.00	75.00
without signature	35.00	50.00	20.00	50.00
Don mug, two handles				
with signature	50.00	75.00	30.00	75.00
without signature	35.00	50.00	20.00	50.00
Egg box				
small	250.00	350.00	100.00	400.00
medium	325.00	475.00	150.00	500.00
large	400.00	575.00	200.00	600.00
Jaffa fruit saucer (plain)	25.00	35.00	15.00	40.00
Lamp	175.00	250.00	100.00	250.00
Lid of hot water plate				
with signature	100.00	150.00	60.00	150.00
without signature	75.00	100.00	45.00	100.00
Malvern beaker	30.00	45.00	20.00	50.00
Money ball	25.00	35.00	15.00	40.00
Picture plaque, small	50.00	75.00	35.00	75.00
Plate, 6½"				
with signature	50.00	75.00	35.00	75.00
without signature	25.00	35.00	20.00	40.00
Plate, 7½"				
with signature	60.00	90.00	40.00	75.00
without signature	30.00	45.00	20.00	50.00
Savings book	30.00	45.00	20.00	50.00
Stratford straight beaker	35.00	50.00	20.00	50.00
Stratford teacup	35.00	45.00	20.00	50.00

Note: A Don mug, two handles, combines designs *Engine Pulling a Carriage* (HW17) and *Snowball Fight* HW141R.

FAIRGROUND THEME
Frank Endersby

Swinging Boats

Design No.:   31 Swinging Boats
Designer: Frank Endersby
Issued: 1995 to the present

Shape	U.S. $	Can. $	U.K. £	Aust. $
Baby plate, round, small	40.00	46.00	12.00	49.00
Cereal / oatmeal bowl	25.00	33.00	9.00	39.00
Plate, 6 ½"	25.00	25.00	7.00	27.00
Plate, 8"	30.00	35.00	9.00	39.00

Swinging Boats (31)

Coconut Shy (32)

Coconut Shy / Playing with Balloons

Design No.:   Front — 32 Coconut Shy
              Reverse — 33 Playing with Balloons
Designer: Frank Endersby
Issued: 1995 to the present

Shape	U.S. $	Can. $	U.K. £	Aust. $
Hug-a-mug, one handle	**30.00**	**33.00**	**9.00**	**39.00**
Hug-a-mug, two handles	**33.00**	**39.00**	**10.00**	**45.00**
Malvern beaker	30.00	45.00	15.00	50.00
Money ball	**35.00**	**40.00**	**13.00**	**45.00**
Stratford teacup	30.00	45.00	15.00	45.00

Playing with Balloons (33)

Family at Breakfast

Family at Breakfast (HW12)

Design No.:	HW12
Designer:	Barbara Vernon
Issued:	By 1937 - by 1952
Combined with:	*Cycling*, HW15R
	Feeding the Baby, HW13
	Fixing Braces, HW3
	Footballer, HW13R

Golfer, HW4R
Kissing under the Mistletoe, HW11R
Leapfrog, HW12R
Pulling On Trousers, HW2
Raising Hat, Style One, HW16R
Smoking in the Doorway, SF2
Washing Day, HW8R

Shape	U.S. $	Can. $	U.K. £	Aust. $
Candle holder	1,500.00	2,500.00	1,000.00	2,500.00
Casino jug, 42s				
with signature	200.00	300.00	150.00	300.00
without signature	150.00	250.00	125.00	250.00
Casino saucer				
with signature	75.00	100.00	45.00	100.00
without signature	50.00	75.00	35.00	75.00
Casino sugar bowl, 30s				
with signature	150.00	225.00	85.00	250.00
without signature	100.00	150.00	65.00	175.00
Casino sugar bowl, 36s				
with signature	200.00	300.00	125.00	325.00
without signature	150.00	225.00	85.00	225.00
Casino teacup				
with signature	100.00	150.00	60.00	150.00
without signature	80.00	130.00	50.00	135.00
Casino teapot, 30s				
with signature	325.00	575.00	225.00	650.00
without signature	300.00	450.00	175.00	575.00
Casino teapot, 36s				
with signature	375.00	575.00	225.00	650.00
without signature	300.00	450.00	175.00	575.00
Cup / mug, large	350.00	500.00	200.00	500.00
Don beaker				
with signature	100.00	150.00	60.00	150.00
without signature	65.00	100.00	40.00	100.0

Shape	U.S. $	Can. $	U.K. £	Aust. $
Don beaker, one handle				
with signature	100.00	150.00	60.00	150.00
without signature	65.00	100.00	40.00	100.00
Don mug, one handle				
with signature	90.00	140.00	60.00	150.00
without signature	75.00	115.00	45.00	125.00
Don mug, two handles				
with signature	100.00	150.00	75.00	165.00
without signature	75.00	115.00	45.00	125.00
Jaffa fruit saucer (wavy)				
with signature	75.00	125.00	45.00	125.00
without signature	50.00	85.00	30.00	100.00
Jam pot	850.00	1,300.00	500.00	1,300.00
Lid of hot water plate				
with signature	85.00	125.00	50.00	125.00
without signature	75.00	100.00	45.00	100.00
Plate, 6 ½"				
with signature	75.00	100.00	45.00	100.00
without signature	50.00	75.00	30.00	75.00
Plate, 7 ½"				
with signature	75.00	100.00	45.00	100.00
without signature	50.00	75.00	30.00	75.00
Rex mug, fine china		Extremely rare		
Saucer, fine china		Very rare		

Family Cycling

Design No.: LF11
Designer: Walter Hayward
Issued: By 1952 - 1970

Shape	U.S. $	Can. $	U.K. £	Aust. $
Baby plate, oval, large				
with signature	275.00	450.00	200.00	475.00
without signature	125.00	200.00	80.00	225.00
Baby plate, round, large				
with signature	200.00	275.00	125.00	300.00
without signature	125.00	200.00	80.00	225.00
Bread / butter plate, handles				
with signature	200.00	275.00	125.00	300.00
without signature	150.00	225.00	100.00	250.00
Cereal / oatmeal bowl				
with signature	95.00	150.00	65.00	150.00
without signature	75.00	110.00	45.00	125.00
Hot water plate				
with signature	175.00	275.00	100.00	275.00
without signature	125.00	200.00	85.00	200.00
Plate, 8 ½"				
with signature	175.00	275.00	100.00	275.00
without signature	125.00	200.00	75.00	200.00
Porridge bowl				
with signature	150.00	200.00	95.00	200.00
without signature	100.00	145.00	60.00	150.00

Family Cycling (LF11)

Family Going out on Washing Day (HW8)

Family Going out on Washing Day

Design No.:	HW8
Designer:	Barbara Vernon
Issued:	By 1937 - by 1967
Combined with:	*Cycling*, HW15R
	Leapfrog, HW12R
	Trumpeter, EC5
	Washing Day, HW8R

Shape	U.S. $	Can. $	U.K. £	Aust. $
Casino jug, 24s				
with signature	225.00	350.00	150.00	350.00
without signature	175.00	250.00	125.00	250.00
Casino saucer				
with signature	75.00	100.00	45.00	100.00
without signature	50.00	75.00	35.00	75.00
Casino sugar bowl, 36s				
with signature	200.00	300.00	125.00	325.00
without signature	150.00	225.00	85.00	225.00
Casino teacup				
with signature	125.00	175.00	75.00	175.00
without signature	75.00	125.00	45.00	125.00
Don beaker				
with signature	125.00	175.00	75.00	175.00
without signature	75.00	125.00	45.00	125.00
Don beaker, one handle				
with signature	125.00	175.00	75.00	175.00
without signature	75.00	125.00	45.00	125.00
Don mug, one handle				
with signature	100.00	150.00	60.00	150.00
without signature	75.00	110.00	45.00	125.00
Don mug, two handles				
with signature	75.00	100.00	45.00	95.00
without signature	50.00	75.00	30.00	75.00
Jaffa fruit saucer				
plain rim	75.00	125.00	50.00	125.00
wavy rim	75.00	125.00	50.00	125.00
Plate, 6 ½"				
with signature	75.00	100.00	45.00	95.00
without signature	50.00	75.00	30.00	75.00

Family in the Garden

Design No.: SF135
Designer: Walter Hayward
Issued: 1967 - by 1998

Shape	U.S. $	Can. $	U.K. £	Aust. $
Albion jug, 1 pint	75.00	150.00	50.00	150.00
Baby plate, round, small	25.00	40.00	10.00	40.00
Baby plate, round, large	85.00	125.00	50.00	130.00
Cake stand	150.00	200.00	75.00	200.00
Cereal / oatmeal bowl	20.00	30.00	9.00	35.00
Jaffa fruit saucer (plain)	25.00	35.00	15.00	35.00
Hot water plate	100.00	150.00	65.00	150.00
Picture plaque, large	50.00	75.00	30.00	75.00
Plate, 8"	20.00	35.00	9.00	50.00

Family in the Garden (SF135)

Family Photograph (LF15)

Family Photograph

Design No.: LF15
Designer: Walter Hayward
Issued: By 1954 - 1970

Shape	U.S. $	Can. $	U.K. £	Aust. $
Baby plate, oval, large				
with signature	225.00	325.00	135.00	350.00
without signature	125.00	200.00	80.00	225.00
Baby plate, round, large				
with signature	250.00	350.00	150.00	350.00
without signature	125.00	200.00	80.00	225.00
Bread / butter plate, handles				
with signature	200.00	275.00	125.00	300.00
without signature	150.00	225.00	100.00	250.00
Cereal / oatmeal bowl				
with signature	100.00	150.00	65.00	160.00
without signature	75.00	110.00	45.00	100.00
Plate, 8"	85.00	125.00	50.00	125.00
Plate, 8 ½"				
with signature	100.00	150.00	60.00	150.00
without signature	75.00	100.00	45.00	100.00
Porridge bowl				
with signature	150.00	225.00	85.00	225.00
without signature	100.00	150.00	60.00	150.00

Family with Pram, Style One (HW15)

Family with Pram (HW15) / Raising Hat (HW16R)

Family with Pram
Style One

Design No.:	HW15
Designer:	Barbara Vernon
Issued:	By 1937 - by 1952
Combined with:	*Cycling*, HW15R
	Footballer, HW13R
	Leapfrog, HW12R
	Proposal, HW11
	Raising Hat, Style One, HW16R
	Raising Hat, Style Two, EC7
	Washing in the Open Air, HW10R

Shape	U.S. $	Can. $	U.K. £	Aust. $
Baby plate, oval, large	225.00	325.00	135.00	350.00
Baby plate, round, large	250.00	350.00	150.00	350.00
Casino saucer	50.00	75.00	30.00	75.00
Casino sugar bowl, 30s	150.00	225.00	85.00	250.00
Casino teacup	85.00	125.00	50.00	135.00
Casino teapot, 24s	300.00	450.00	175.00	575.00
Casino teapot, 30s	375.00	575.00	225.00	650.00
Don beaker	85.00	125.00	50.00	95.00
Don beaker, one handle	85.00	125.00	50.00	95.00
Don mug, one handle	85.00	125.00	50.00	95.00
Don mug, two handles	95.00	135.00	50.00	130.00
Jaffa fruit saucer	85.00	135.00	55.00	125.00
Jam pot	850.00	1,300.00	500.00	1,300.00
Lid of hot water plate	85.00	125.00	50.00	100.00
Plate, 6½"	75.00	100.00	45.00	100.00

Note: This design should appear with the Barbara Vernon facsimile signature. The large round and oval baby plates, a Casino teapot 30s, and a 7½" plate have been found combining *Family with Pram* (Style One) HW15 and *Raising Hat* (Style One) HW16R.

Family with Pram
Style Two

Design No.:	Front — CT14 Family with Pram
	Reverse — CT6 Standing by Pram
Designer:	Colin Twinn
Issued:	1989 - 1993
Combined with:	*Bunny on Rocking Horse*, CT29
	Father Bunnykins with Fishing Rod, CT27
	Home from Fishing, CT26
	Nursery, First Version, CT19

Family with Pram, Style Two (CT14)

Shape	U.S. $	Can. $	U.K. £	Aust. $
Albion jug, ½ pint	90.00	135.00	55.00	135.00
Cake stand	100.00	150.00	65.00	150.00
Divided dish	45.00	65.00	30.00	75.00
Hug-a-mug, one handle	25.00	35.00	15.00	40.00
Hug-a-mug, two handles	30.00	45.00	20.00	40.00
Lamp	175.00	250.00	75.00	250.00
Malvern beaker	35.00	50.00	20.00	50.00
Money ball	25.00	35.00	12.00	40.00
Stratford teacup	30.00	45.00	20.00	60.00

Standing by Pram (CT6)

Feeding the Baby

Feeding the Baby (HW13)

Design No.:   HW13
Designer: Barbara Vernon
Issued: By 1937 - by 1967
Combined with: *Cycling*, HW15R
                 Family at Breakfast, HW12
                 Footballer, HW13R
                 Golfer, HW4R

Kissing under the Mistletoe, HW11R
Leapfrog, HW12R
Raising Hat, Style One, HW16R
Santa Claus, SF9
Sleeping in a Rocking Chair, EC1
Top Hat, HW14R
Washing in the Open Air, HW10R

Shape	U.S. $	Can. $	U.K. £	Aust. $
Baby plate, round, small				
with signature	135.00	200.00	85.00	200.00
without signature	100.00	150.00	65.00	150.00
Candle holder	1,500.00	2,500.00	900.00	2,500.00
Casino jug, 36s				
with signature	150.00	225.00	90.00	225.00
without signature	135.00	200.00	80.00	200.00
Casino jug, 42s				
with signature	135.00	200.00	85.00	200.00
without signature	125.00	175.00	70.00	175.00
Casino saucer				
with signature	60.00	100.00	36.00	100.00
without signature	50.00	75.00	35.00	75.00
Casino sugar bowl, 30s				
with signature	200.00	300.00	125.00	325.00
without signature	150.00	225.00	85.00	225.00
Casino teacup				
with signature	95.00	140.00	60.00	150.00
without signature	75.00	100.00	45.00	100.00
Don beaker				
with signature	125.00	175.00	75.00	175.00
without signature	75.00	125.00	45.00	125.00

Shape	U.S. $	Can. $	U.K. £	Aust. $
Don beaker, one handle				
with signature	95.00	140.00	60.00	140.00
without signature	70.00	100.00	40.00	100.00
Don mug, one handle				
with signature	75.00	100.00	45.00	95.00
without signature	60.00	90.00	35.00	90.00
Don mug, two handles				
with signature	85.00	125.00	55.00	125.00
without signature	50.00	75.00	30.00	75.00
Jaffa fruit saucer				
plain rim	95.00	140.00	85.00	150.00
wavy rim	95.00	140.00	85.00	150.00
Lid of hot water plate				
with signature	85.00	125.00	55.00	125.00
without signature	75.00	100.00	45.00	100.00
Plate, 6 ½"				
with signature	75.00	100.00	50.00	100.00
without signature	50.00	75.00	30.00	75.00
Teacup, fine china		Very rare		

FIRE STATION THEME
Frank Endersby

Washing the Fire Engine

Design No.: 10 Washing the Fire Engine
Designer: Frank Endersby
Issued: 1995 to the present

Shape	U.S. $	Can. $	U.K. £	Aust. $
Cereal / oatmeal bowl	25.00	33.00	9.00	39.00
Jaffa fruit saucer	25.00	30.00	9.00	35.00
Plate, 6 ½"	25.00	25.00	7.00	27.00
Plate, 8"	30.00	35.00	9.00	39.00

Washing the Fire Engine (10)

Pumping Water (11)

Pumping Water / Trying on Hat

Design No.: Front — 11 Pumping Water
Reverse — 12 Trying on Hat
Designer: Frank Endersby
Issued: 1995 to the present

Shape	U.S. $	Can. $	U.K. £	Aust. $
Hug-a-mug, one handle	**30.00**	**33.00**	**9.00**	**39.00**
Hug-a-mug, two handles	**33.00**	**39.00**	**10.00**	**45.00**
Malvern beaker	30.00	45.00	20.00	45.00
Money ball	**35.00**	**40.00**	**13.00**	**45.00**
Stratford teacup	30.00	45.00	20.00	45.00

Note: Bold type in the listing tables indicate a current design on a current shape.

Trying on Hat (12)

FISHING THEME
Frank Endersby

Fishing at the Pond

Fishing at the Pond (4)

Design No.   4 Fishing at the Pond
Designer: Frank Endersby
Issued: 1995 to the present

Shape	U.S. $	Can. $	U.K. £	Aust. $
Baby plate, round, small	40.00	46.00	12.00	49.00
Jaffa fruit saucer	25.00	30.00	9.00	35.00
Plate, 6 ½"	25.00	25.00	7.00	27.00
Plate, 8"	30.00	35.00	9.00	39.00

Resting by Pond (5)

Resting by Pond / Carrying Net

Design No.   Front — 5 Resting by Pond
             Reverse — 6 Carrying Net
Designer: Frank Endersby
Issued: 1995 to the present

Shape	U.S. $	Can. $	U.K. £	Aust. $
Hug-a-mug, one handle	30.00	33.00	9.00	39.00
Hug-a-mug, two handles	33.00	39.00	10.00	45.00
Money ball	35.00	40.00	13.00	45.00
Stratford teacup	30.00	45.00	20.00	45.00

Carrying Net (6)

Fishing in the Goldfish Bowl

Design No.: HW3R
Designer: Barbara Vernon
Issued: By 1937 - by 1952
Combined with: *Fixing Braces*, HW3
Mr. Piggly's Stores, SF14
Netting a Cricket, HW6
Playing with Cup and Spoon, EC6
Pressing Trousers, HW14
Pulling on Trousers, HW2

Shape	U.S. $	Can. $	U.K. £	Aust. $
Casino jug, 24s	250.00	375.00	175.00	400.00
Casino jug, 36s	175.00	250.00	100.00	250.00
Casino teacup	125.00	175.00	75.00	200.00
Don beaker	150.00	225.00	75.00	225.00
Don mug, one handle	175.00	250.00	75.00	250.00

Note: This design should appear with the Barbara Vernon facsimile
signature.

Fishing in the Goldfish Bowl (HW3R)

Fishing on the Pier (LF3)

Fishing on the Pier

Design No.: LF3
Designer: Barbara Vernon
Issued: By 1940 - by 1952

Shape	U.S. $	Can. $	U.K. £	Aust. $
Baby plate, round, large				
with signature	250.00	350.00	150.00	350.00
without signature	125.00	200.00	80.00	225.00
Bread / butter plate, handles				
with signature	200.00	275.00	125.00	300.00
without signature	150.00	225.00	100.00	250.00
Cereal / oatmeal bowl				
with signature	125.00	175.00	75.00	175.00
without signature	75.00	110.00	45.00	125.00
Plate, 8 ½"				
with signature	175.00	275.00	100.00	275.00
without signature	125.00	200.00	75.00	200.00
Porridge bowl				
with signature	175.00	250.00	100.00	250.00
without signature	125.00	200.00	75.00	200.00

Fixing Braces (HW3)

Fixing Braces

Design No.: HW3
Designer: Barbara Vernon
Issued: By 1937 - by 1952
Combined with: *Embracing at a Window*, HW5
Family at Breakfast, HW12
Fishing in the Goldfish Bowl, HW3R
Leapfrog, HW12R
Smoking in the Doorway, SF2

Shape	U.S. $	Can. $	U.K. £	Aust. $
Candle holder	1,500.00	2,500.00	900.00	2,500.00
Casino jug, 24s	300.00	450.00	180.00	450.00
Casino jug, 36s	175.00	250.00	125.00	250.00
Casino saucer	75.00	100.00	45.00	100.00
Casino teacup	125.00	175.00	90.00	175.00
Cup / mug, large	350.00	500.00	200.00	500.00
Don beaker	125.00	175.00	75.00	175.00
Don beaker, one handle	135.00	200.00	80.00	200.00
Don mug, one handle	125.00	175.00	75.00	175.00
Don mug, two handles	125.00	175.00	75.00	175.00
Jaffa fruit saucer				
plain rim	175.00	250.00	100.00	250.00
wavy rim	125.00	175.00	75.00	175.00
Night light, fine china	1,000.00	1,500.00	650.00	1,500.00
Plate, 6½"	100.00	150.00	75.00	175.00

Note: This design should appear with the Barbara Vernon facsimile signature.

Flying Kites

Design No.: SF133
Designer: Walter Hayward
Issued: 1967 - by 1998

Shape	U.S. $	Can. $	U.K. £	Aust. $
Baby plate, round, small	25.00	40.00	12.00	45.00
Cake stand	150.00	200.00	90.00	200.00
Cereal / oatmeal bowl	22.00	30.00	9.00	35.00
Jaffa fruit saucer (plain)	20.00	28.00	8.00	30.00
Hot water plate	100.00	150.00	65.00	150.00
Picture plaque, large	50.00	75.00	30.00	75.00
Plate, 6 ½"	17.00	25.00	7.00	30.00
Plate, 8"	20.00	35.00	10.00	35.00

Flying Kites (SF133)

Footballer

Design No.:	HW13R
Designer:	Barbara Vernon
Issued:	By 1937 - by 1967
Combined with:	*Cuddling under a Mushroom*, HW4
	Family at Breakfast, HW12
	Family with Pram , Style One, HW15
	Feeding the Baby, HW13
	Lambeth Walk, HW16
	Pressing Trousers, HW14
	Proposal, HW11
	Sleepeing in a Rocking Chair, EC1

Footballer (HW13R)

Shape	U.S. $	Can. $	U.K. £	Aust. $
Casino cream jug				
with signature	135.00	200.00	85.00	200.00
without signature	125.00	175.00	70.00	175.00
Casino sugar bowl, 36s				
with signature	150.00	225.00	85.00	250.00
without signature	100.00	150.00	65.00	175.00
Casino teacup				
with signature	100.00	150.00	65.00	150.00
without signature	75.00	125.00	45.00	125.00
Don beaker				
with signature	125.00	175.00	75.00	175.00
without signature	75.00	125.00	45.00	125.00
Don beaker, one handle				
with signature	100.00	150.00	60.00	150.00
without signature	70.00	100.00	40.00	100.00
Don mug, one handle				
with signature	100.00	150.00	60.00	150.00
without signature	75.00	125.00	45.00	125.00
Don mug, two handles				
with signature	75.00	100.00	45.00	95.00
without signature	50.00	75.00	30.00	75.00
Lid of hot water plate				
with signature	85.00	125.00	50.00	125.00
without signature	75.00	100.00	45.00	`00.00
Rex mug, fine china		Extremely rare		
Teacup, fine china		Very rare		

Note: The Rex mug combines *Lambeth Walk*, first version (HW16) and *Footballer* (HW13R).

Frightening Spider (SF4)

Frightening Spider with
Dorothy Vernon facsimile name

Frightening Spider

Design No.:	SF4
Designer:	Barbara Vernon
Issued:	By 1937 - by 1952
Combined with:	*Conducting the Orchestra*, LF5
	Pressing Trousers, HW14

Shape	U.S. $	Can. $	U.K. £	Aust. $
Baby plate, round, large	250.00	350.00	150.00	350.00
Baby plate, round, small	135.00	200.00	85.00	200.00
Casino jug, 24s	225.00	350.00	150.00	250.00
Casino jug, 36s	150.00	225.00	90.00	225.00
Casino saucer	75.00	100.00	45.00	100.00
Casino teapot, 24s	300.00	450.00	175.00	575.00
Cereal / oatmeal bowl	100.00	150.00	65.00	150.00
Jaffa fruit saucer				
plain rim	125.00	175.00	75.00	175.00
wavy rim	115.00	160.00	70.00	160.00
Hot water plate	175.00	275.00	110.00	275.00
Plate, 6 ½"	150.00	225.00	90.00	225.00
Plate, 7 ½"	175.00	275.00	110.00	250.00
Plate, 8"	200.00	300.00	130.00	300.00

Note: This design should appear with the Barbara Vernon facsimile signature. A round baby plate has been recorded featuring the facsimile name of Dorothy Vernon instead of Barbara Vernon.

Fun in the Snow
Christmas Tree Ornament

This Christmas tree ornament, which has a rabbit-shaped rim, was commissioned by Royal Doulton U.S.A. and produced in the U.S.A. The words *Fun in the Snow* appear on the reverse.

Design No.: None
Designer: Frank Endersby
Issued: 1995 - 1995
Series: Christmas Tree Ornaments

Shape	U.S. $	Can. $	U.K. £	Aust. $
Christmas tree ornament	35.00	45.00	30.00	45.00

Note: For other Christmas ornaments in this series see pages 43, 45, 144 and 166.

Fun in the Snow

Game of Golf (SF11)

Game of Golf

Design No.: SF11
Designer: Barbara Vernon
Issued: By 1940 - by 1952

Shape	U.S. $	Can. $	U.K. £	Aust. $
Baby plate, round, small				
with signature	350.00	550.00	200.00	575.00
without signature	275.00	450.00	175.00	450.00
Baby plate, round, large				
with signature	350.00	550.00	200.00	575.00
without signature	275.00	450.00	175.00	450.00
Casino jug, 36s				
with signature	275.00	400.00	175.00	400.00
without signature	225.00	350.00	125.00	350.00
Casino saucer				
with signature	100.00	150.00	65.00	150.00
without signature	75.00	100.00	45.00	100.00
Casino teapot, 24s				
with signature	500.00	750.00	300.00	750.00
without signature	375.00	550.00	225.00	575.00
Cereal / oatmeal bowl				
with signature	250.00	375.00	150.00	375.00
without signature	200.00	300.00	125.00	325.00
Jaffa fruit saucer				
plain rim	200.00	300.00	125.00	300.00
wavy rim	125.00	200.00	75.00	200.00
Plate, 6 ½"				
with signature	250.00	375.00	150.00	400.00
without signature	200.00	300.00	125.00	325.00
Plate, 7 ½"				
with signature	250.00	325.00	150.00	400.00
without signature	200.00	300.00	125.00	325.00

Note: See also *Golfer* (HW4R) page 90.

GARAGE THEME
Frank Endersby

Petrol in the Sports Car (37)

Petrol in the Sports Car

Design No.: 37 Petrol in the Sports Car
Designer: Frank Endersby
Issued: 1995 to the present

Shape	U.S. $	Can. $	U. K. £	Aust. $
Baby plate, round, small	40.00	46.00	12.00	49.00
Plate, 6"	25.00	25.00	7.00	27.00
Plate, 8"	30.00	35.00	9.00	39.00

Pumping Tyre (38)

Pumping Tyre / Sitting on Oil Drum

Design No.: Front — 38 Pumping Tyre
Reverse — 39 Sitting on Oil Drum
Designer: Frank Endersby
Issued: 1995 to the present

Shape	U.S. $	Can. $	U. K. £	Aust. $
Hug-a-mug, one handle	30.00	33.00	9.00	39.00
Hug-a-mug, two handles	33.00	39.00	10.00	45.00
Malvern beaker	30.00	45.00	15.00	50.00

Sitting on Oil Drum (39)

Gardener with Wheelbarrow

Design No.:   HW9R
Designer: Barbara Vernon
Issued: By 1937 - by 1967
Combined with: *Gardening*, Style One, HW9
                  Netting a Cricket, HW6

Shape	U.S. $	Can. $	U.K. £	Aust. $
Casino jug, 42s				
with signature	135.00	200.00	85.00	200.00
without signature	125.00	175.00	75.00	175.00
Casino sugar bowl, 36s				
with signature	150.00	225.00	90.00	225.00
without signature	135.00	200.00	80.00	200.00
Casino teacup				
with signature	125.00	175.00	75.00	175.00
without signature	75.00	125.00	45.00	125.00
Cup / mug, large	350.00	500.00	200.00	500.00
Don beaker				
with signature	125.00	175.00	75.00	175.00
without signature	75.00	125.00	45.00	125.00
Don mug, one handle				
with signature	75.00	125.00	60.00	125.00
without signature	65.00	100.00	40.00	100.00
Don mug, two handles				
with signature	75.00	125.00	60.00	125.00
without signature	75.00	100.00	45.00	100.00
Lid of hot water plate				
with signature	85.00	125.00	50.00	125.00
without signature	75.00	100.00	45.00	100.00

Gardener with Wheelbarrow (HW9R)

Gardening, Style One (HW9)

Gardening
Style One

The don mug, one handle, was also available with a sterling silver rim see Roden advertising page viii.

Design No.:   HW9
Designer: Barbara Vernon
Issued: By 1937 - by 1967
Combined with: *Gardener with Wheelbarrow*, HW9R
                  Leapfrog, HW12R
                  Washing in the Open Air, HW10R

Shape	U.S. $	Can. $	U.K. £	Aust. $
Baby plate, round, 6"				
with signature	135.00	200.00	85.00	200.00
without signature	100.00	150.00	65.00	150.00
Casino jug, 36s				
with signature	150.00	225.00	90.00	225.00
without signature	135.00	200.00	80.00	200.00
Casino jug, 42s				
with signature	135.00	200.00	80.00	200.00
without signature	125.00	175.00	70.00	175.00
Casino saucer				
with signature	75.00	100.00	45.00	100.00
without signature	50.00	75.00	35.00	75.00
Casino sugar bowl, 36s				
with signature	150.00	225.00	85.00	250.00
without signature	100.00	150.00	65.00	175.00
Casino teacup				
with signature	75.00	110.00	45.00	125.00
without signature	50.00	75.00	30.00	75.00
Casino teapot, 24s				
with signature	300.00	450.00	175.00	575.00
without signature	250.00	400.00	150.00	525.00
Cereal / oatmeal bowl				
with signature	85.00	135.00	60.00	150.00
without signature	60.00	90.00	35.00	100.00
Don beaker				
with signature	75.00	125.00	45.00	125.00
without signature	60.00	90.00	35.00	95.00
Don beaker, one handle				
with signature	75.00	125.00	45.00	125.00
without signature	60.00	90.00	35.00	95.00
Don mug, one handle				
with signature	75.00	110.00	45.00	125.00
without signature	60.00	90.00	35.00	95.00
Don mug, two handles				
with signature	75.00	110.00	45.00	125.00
without signature	60.00	90.00	35.00	95.00
Jaffa fruit saucer				
plain rim	60.00	90.00	35.00	95.00
wavy rim	75.00	110.00	45.00	125.00
Lid of hot water plate				
with signature	85.00	125.00	50.00	125.00
without signature	75.00	100.00	45.00	100.00
Plate, 6½"				
with signature	65.00	100.00	40.00	100.00
without signature	50.00	75.00	30.00	75.00

GARDENING THEME
Frank Endersby

Gardening
Style Two

Design No.: 55 Gardening
Designer: Frank Endersby
Issued: 1995 to the present

Shape	U.S. $	Can. $	U.K. £	Aust. $
Baby plate, round, small	40.00	46.00	12.00	49.00
Cake stand	150.00	200.00	90.00	200.00
Plate, 6 ½"	25.00	25.00	7.00	27.00
Plate, 8"	30.00	35.00	9.00	39.00

Gardening, Style Two (55)

Playing in Tree House (56)

Playing in Tree House / Resting in Wheelbarrow

Design No.: Front — 56 Playing in Tree House
            Reverse — 57 Resting in Wheelbarrow
Designer: Frank Endersby
Issued: 1995 to the present

Shape	U.S. $	Can. $	U.K. £	Aust. $
Hug-a-mug, one handle	30.00	33.00	9.00	39.00
Hug-a-mug, two handles	33.00	39.00	10.00	45.00

Resting in Wheelbarrow (57)

Geography Lesson (LF17)

Geography Lesson

Design No.: LF17
Designer: Walter Hayward
Issued: 1954 - 1970

Shape	U.S. $	Can. $	U.K. £	Aust. $
Baby plate, oval, large				
with signature	225.00	325.00	135.00	350.00
without signature	125.00	200.00	80.00	225.00
Baby plate, round, large				
with signature	250.00	350.00	150.00	350.00
without signature	125.00	200.00	80.00	225.00
Bread / butter plate, handles				
with signature	200.00	275.00	125.00	300.00
without signature	150.00	225.00	100.00	250.00
Cereal / oatmeal bowl				
with signature	95.00	150.00	65.00	160.00
without signature	75.00	110.00	45.00	125.00
Plate, 8"	125.00	200.00	75.00	200.00
Plate, 8 ½"				
with signature	150.00	250.00	100.00	250.00
without signature	125.00	200.00	75.00	200.00
Porridge bowl				
with signature	150.00	200.00	85.00	200.00
without signature	100.00	145.00	75.00	150.00

Getting Dressed

Design No.: LF2
Designer: Barbara Vernon
Issued: By 1940 - by 1952

Shape	U.S. $	Can. $	U.K. £	Aust. $
Baby plate, round, large				
with signature	225.00	325.00	150.00	350.00
without signature	125.00	200.00	80.00	225.00
Bread / butter plate, handles				
with signature	200.00	275.00	125.00	300.00
without signature	125.00	200.00	100.00	250.00
Hot water plate				
with signature	175.00	275.00	110.00	275.00
without signature	125.00	200.00	90.00	200.00
Plate, 8 ½"				
with signature	200.00	300.00	125.00	275.00
without signature	125.00	200.00	75.00	200.00
Porridge bowl				
with signature	175.00	225.00	100.00	225.00
without siignature	100.00	150.00	75.00	150.00

Getting Dressed (LF2)

Going Shopping

Design No.: SF10
Designer: Barbara Vernon
Issued: By 1940 - by 1952

Shape	U.S. $	Can. $	U.K. £	Aust. $
Baby plate, round, small				
with signature	150.00	225.00	90.00	225.00
without signature	125.00	175.00	70.00	175.00
Casino jug, 30s				
with signature	175.00	250.00	125.00	250.00
without signature	150.00	200.00	80.00	200.00
Casino saucer				
with signature	70.00	100.00	45.00	100.00
without signature	50.00	75.00	35.00	75.00
Casino teapot				
with signature	200.00	300.00	125.00	325.00
without signature	150.00	225.00	85.00	225.00
Cereal bowl, fine china	400.00	625.00	250.00	600.00
Cereal / oatmeal bowl				
with signature	85.00	125.00	50.00	125.00
without signature	65.00	100.00	40.00	100.00
Don beaker, one handle				
with signature	100.00	150.00	60.00	150.00
without signature	65.00	100.00	40.00	100.00
Jaffa fruit saucer (wavy)				
with signature	100.00	150.00	65.00	150.00
without signature	75.00	125.00	50.00	125.00
Hot water plate				
with signature	175.00	275.00	100.00	275.00
without signature	125.00	200.00	85.00	200.00
Plate, 6 ½"				
with signature	100.00	150.00	60.00	150.00
without signature	50.00	75.00	30.00	75.00
Plate, 7 ½"				
with signature	100.00	150.00	60.00	150.00
without signature	75.00	110.00	50.00	125.00

Going Shopping (SF10)

Golfer (HW4R)

Golfer

Design No.:	HW4R
Designer:	Barbara Vernon
Issued:	By 1937 - by 1952
Combined with:	*Cuddling under a Mushroom*, HW4
	Cycling, HW15R
	Family at Breakfast, HW12
	Feeding the Baby, HW13
	Proposal, HW11
	Pulling on Trousers, HW2

Shape	U.S. $	Can. $	U.K. £	Aust. $
Casino jug, 36s	250.00	400.00	150.00	450.00
Casino teacup	250.00	400.00	150.00	450.00
Don beaker	125.00	175.00	75.00	175.00
Don beaker, one handle	135.00	185.00	80.00	185.00
Don mug, one handle	250.00	400.00	150.00	425.00
Don mug, two handles	150.00	225.00	90.00	250.00

Note: This design should appear with the Barbara Vernon facsimile signature. See also *Game of Golf* (SF11) page 83.

Greetings

Design No.:	HW7
Designer:	Barbara Vernon
Issued:	By 1937 - by 1952
Combined with:	*Dunce*, HW1R

Shape	U.S. $	Can. $	U.K. £	Aust. $
Baby plate, round, small	135.00	200.00	100.00	225.00
Casino jug, 36s	150.00	225.00	90.00	225.00
Casino jug, 42s	135.00	200.00	85.00	200.00
Casino saucer	75.00	100.00	45.00	100.00
Casino teacup	115.00	165.00	70.00	165.00
Casino teapot, 24s	300.00	450.00	175.00	500.00
Casino teapot, 30s	300.00	450.00	175.00	475.00
Cereal / oatmeal bowl	100.00	150.00	65.00	150.00
Don beaker	125.00	175.00	75.00	175.00
Don beaker, one handle	135.00	180.00	80.00	185.00
Don mug, one handle	125.00	175.00	75.00	175.00
Don mug, two handles	135.00	180.00	80.00	180.00
Jaffa fruit saucer				
plain rim	95.00	140.00	50.00	125.00
wavy rim	150.00	225.00	100.00	250.00
Lid of hot water plate	85.00	125.00	50.00	150.00
Plate, 6 ½"	95.00	140.00	60.00	150.00
Plate, 7 ½"	100.00	150.00	65.00	160.00
Plate 7", fine china		Very rare		

Greetings (HW7)

Note: This design should appear with the Barbara Vernon facsimile signature.

HAPPY BIRTHDAY FROM BUNNYKINS
Walter Hayward

Style One

Design No.:	Front — SF136 Happy Birthday from Bunnykins
	Reverse — Birthday Inscription
Designer:	Walter Hayward
Issued:	1982 - 1989
Inscription:	'Birthdays are lots and lots of fun,
	With cards and gifts for everyone.
	There are cakes and jellies and lots to eat,
	Parties and games and your favourite treat.
	So on this your very special day
	The Bunnykins wish you a Happy Birthday!'

Shape	U.S. $	Can. $	U.K. £	Aust. $
Plate, 8"	75.00	100.00	35.00	100.00

Happy Birthday from Bunnykins, Style One, (SF136)

Reverse Birthday Inscription

HAPPY BIRTHDAY FROM BUNNYKINS
Colin Twinn

Happy Birthday from Bunnykins
Style Two, First Version (CT37)

Style Two, First Version

The rhyme used on the reverse of this plate is the same as that used on style one, however a new border and copyright date are shown.

Design No.: Front — CT37 Happy Birthday from Bunnykins
Reverse — CT64 Birthday Inscription
Designer: Colin Twinn
Issued: 1990 - 1992
Inscription: 'Birthdays are lots and lots of fun,
With cards and gifts for everyone.
There are cakes and jellies and lots to eat,
Parties and games and your favourite treat.
So on this your very special day
The Bunnykins wish you a Happy Birthday!'

Shape	U.S. $	Can. $	U.K. £	Aust. $
Plate, 8"	75.00	100.00	40.00	100.00

Birthday Inscription (CT64)

Happy Birthday from Bunnykins
Style Two, Second Version (CT60)

Style Two, Second Version

Design No.: Front — CT60 Happy Birthday from Bunnykins
Reverse — CT61 Inscription
Designer: Colin Twinn
Issued: 1992 - 1992

Shape	U.S. $	Can. $	U.K. £	Aust. $
Hug-a-mug, one handle	35.00	60.00	25.00	75.00
Money ball				
with 1992	50.00	75.00	30.00	75.00
without 1992	50.00	75.00	30.00	75.00

Note: Two money balls were issued for the U.S. Special Events Tour in 1992. The ball sold on the Spring tour depicted *Queen of the May* (CT7) page 128, and the Fall tour ball was as listed below. The Special Events Tour money ball was inscribed 'U.S. Special Event Tour 1992' and 'To..... From......' to be completed by the customer.

Happy Birthday Bunnykins Inscription (CT61)

HAPPY EASTER FROM BUNNYKINS
Colin Twinn

First Version, Large Design

Design No.: Front — CT40 Happy Easter from Bunnykins
Reverse no. one - without inscription
Reverse no. two — CT67 with inscription
Designer: Colin Twinn
Issued: 1990 - 1992
Rhyme: 'The Easter Bunnykins romp and play,
Loving the joy of this Easter Day.
Gone is the frost, the long winter lost,
The sunshine brings light and new blossoms bright,
So Bunnykins send you this warm invitation
To Easter's party, a grand celebration'.

Shape	U.S. $	Can. $	U.K. £	Aust. $
Plate, 8"	75.00	100.00	40.00	100.00

Happy Easter from Bunnykins
First Version (CT40)

Happy Easter from Bunnykins
Second Version (CT62)

Second Version, Small Design

Design No.: Front — CT62 Happy Easter from Bunnykins
Reverse — CT63 Happy Easter inscription
Designer: Colin Twinn
Issued: 1992 - 1992

Shape	U.S. $	Can. $	U.K. £	Aust. $
Hug-a-mug, one handle	40.00	65.00	25.00	75.00

Happy Easter Inscription (CT63)

Hat Shop / Trying on Hats

Hat Shop (HW28)   Trying on Hats (HW28R)

Design No.:	Front — HW28 Hat Shop
	Reverse — HW28R Trying on Hats
Designer:	Walter Hayward
Issued:	1954 - by 1998

Combined with: *Afternoon Tea*, HW116
Dancing with Doll, HW115R
Drummer and Bugler, EC126
Serving Tea, HW116R

Shape	U.S. $	Can. $	U.K. £	Aust. $
Albion cream jug	50.00	75.00	30.00	75.00
Albion jug, ½ pint	50.00	75.00	30.00	75.00
Albion jug, 1 pint	75.00	100.00	50.00	150.00
Albion teapot	50.00	75.00	30.00	75.00
Casino jug, 36s				
with signature	125.00	175.00	85.00	175.00
without signature	100.00	150.00	60.00	150.00
Casino jug, 42s				
with signature	100.00	150.00	60.00	150.00
without signature	75.00	100.00	45.00	100.00
Casino saucer				
with signature	35.00	50.00	20.00	60.00
without signature	10.00	15.00	5.00	15.00
Casino teacup				
with signature	50.00	75.00	30.00	75.00
without signature	25.00	35.00	15.00	35.00
Divided dish	45.00	65.00	30.00	65.00
Don beaker				
with signature	50.00	75.00	30.00	75.00
without signature	35.00	50.00	20.00	50.00
Don beaker , one handle				
with signature	50.00	75.00	30.00	75.00
without signature	35.00	50.00	20.00	50.00
Don mug, one handle				
with signature	50.00	75.00	30.00	75.00
without signature	35.00	50.00	20.00	50.00

Shape	U.S. $	Can. $	U.K. £	Aust. $
Don mug, two handles				
with signature	50.00	75.00	30.00	75.00
without signature	35.00	50.00	20.00	50.00
Egg box				
small	250.00	350.00	100.00	400.00
medium	325.00	475.00	150.00	500.00
large	400.00	575.00	200.00	600.00
Jaffa fruit saucer (plain)	40.00	60.00	25.00	60.00
Hug-a-mug, one handle	30.00	45.00	20.00	45.00
Hug-a-mug, two handles	35.00	50.00	20.00	55.00
Lamp	175.00	250.00	100.00	225.00
Lid of hot water plate				
with signature	85.00	125.00	50.00	125.00
without signature	75.00	100.00	45.00	100.00
Malvern beaker	30.00	45.00	20.00	50.00
Money ball	25.00	35.00	15.00	40.00
Picture plaque, small	40.00	60.00	25.00	65.00
Plate, 6½"				
with signature	50.00	75.00	30.00	75.00
without signature	20.00	30.00	10.00	35.00
Savings book	30.00	45.00	20.00	50.00
Stratford straight beaker	30.00	45.00	20.00	50.00
Stratford teacup	30.00	45.00	20.00	50.00

Note: *Trying on Hats* (HW28R) was paired with *Dancing with Doll* (HW115R) on the Savings book. The divided dish combines *Afternoon Tea* (HW116), *Serving Tea* (HW116R) and *Trying on Hats* (HW28R) and the lid of the hot water plate combines *Hat Shop* (HW28), *Trying on Hats* (HW28R) and *Drummer and Bugler* (EC126).

Haymaking / Lunch Break

Haymaking (HW29) Lunch Break (HW29R)

Design No.:	Front — HW29 Haymaking
	Reverse — HW29R Lunch Break
Designer:	Walter Hayward
Issued:	1954 - by 1998

Combined with:	*Dancing with Doll*, HW115R
	Holding Hat and Coat, EC4
	Sleeping in a Rocking Chair, EC1

Shape	U.S. $	Can. $	U.K. £	Aust. $
Albion cream jug	50.00	75.00	30.00	75.00
Albion jug, ½ pint	50.00	75.00	30.00	75.00
Albion teapot	50.00	75.00	30.00	75.00
Casino jug, 36s				
with signature	125.00	175.00	85.00	175.00
without signature	100.00	150.00	60.00	175.00
Casino jug, 42s				
with signature	100.00	150.00	60.00	150.00
without signature	75.00	100.00	45.00	125.00
Casino saucer				
with signature	35.00	50.00	20.00	60.00
without signature	10.00	15.00	15.00	15.00
Casino teacup				
with signature	50.00	75.00	30.00	75.00
without signature	25.00	25.00	15.00	35.00
Casino teapot, 30s				
with signature	275.00	400.00	175.00	450.00
without signature	250.00	350.00	150.00	350.00
Don beaker				
with signature	50.00	75.00	30.00	75.00
without signature	35.00	50.00	20.00	50.00
Don beaker, one handle				
with signature	50.00	75.00	30.00	75.00
without signature	35.00	50.00	20.00	50.00

Shape	U.S. $	Can. $	U.K. £	Aust. $
Don mug, one handle				
with signature	50.00	75.00	30.00	75.00
without signature	35.00	50.00	20.00	50.00
Don mug, two handles				
with signature	50.00	75.00	30.00	75.00
without signature	35.00	50.00	20.00	50.00
Egg box				
small	275.00	350.00	100.00	400.00
medium	325.00	475.00	150.00	500.00
large	400.00	575.00	200.00	600.00
Hug-a-mug, one handle	25.00	35.00	10.00	40.00
Hug-a-mug, two handles	25.00	35.00	10.00	40.00
Jaffa fruit saucer (plain)	50.00	75.00	30.00	75.00
Lamp	175.00	250.00	100.00	200.00
Lid of hot water plate				
with signature	100.00	150.00	60.00	150.00
without signature	75.00	100.00	45.00	100.00
Malvern beaker	30.00	45.00	20.00	50.00
Money ball	25.00	35.00	15.00	40.00
Picture plaque, small	40.00	60.00	25.00	65.00
Plate, 6½"				
with signature	50.00	75.00	30.00	75.00
without signature	20.00	30.00	10.00	35.00
Savings book	30.00	45.00	20.00	50.00
Stratford straight beaker	30.00	45.00	20.00	50.00
Stratford teacup	30.00	45.00	20.00	50.00

Note: The savings book combines *Lunch Break* (HW29R) and *Dancing with Doll* (HW115R).

Hikers (EC124)

Hikers

Design No.:	EC124
Designer:	Walter Hayward
Issued:	1959 to the present
Combined with:	*Daisy Chains*, HW25
	The Doll's House, HW120
	Drummer, EC2
	Drummer and Bugler, EC126
	Nipped by a Crab, HW21R
	Playing with Doll and Teddy, HW120R
	Raising Hat, Style Two, EC7
	Reading, EC122
	Row Boat, HW21
	Sleeping in a Rocking Chair, EC1
	Trumpeter, EC5

Shape	U.S. $	Can. $	U.K. £	Aust. $
Albion sugar bowl	40.00	60.00	25.00	55.00
Beaker cover	75.00	100.00	35.00	100.00
Egg cup				
Style One	35.00	60.00	25.00	65.00
Style Two	60.00	100.00	35.00	125.00
Style Three	**10.00**	**15.00**	**5.00**	**15.00**
Hug-a-mug, 1993	25.00	35.00	10.00	40.00
Lid of hot water plate	100.00	150.00	40.00	175.00

Note: This scene was combined with *Daisy Chains*, HW25 on a hug-a-mug for the U.S. Special Events Tour in 1993.

Hobby Horse
Style Two

Design No.:	EC121
Designer:	Walter Hayward
Issued:	1959 to the present
Combined with:	*Cowboy on Rocking Horse*, HW140R
	Cowboys and Indians, HW140
	Drummer and Bugler, EC126
	Lasso Games, HW117
	Lassoing, HW117R
	Playing with Cup and Spoon, EC6
	Playing with Doll and Pram, EC123
	Raising Hat, Style Two, EC7

Shape	U.S. $	Can. $	U.K. £	Aust. $
Albion sugar bowl	40.00	60.00	25.00	55.00
Beaker cover	100.00	150.00	65.00	145.00
Egg cup				
Style One	35.00	60.00	25.00	65.00
Style Two	60.00	100.00	35.00	125.00
Style Three	**10.00**	**15.00**	**5.00**	**15.00**
Lid of hot water plate	100.00	150.00	40.00	175.00

Hobby Horse, Style Two (EC121)

Holding Hat and Coat

Design No.:   EC4
Designer: Barbara Vernon
Isued: 1937 to the present
Combined with: *Bedtime with Dollies*, EC125
                   Drummer, EC2
                   Haymaking, HW29
                   Lunch Break, HW29R
                   Playing with Cup and Spoon, EC6
                   Playing with Doll and Pram, EC123
                   Sheltering Under an Umbrella, EC3
                   Skipping, HW20R
                   Swinging, HW20
                   Trumpeter, EC5
                   Wheelbarrow Race, (HW22)

Holding Hat and Coat (EC4)

Shape	U.S. $	Can. $	U.K. £	Aust. $
Albion sugar bowl	40.00	60.00	25.00	55.00
Beaker cover				
with signature	150.00	225.00	90.00	250.00
without signature	100.00	150.00	60.00	150.00
Casino sugar bowl, 36s				
with signature	150.00	225.00	85.00	250.00
without signature	35.00	50.00	25.00	55.00
Egg cup				
Style one	35.00	60.00	25.00	65.00
Style two				
with signature	175.00	250.00	100.00	275.00
without signature	60.00	100.00	35.00	100.00
Style three	**10.00**	**15.00**	**5.00**	**15.00**
Lid of hot water plate				
with signature	85.00	125.00	50.00	125.00
without signature	75.00	100.00	45.00	100.00
Money ball	25.00	35.00	12.00	40.00

Note: *Wheelbarrow Race* (HW22) is combined with *Holding Hat and Coat* (EC4) on a money ball.

Home Decorating (SF131)

Home Decorating

Design No.:   SF131
Designer: Walter Hayward
Issued: 1967 - by 1998

Shape	U.S. $	Can. $	U.K. £	Aust. $
Baby plate, round, small	25.00	40.00	12.00	45.00
Cake stand	150.00	200.00	90.00	200.00
Casino saucer	40.00	60.00	25.00	45.00
Cereal / oatmeal bowl	20.00	30.00	9.00	35.00
Hot water plate	125.00	200.00	80.00	150.00
Jaffa fruit saucer (plain)	20.00	30.00	10.00	35.00
Picture plaque, large	50.00	75.00	30.00	75.00
Plate, 6 ½"	17.00	25.00	7.00	35.00
Plate, 8"	30.00	45.00	9.00	50.00
Plate, 10"	40.00	60.00	12.00	65.00

Home from Fishing
First Variation (CT18)

Home From Fishing
First Variation, Large Size

Design No.: CT18 Home from Fishing
Designer: Colin Twinn
Issued: 1990 - 1993

Shape	U.S. $	Can. $	U.K. £	Aust. $
Albion jug, 1 pint	100.00	150.00	60.00	150.00
Baby plate, round, small	20.00	30.00	15.00	35.00
Divided dish	45.00	65.00	30.00	75.00
Jaffa fruit saucer	50.00	75.00	30.00	80.00
Picture plaque, large	50.00	75.00	30.00	80.00
Picture plaque, small	40.00	60.00	25.00	70.00
Plate, 8"	25.00	40.00	15.00	45.00

Home from Fishing
Second Variation (CT26)

Home From Fishing
Second Variation, Small Size /
Father Bunnykins with Fishing Rod

Design No.: Front — CT26 Home from Fishing
　　　　　　Reverse — CT27 Father Bunnykins with Fishing Rod
Designer: Colin Twinn
Issued: 1990 - 1993
Combined with: *Bunny on Rocking Horse*, CT29
　　　　　　Family with Pram, Style Two, CT14
　　　　　　Standing by Pram, CT6

Shape	U.S. $	Can. $	U.K £	Aust. $
Albion cream jug	50.00	75.00	25.00	80.00
Albion jug, ½ pint	40.00	75.00	30.00	70.00
Albion teapot	50.00	100.00	30.00	125.00
Hug-a-mug, two handles	25.00	35.00	10.00	40.00
Lamp	175.00	250.00	75.00	250.00
Malvern beaker	45.00	65.00	30.00	70.00
Money ball	25.00	35.00	15.00	40.00
Picture plaque, small	40.00	60.00	25.00	65.00
Savings book	30.00	50.00	15.00	60.00
Stratford straight beaker	35.00	50.00	20.00	60.00
Stratford teacup	30.00	45.00	15.00	45.00

Note: *Bunny on Rocking Horse* (CT29) is combined with *Home from Fishing* (CT26) on a savings book.

Father Bunnykins with Fishing Rod (CT27)

Hoopla

Design No.: LF129
Designer: Walter Hayward
Issued: 1967 - 1970

Shape	U.S. $	Can. $	U.K. £	Aust. $
Baby plate, oval, large	500.00	750.00	300.00	775.00
Baby plate, round, large	500.00	750.00	300.00	800.00
Plate, 8 ½"	850.00	1,250.00	500.00	1,300.00

Hoopla (LF129)

ICE CREAM THEME
Colin Twinn

Ice Cream Seller, First Variation (CT5)

Ice Cream Seller
First Variation, Large Size

Design No.:   CT5 Ice Cream Seller
Designer: Colin Twinn
Issued: 1989 - 1993
Combined with: *Pushing the Wheelbarrow*, CT3
                  Splashing at Sink, CT33
                  Washing Up, CT32

Shape	U.S. $	Can. $	U.K	Aust. $
Hug-a-mug, one handle	20.00	30.00	10.00	30.00
Hug-a-mug, two handles	25.00	35.00	15.00	50.00
Lamp	175.00	250.00	75.00	225.00
Malvern beaker	30.00	45.00	20.00	60.00
Money ball	25.00	35.00	15.00	40.00
Picture plaque, small	50.00	75.00	30.00	75.00
Stratford straight beaker	40.00	50.00	20.00	60.00
Stratford teacup	30.00	45.00	15.00	45.00

Ice Cream Seller
Second Variation, Small Size

Design No.:   CT11 Ice Cream Seller
Designer: Colin Twinn
Issued: 1989 - 1993

Shape	U.S. $	Can. $	U.K. £	Aust. $
Albion jug, 1 pint	100.00	150.00	80.00	150.00
Albion teapot	50.00	100.00	30.00	125.00
Baby plate, round, small	20.00	30.00	12.00	35.00
Cake stand	150.00	225.00	90.00	200.00
Cereal / oatmeal bowl	25.00	35.00	10.00	35.00
Plate, 6"	20.00	25.00	7.00	25.00

Ice Cream Seller, Second Variation (CT11)

Ice Cream Vendor / Hiker Resting with Ice Cream

Ice Cream Vendor (HW23)   Hiker Resting with Ice Cream (HW23R)

Design No.: Front — HW23 Ice Cream Vendor
             Reverse — HW23R Hiker Resting with Ice Cream

Designer: Walter Hayward
Issued: By 1952 - by 1998

Shape	U.S. $	Can. $	U.K. £	Aust. $
Albion cream jug	50.00	75.00	30.00	75.00
Albion jug, ½ pint	50.00	75.00	30.00	75.00
Albion jug, 1 pint	75.00	100.00	50.00	150.00
Albion teapot	50.00	75.00	30.00	75.00
Baby plate, round, small				
with signature	50.00	75.00	35.00	75.00
without signature	25.00	40.00	12.00	45.00
Casino jug, 30s				
with signature	150.00	225.00	90.00	225.00
without signature	125.00	175.00	80.00	200.00
Casino jug, 36s				
with signature	125.00	175.00	85.00	200.00
without signature	100.00	150.00	60.00	175.00
Casino jug, 42s				
with signature	100.00	150.00	60.00	150.00
without signature	75.00	100.00	45.00	125.00
Casino saucer				
with signature	35.00	50.00	20.00	60.00
without signature	10.00	15.00	5.00	15.00
Casino sugar bowl, 30s				
with signature	200.00	300.00	125.00	325.00
without signature	150.00	225.00	85.00	200.00
Casino sugar bowl, 36s				
with signature	150.00	225.00	85.00	250.00
without signature	125.00	175.00	70.00	175.00
Casino teacup				
with signature	50.00	75.00	30.00	75.00
without signature	25.00	35.00	15.00	35.00
Casino teapot, 30s				
with signature	275.00	400.00	125.00	425.00
without signature	250.00	400.00	150.00	525.00

Shape	U.S. $	Can. $	U.K. £	Aust. $
Divided dish	45.00	65.00	30.00	65.00
Don beaker				
with signature	40.00	60.00	25.00	65.00
without signature	30.00	45.00	20.00	50.00
Don beaker, one handle				
with signature	40.00	60.00	25.00	65.00
without signature	30.00	45.00	20.00	50.00
Don mug, one handle				
with signature	70.00	105.00	40.00	100.00
without signature	50.00	75.00	30.00	75.00
Don mug, two handles				
with signature	70.00	105.00	40.00	100.00
without signature	50.00	75.00	30.00	75.00
Hug-a-mug, one handle	25.00	35.00	15.00	40.00
Hug-a-mug, two handles	25.00	35.00	15.00	40.00
Jaffa fruit saucer				
plain rim	45.00	70.00	30.00	75.00
wavy rim	100.00	150.00	60.00	150.00
Lamp	175.00	250.00	100.00	250.00
Lid of hot water plate				
with signature	100.00	150.00	60.00	150.00
without signature	75.00	100.00	45.00	100.00
Money ball	25.00	35.00	15.00	40.00
Picture plaque, small	40.00	60.00	25.00	65.00
Plate, 6½"				
with signature	50.00	75.00	30.00	75.00
without signature	20.00	30.00	10.00	35.00
Savings book	30.00	45.00	20.00	50.00
Stratford straight beaker	30.00	45.00	20.00	50.00
Stratford teacup	30.00	45.00	20.00	50.00

Ice Skating (SF24)

Jack and Jill (CT9)

Ice Skating

Design No.: SF24
Designer: Walter Hayward
Issued: 1954 - 1967

Shape	U.S. $	Can. $	U.K. £	Aust. $
Baby plate, round, small				
with signature	135.00	200.00	85.00	200.00
without signature	100.00	150.00	65.00	150.00
Baby plate, round, large				
with signature	250.00	350.00	150.00	375.00
without signature	125.00	200.00	80.00	200.00
Casino saucer				
with signature	75.00	100.00	45.00	100.00
without signature	50.00	75.00	3500	75.00
Cereal / oatmeal bowl				
with signature	100.00	150.00	65.00	165.00
with signature	75.00	110.00	45.00	125.00
Hot water plate				
with signature	175.00	275.00	110.00	275.00
without signature	125.00	200.00	85.00	200.00
Plate, 6 ½"				
with signature	75.00	100.00	45.00	100.00
without signature	50.00	75.00	30.00	75.00
Plate, 7 ½"				
with signature	90.00	135.00	60.00	125.00
without signature	75.00	110.00	50.00	110.00
Plate, 8½"				
with signature	100.00	150.00	65.00	125.00
without signature	75.00	110.00	50.00	125.00

Jack and Jill

Design No.: Front — CT9 Jack and Jill
Reverse — CT10 Jack and Jill Nursery Rhyme
Designer: Colin Twinn
Issued: 1989 - 1993

Shape	U.S. $	Can. $	U.K. £	Aust. $
Hug-a-mug, one handle	75.00	100.00	50.00	100.00

Jack and Jill Nursery Rhyme (CT10)

Juggling

Design No.: LF127
Designer: Walter Hayward
Issued: 1967 - 1970

Shape	U.S. $	Can. $	U.K. £	Aust. $
Baby plate, round, large	1,000.00	1,500.00	600.00	1,500.00
Plate, 8 ½"	1,000.00	1,500.00	600.00	1,500.00

Juggling (LF127)

Kissing Under the Mistletoe (with mistletoe)

Kissing Under the Mistletoe
First Version, With Mistletoe

Design No.: HW11R
Designer: Barbara Vernon
Issued: By 1937 - by 1947
Combined with: *Cycling*, HW15R
Family at Breakfast, HW12
Feeding the Baby, HW13
Proposal, HW11
Reading the Times, HW2R

Shape	U.S. $	Can. $	U.K. £	Aust. $
Casino jug, 36s	350.00	525.00	200.00	550.00
Casino jug, 42s	300.00	450.00	175.00	450.00
Casino teacup	125.00	175.00	75.00	200.00
Don beaker	150.00	225.00	90.00	250.00
Don beaker, one handle	150.00	225.00	90.00	250.00
Don mug, one handle	175.00	250.00	110.00	275.00
Don mug, two handles	175.00	250.00	110.00	275.00
Teacup, fine china		Very rare		

Kissing Under the Mistletoe
Second Version, Without Mistletoe

Design No.: HW11R
Designer: Barbara Vernon
Issued: c.1947 - by 1967
Combined with: *Cycling*, HW15R
Family at Breakfast, HW12
Feeding the Baby, HW13
Proposal, HW11
Reading the Times, HW2R

Shape	U.S. $	Can. $	U.K. £	Aust. $
Casino jug, 42s				
with signature	135.00	200.00	85.00	200.00
without signature	125.00	175.00	75.00	175.00
Casino teacup				
with signature	125.00	175.00	75.00	195.00
without signature	75.00	125.00	45.00	125.00
Don beaker				
with signature	125.00	175.00	80.00	185.00
without signature	75.00	125.00	45.00	125.00
Don beaker, one handle				
with signature	150.00	225.00	90.00	225.00
without signature	125.00	200.00	75.00	200.00
Don mug, one handle				
with signature	125.00	175.00	75.00	200.00
without signature	100.00	150.00	60.00	150.00
Don mug, two handles				
with signature	135.00	200.00	80.00	200.00
without signature	100.00	150.00	65.00	150.00
Rex mug, fine china		Extremely Rare		

Kissing Under the Mistletoe (without mistletoe)

Lambeth Walk
First Version, 'Lambeth Walk' on Music Sheet

Design No.:	HW16
Designer:	Barbara Vernon
Issued:	By 1937 - By 1949
Combined with:	*Footballer*, HW13R
	Leapfrog, HW12R
	Raising Hat, Style One, HW16R
	Top Hat, HW14R

Shape	U.S. $	Can. $	U.K. £	Aust. $
Casino jug, 30s	175.00	250.00	125.00	250.00
Casino jug, 36s	150.00	225.00	90.00	225.00
Casino saucer	75.00	100.00	45.00	100.00
Casino teacup	125.00	175.00	75.00	175.00
Don beaker	125.00	175.00	75.00	175.00
Don mug, one handle	100.00	150.00	65.00	150.00
Don mug, two handles	100.00	150.00	65.00	150.00
Jam pot	850.00	1,250.00	500.00	1,300.00
Lid of hot water plate	85.00	120.00	50.00	125.00
Rex mug, fine china	Extremely rare			
Saucer, fine china	Very rare			

Lambeth Walk, First Version (HW16)

Note: This design should appear with the Barbara Vernon facsimile signature. The Rex mug combines *Footballer* (HW13R) and *Lambeth Walk*, first version (HW16)

Lambeth Walk, Second Version,
Musical Score on Music Sheet, Bird Sits Atop Sheet

After 1949 the words *Lambeth Walk* were replaced by a musical score, and a small bird sat atop the music sheet.

Lambeth Walk, Second Version (HW16)

Combined with: *Footballer*, HW13R
Leapfrog, HW12R
Raising Hat, Style One, HW16R
Sleeping in a Rocking Chair, EC1
Top Hat, HW14R

Design No.: HW16
Designer: Barbara Vernon
Issued: By 1949 - 1967

Shape	U.S. $	Can. $	U.K. £	Aust. $
Baby plate, round, 6"				
with signature	125.00	175.00	75.00	175.00
without signature	100.00	150.00	60.00	150.00
Casino jug, 30s				
with signature	175.00	250.00	100.00	250.00
without signature	150.00	225.00	90.00	225.00
Casino jug, 36s				
with signature	150.00	225.00	90.00	225.00
without signature	125.00	200.00	75.00	200.00
Casino jug, 42s				
with signature	125.00	200.00	80.00	200.00
without signature	100.00	150.00	60.00	150.00
Casino saucer				
with signature	75.00	100.00	45.00	100.00
without signature	50.00	75.00	30.00	75.00
Casino sugar bowl, 30s				
with signature	200.00	300.00	125.00	300.00
without signature	150.00	225.00	90.00	225.00
Casino teacup				
with signature	150.00	225.00	90.00	200.00
without signature	75.00	100.00	45.00	100.00
Casino teapot, 24s				
with signature	400.00	600.00	250.00	600.00
without signature	350.00	525.00	225.00	525.00

Shape	U.S. $	Can. $	U.K. £	Aust. $
Don beaker				
with signature	125.00	200.00	75.00	200.00
without signature	100.00	150.00	60.00	150.00
Don beaker, one handle				
with signature	135.00	200.00	80.00	200.00
without signature	100.00	150.00	60.00	150.00
Don mug, one handle				
with signature	125.00	200.00	75.00	200.00
without signature	100.00	150.00	60.00	150.00
Don mug, two handles				
with signature	135.00	200.00	80.00	200.00
without signature	100.00	150.00	60.00	150.00
Egg cup				
Style One	50.00	75.00	30.00	75.00
Style Two	100.00	150.00	60.00	150.00
Jam pot	1,000.00	1,500.00	600.00	1,500.00
Lid of hot water plate				
with signature	150.00	225.00	90.00	225.00
without signature	100.00	150.00	60.00	150.00
Plate, 6 ½"				
with signature	100.00	150.00	60.00	100.00
without signature	75.00	100.00	45.00	75.00
Sugar bowl with handles		Exremely rare		

Lasso Games / Lassoing

Design No.:	Front — HW117 Lasso Games
	Reverse — HW117R Lassoing
Designer:	Walter Hayward
Issued:	1959 - 1967
Combined with:	*Hobby Horse*, Style Two, EC121

Shape	U.S. $	Can. $	U.K. £	Aust. $
Casino teacup	90.00	150.00	60.00	150.00
Don beaker	75.00	125.00	50.00	100.00
Don beaker, one handle	90.00	150.00	60.00	150.00
Don mug, one handle	75.00	125.00	50.00	100.00
Don mug, two handles	90.00	150.00	60.00	150.00
Jaffa fruit saucer	75.00	125.00	50.00	100.00
Lid of hot water plate	100.00	150.00	60.00	150.00
Plate, 6½"	65.00	100.00	45.00	100.00

Lasso Games (HW117)

Leapfrog

Design No.:	HW12R
Designer:	Barbara Vernon
Issued:	By 1937 - by 1952
Combined with:	*Asleep in the Open Air*, HW10
	Embracing at a Window, HW5
	Family at Breakfast, HW12
	Family Going out on Washing Day, HW8
	Family with Pram, Style One, HW15
	Feeding the Baby, HW13
	Fixing Braces, HW3
	Gardening, Style One, HW9
	Lambeth Walk, HW16
	Proposal, HW11
	Pressing Trousers, HW14
	Washing in the Open Air, HW10R

Shape	U.S. $	Can. $	U.K. £	Aust. $
Casino jug, 36s				
with signature	150.00	225.00	90.00	225.00
without signature	135.00	200.00	80.00	200.00
Casino jug, 42s				
with signature	135.00	200.00	85.00	200.00
without signature	125.00	175.00	70.00	175.00
Casino sugar bowl, 30s				
with signature	200.00	300.00	125.00	325.00
without signature	150.00	225.00	85.00	225.00
Casino teacup				
with signature	95.00	150.00	65.00	150.00
without signature	75.00	125.00	55.00	125.00
Don beaker				
with signature	100.00	150.00	60.00	150.00
without signature	75.00	125.00	45.00	125.00
Don beaker, one handle				
with signature	100.00	150.00	60.00	150.00
without signature	75.00	125.00	45.00	125.00
Don mug, one handle				
with signature	95.00	150.00	60.00	150.00
without signature	75.00	125.00	45.00	125.00
Jam pot	850.00	1,275.00	500.00	1,300.00
Teacup, fine china		Very rare		

Lassoing (HW117R)

Leapfrog (HW12R)

Letterbox (SF13)

Letterbox

Design No.: SF13
Designer: Walter Hayward after Barbara Vernon
Issued: By 1952 - by 1998

Shape	U.S. $	Can. $	U.K. £	Aust. $
Baby plate, round, small				
with signature	50.00	75.00	35.00	73.00
without signature	20.00	30.00	12.00	30.00
Cake stand	150.00	200.00	65.00	200.00
Casino saucer				
with signature	35.00	50.00	15.00	50.00
without signature	10.00	15.00	5.00	15.00
Casino teapot, 24s				
with signature	275.00	425.00	175.00	525.00
without signature	250.00	400.00	150.00	525.00
Cereal / oatmeal bowl				
with signature	50.00	75.00	25.00	75.00
without signature	25.00	30.00	10.00	30.00
Jaffa fruit saucer (plain)				
with signature	100.00	150.00	65.00	150.00
without signature	35.00	50.00	15.00	60.00
Hot water plate				
with signature	125.00	200.00	85.00	200.00
without signature	100.00	150.00	60.00	150.00
Plate, 6 ½"				
with signature	90.00	135.00	50.00	135.00
without signature	20.00	30.00	10.00	25.00
Plate, 7 ½"				
with signature	100.00	150.00	60.00	150.00
without signature	20.00	30.00	10.00	30.00
Plate, 8"	20.00	30.00	10.00	30.00

Note: A money box in the shape of a post box was modelled but not put into production. Two examples have been recorded, one in the Royal Doulton Archives and another in a private collection. For an illustration of the front see the back cover, and for the reverse see page 2.

Medicine Time

Design No.: SF1
Designer: Barbara Vernon
Issued: By 1937 - by 1952

Shape	U.S. $	Can. $	U.K. £	Aust. $
Baby plate, round, small				
with signature	135.00	200.00	85.00	200.00
without signature	100.00	150.00	65.00	150.00
Baby plate, round, large				
with signature	200.00	300.00	125.00	300.00
without signature	125.00	200.00	80.00	200.00
Candle holder	1,500.00	2,500.00	900.00	2,500.00
Casino jug, 30s				
with signature	175.00	250.00	125.00	250.00
without signature	150.00	200.00	80.00	200.00
Casino saucer				
with signature	75.00	100.00	45.00	100.00
without signature	50.00	75.00	35.00	75.00
Casino teapot, 30s				
with signature	375.00	575.00	225.00	650.00
without signature	300.00	450.00	175.00	575.00
Cereal / oatmeal bowl				
with signature	135.00	200.00	80.00	200.00
without signature	100.00	150.00	65.00	150.00
Hot water plate				
with signature	130.00	200.00	80.00	200.00
without signature	100.00	150.00	65.00	150.00
Night light, fine china	3,500.00	5,000.00	2,000.00	5,000.00
Plate, 6 ½"				
with signature	100.00	150.00	60.00	150.00
without signature	75.00	100.00	45.00	100.00
Plate, 8"	100.00	150.00	60.00	150.00
Shallow bowl, fine china		Extremely rare		

Medicine Time (SF1)

MERRY CHRISTMAS FROM BUNNYKINS
Walter Hayward

Merry Christmas from Bunnykins, Style One (SF137)

Style One

The reverse decoration on this plate has a a single holly leaf wreath border and a 1936 copyright date.

Design No.: Front — SF137 Merry Christmas from Bunnykins
            Reverse — Inscription
Designer: Walter Hayward
Issued: 1981 - 1989
Rhyme: 'Bunnykins are just like you
             For they love Christmas too,
             They sing and dance as you can see
             And play around the Christmas tree,
             And each year they always say
             "We wish it were Christmas every day.'

Shape	U.S. $	Can. $	U.K. £	Aust. $
Plate, 8"	65.00	85.00	35.00	85.00

Reverse Inscription (SF137)

MERRY CHRISTMAS FROM BUNNYKINS
Colin Twinn

Style Two
First Variation, Large Size

The reverse deocration on this plate has a multiple holly leaf wreath border and a 19?? copyright date.

Design No.:	Front — CT39 Merry Christmas from Bunnykins
	Reverse — CT66 Inscription
Designer:	Colin Twinn
Issued:	1990 - 1993
Rhyme:	'Bunnykins are just like you
	For they love Christmas too,
	They sing and dance as you can see
	And play around the Christmas tree,
	And each year they always say
	"We wish it were Christmas every day.'

Shape	U.S. $	Can. $	U.K. £	Aust. $
Plate, 8"	65.00	85.00	35.00	85.00

Merry Christmas from Bunnykins
First Variation (CT39)

Merry Christmas from Bunnykins
Second Variation (CT43)

Style Two
Second Variation, Small Size

Design No.:	Front — CT43 Merry Christmas from Bunnykins
	Reverse — CT44 Inscription
Designer:	Colin Twinn
Issued:	1992 - 1994

Shape	U.S. $	Can. $	U.K. £	Aust. $
Hug-a-mug, one handle	50.00	75.00	30.00	85.00

Family Christmas Scene (CT72)

Style Three
Family Christmas Scene
First Version, Large Size

Design No.: CT72 Family Christmas Scene
CT73 Christmas Inscription
Designer: Colin Twinn
Issued: 1993 - 1994
Inscription: 'Bunnykins are just like you
For they love Christmas too
They sing and dance as you can see
And play around the Christmas Tree
And each year they always say
"We wish it were Christmas every day.'

Shape	U.S. $	Can. $	U.K. £	Aust. $
Plate, 8"	60.00	90.00	35.00	85.00

Inscription (CT73)

Merry Christmas from Bunnykins (CT74)

Style Three
Family Christmas Scene
Second Version, Small Size

Design No.: Front — CT74 Family Christmas Scene
Reverse — CT75 Merry Christmas from Bunnykins
Inscription
Designer: Colin Twinn
Issued: 1993-1994

Shape	U.S. $	Can. $	U.K. £	Aust. $
Hug-a-mug, one handle	70.00	90.00	45.00	85.00
Money ball	70.00	90.00	45.00	85.00

Merry Christmas Inscription (CT75)

Mr. Piggly's Stores

Design No.: SF14
Designer: Walter Hayward after Barbara Vernon
Issued: By 1952 - by 1998
Combined with: *Fishing in the Goldfish Bowl*, HW3R

Shape	U.S. $	Can. $	U.K. £	Aust. $
Baby plate, round, 6"				
with signature	50.00	75.00	35.00	85.00
without signature	25.00	30.00	12.00	30.00
Bread / butter plate, handles				
with signature	200.00	275.00	125.00	300.00
without signature	150.00	225.00	100.00	250.00
Casino jug, 24s				
with signature	225.00	350.00	150.00	350.00
without signature	175.00	250.00	125.00	250.00
Casino saucer				
with signature	35.00	55.00	15.00	55.00
without signature	10.00	15.00	5.00	15.00
Casino teapot, 30s				
with signature	275.00	450.00	175.00	750.00
without signature	250.00	400.00	150.00	600.00
Cereal / oatmeal bowl				
with signature	40.00	65.00	20.00	65.00
without signature	25.00	30.00	10.00	30.00
Hot water plate				
with signature	125.00	200.00	85.00	200.00
without signature	100.00	150.00	65.00	150.00
Jaffa fruit saucer (plain)				
with signature	95.00	150.00	40.00	150.00
without signature	50.00	75.00	20.00	25.00
Plate, 6 ½"				
with signature	90.00	135.00	50.00	135.00
without signature	20.00	30.00	10.00	25.00
Plate, 7 ½"				
with signature	100.00	150.00	60.00	150.00
without signature	20.00	30.00	10.00	30.00
Plate, 8½"				
with signature	65.00	125.00	30.00	150.00
without signature	25.00	30.00	10.00	30.00
Porridge bowl				
with signature	100.00	150.00	50.00	150.00
without signature	60.00	100.00	25.00	100.00

Mr. Piggly's Stores (SF14)

Mrs. Moppet's Tea Room (LF6)

Mrs. Moppet's Tea Room

Design No.: LF6
Designer: Barbara Vernon
Issued: By 1940 - by 1952

Shape	U.S. $	Can. $	U.K. £	Aust. $
Baby plate, oval, large				
with signature	225.00	325.00	135.00	350.00
without signature	125.00	200.00	80.00	225.00
Baby plate, round, large				
with signature	250.00	350.00	150.00	300.00
without signature	125.00	200.00	80.00	225.00
Bread / butter plate, handles				
with signature	200.00	275.00	125.00	300.00
without signature	150.00	225.00	100.00	250.00
Cereal / oatmeal bowl				
with signature	125.00	175.00	75.00	200.00
without signature	100.00	150.00	65.00	150.00
Plate, 8 ½"				
with signature	150.00	225.00	90.00	225.00
without signature	80.00	125.00	50.00	150.00
Porridge bowl				
with signature	165.00	250.00	95.00	225.00
without signature	125.00	175.00	75.00	200.00

Netting a Cricket

Design No.:	HW6
Designer:	Barbara Vernon
Issued:	By 1937 - by 1952
Combined with:	*Cuddling under a Mushroom*, HW4
	Dunce, HW1R
	Fishing in the Goldfish Bowl, HW3R
	Gardener with Wheelbarrow, HW9R
	Pressing Trousers, HW14
	Pulling on Trousers, HW2
	Reading the Times, HW2R

Netting a Cricket (HW6)

Shape	U.S. $	Can. $	U.K. £	Aust. $
Casino sugar bowl, 30s				
with signature	175.00	250.00	125.00	250.00
without signature	150.00	200.00	80.00	200.00
Casino sugar bowl, 36s				
with signature	150.00	225.00	85.00	250.00
without signature	100.00	150.00	65.00	175.00
Casino teacup				
with signature	95.00	145.00	65.00	150.00
without signature	75.00	125.00	45.00	125.00
Don beaker				
with signature	95.00	145.00	65.00	145.00
without signature	75.00	125.00	45.00	125.00
Don beaker, one handle				
with signature	115.00	175.00	70.00	175.00
without signature	85.00	125.00	50.00	125.00
Don mug, one handle				
with signature	95.00	145.00	60.00	145.00
without signature	75.00	125.00	45.00	125.00
Don mug, two handles				
with signature	115.00	175.00	70.00	175.00
without signature	85.00	125.00	50.00	125.00
Jaffa fruit saucer				
plain rim	150.00	225.00	90.00	225.00
wavy rim	115.00	175.00	70.00	175.00
Jam pot	850.00	1,275.00	500.00	1,300.00
Plate, 6 ½"				
with signature	95.00	145.00	65.00	150.00
without signature	75.00	125.00	45.00	125.00

NEW ARRIVAL THEME
Colin Twinn

Family Group with Father Standing (CT97)

Family Group with Father Standing

Design No.: CT97 Family Group with Father Standing
Designer: Colin Twinn
Issued: 1995 - 1997

Shape	U.S. $	Can. $	U.K. £	Aust. $
Baby plate, round, small	40.00	60.00	25.00	60.00
Plate, 8"	40.00	60.00	25.00	60.00

Family Group with Father Kneeling (CT98)

Family Group with Father Kneeling

Design No.: Front — CT98 Family group with Father Kneeling
Reverse — CT99 New Arrival Inscription
Designer: Colin Twinn
Issued: 1995 - 1997

Shape	U.S. $	Can. $	U.K. £	Aust. $
Hug-a-mug, one handle	30.00	45.00	20.00	45.00
Money ball	30.00	45.00	20.00	45.00

New Arrival Inscription (CT99)

NEW BABY THEME
Frank Endersby

Showing Baby at Window

Design No.: 40 Showing Baby at Window
Designer: Frank Endersby
Issued: 1996 to the present

Shape	U.S. $	Can. $	U.K. £	Aust. $
Plate, 6 ½"	25.00	25.00	7.00	27.00
Plate, 8"	30.00	3500	9.00	39.00

Showing Baby at Window (40)

Pushing Pram (41)

Pushing Pram / Playing with Ball

Design No.: Front — 41 Pushing Pram
　　　　　　Reverse — 42 Playing with Ball
Designer: Frank Endersby
Issued: 1996 to the present

Shape	U.S. $	Can. $	U.K. £	Aust. $
Hug-a-mug, one handle	30.00	33.00	9.00	39.00
Hug-a-mug, two handles	33.00	39.00	10.00	45.00
Malvern beaker	50.00	75.00	25.00	75.00
Money ball	35.00	40.00	13.00	45.00
Stratford teacup	30.00	45.00	15.00	45.00

Note: Bold type in the listing tables indicate a current design on a current shape.

Playing with Ball (42)

NURSERY THEME
Colin Twinn

Nursery, First Version (CT19)

Nursery
First Version, Small Size

Design No.:	CT19 Nursery
Designer:	Colin Twinn
Issued:	1990 - 1993
Combined with:	*Family with Pram*, Style Two, CT14
	Standing by Pram, CT6

Shape	U.S. $	Can. $	U.K. £	Aust. $
Albion jug, 1 pint	125.00	175.00	75.00	150.00
Baby plate, round, small	50.00	75.00	30.00	75.00
Cake stand	150.00	200.00	75.00	150.00
Cereal / oatmeal bowl	35.00	50.00	20.00	55.00
Lamp	150.00	225.00	75.00	225.00
Money ball	35.00	50.00	20.00	55.00
Plate, 6 ½ "	35.00	50.00	20.00	55.00
Plate, 8 "	30.00	45.00	18.00	50.00
Picture plaque, large	45.00	70.00	30.00	75.00

Nursery (CT28)

Nursery
Second Version, Large Size / Bunny on Rocking Horse

Design No.:	Front — CT28 Nursery
	Reverse — CT29 Bunny on Rocking Horse
Designer:	Colin Twinn
Issued:	1990 - 1993
Combined with:	*Family with Pram*, Style Two, CT14
	Father Bunnykins with Fishing Rod, (CT27)

Shape	U.S. $	Can. $	U.K. £	Aust. $
Albion jug, 1 pint	100.00	150.00	65.00	150.00
Albion teapot	50.00	100.00	30.00	125.00
Egg cup				
Style Three	20.00	30.00	10.00	30.00
Hug-a-mug, one handle	25.00	50.00	15.00	60.00
Hug-a-mug, two handles	30.00	50.00	20.00	60.00
Money ball	25.00	35.00	15.00	40.00
Picture plaque, small	50.00	75.00	30.00	75.00
Savings book	35.00	60.00	20.00	60.00
Stratford straight beaker	30.00	45.00	20.00	50.00
Stratford teacup	30.00	45.00	20.00	50.00

Bunny on Rocking Horse (CT29)

Bunny with Mirror

Design No.:	Front — CT35 Bunny with Mirror
Designer:	Colin Twinn
Issued:	1990 - 1993
Combined with:	*Bunnies in the Bath*, Second Version, CT34
	Picking Daisies, CT4

Shape	U.S. $	Can. $	U.K. £	Aust. $
Albion sugar bowl	40.00	60.00	25.00	55.00
Divided dish	50.00	75.00	30.00	75.00
Egg cup				
Style Three	20.00	30.00	10.00	30.00

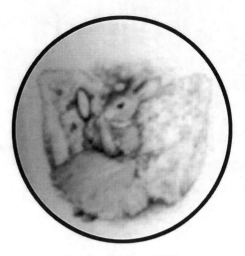

Bunny with Mirror (CT35)

Orange Vendor (SF12)

Orange Vendor

Design No.: SF12
Designer: Walter Hayward after Barbara Vernon
Issued: By 1952 - 1967

Shape	U.S. $	Can. $	U.K. £	Aust. $
Baby plate, round, small				
with signature	125.00	175.00	75.00	175.00
without signature	75.00	100.00	45.00	115.00
Baby plate, round, large				
with signature	175.00	350.00	110.00	375.00
without signature	150.00	300.00	90.00	325.00
Casino jug, 30s				
with signature	175.00	300.00	110.00	300.00
without signature	150.00	200.00	90.00	200.00
Casino saucer				
with signature	65.00	100.00	40.00	100.00
without signature	40.00	60.00	30.00	65.00
Casino teapot, 30s				
with signature	375.00	575.00	275.00	750.00
without signature	300.00	450.00	175.00	575.00
Cereal / oatmeal bowl				
with signature	50.00	75.00	25.00	75.00
without signature	25.00	30.00	10.00	30.00
Hot water plate				
with signature	125.00	200.00	85.00	200.00
without signature	100.00	150.00	65.00	150.00
Jaffa fruit saucer (plain)				
with signature	95.00	150.00	45.00	150.00
without signature	50.00	75.00	20.00	75.00
Plate, 6 ½"				
with signature	65.00	125.00	35.00	150.00
without signature	20.00	30.00	10.00	20.00
Plate, 7 ½"				
with signature	65.00	125.00	35.00	150.00
without signature	20.00	30.00	10.00	35.00
Plate, 8½"				
with signature	65.00	125.00	35.00	150.00
without signature	25.00	30.00	10.00	30.00

Picnic
Style One, First Version (without trees)

Design No.: Unknown
Designer: Walter Hayward after Barbara Vernon
Issued: 1940

Shape	U.S. $	Can. $	U.K. £	Aust. $
Baby plate, oval, small	600.00	950.00	350.00	1,000.00
Baby plate, round, large	750.00	1,100.00	450.00	1,200.00
Plate, 8 ½"	400.00	600.00	250.00	650.00

Note: This design should appear with the Barbara Vernon facsimile signature.

Picnic, Style One, First Version

Picnic, Style One, Second Version (LF10)

Picnic
Style One, Second Version (with trees)

This scene was redrawn to better fit, or conform to round shapes.

Design No.: LF10
Designer: Walter Hayward after Barbara Vernon
Issued: By 1940 - 1970

Shape	U.S. $	Can. $	U.K. £	Aust. $
Baby plate, oval, large				
with signature	350.00	500.00	200.00	525.00
without signature	200.00	300.00	125.00	300.00
Baby plate, round, large				
with signature	250.00	350.00	150.00	350.00
without signature	125.00	200.00	80.00	225.00
Bread / butter plate, handles				
with signature	200.00	275.00	125.00	300.00
without signature	150.00	225.00	100.00	250.00
Cereal / oatmeal bowl				
with signature	100.00	150.00	65.00	165.00
without signature	75.00	110.00	45.00	125.00
Hot water plate				
with signature	175.00	275.00	110.00	275.00
without signature	125.00	200.00	85.00	200.00
Porridge bowl				
with signature	150.00	225.00	90.00	200.00
without signature	100.00	150.00	60.00	135.00
Plate, 8 ½"				
with signature	100.00	150.00	60.00	150.00
without signature	75.00	125.00	45.00	125.00

PICNIC and CAKE STALL THEME
Colin Twinn

Picnic and Cake Stall (CT2)

Picnic and Cake Stall

Design No.: CT2 Picnic and Cake Stall
Designer: Colin Twinn
Issued: 1989 - 1993

Shape	U.S. $	Can. $	U.K. £	Aust. $
Plate, 8"	50.00	75.00	30.00	55.00
Plate 10 ½"	60.00	90.00	45.00	100.00

Cake Stall (CT12)

Cake Stall / Picking Daisies

Design No.: Front — CT12 Cake Stall
Reverse — CT4 Picking Daisies
Designer: Colin Twinn
Issued: 1989 - 1993
Combined with: *Bunny with Mirror*, CT35
Queen of the May, Second Variation, CT13

Shape	U.S. $	Can. $	U.K. £	Aust. $
Albion cream jug	50.00	75.00	30.00	65.00
Albion jug, ½ pint	50.00	75.00	30.00	75.00
Albion teapot	50.00	100.00	35.00	125.00
Hug-a-mug, one handle	40.00	60.00	25.00	65.00
Hug-a-mug, two handles	40.00	60.00	25.00	65.00
Malvern beaker	40.00	60.00	25.00	65.00
Stratford straight beaker	40.00	60.00	25.00	65.00
Stratford teacup	40.00	60.00	25.00	65.00

Note: *Queen of the May* (CT17) is combined with *Picking Daisies* (CT4) on a one-handled, hug-a-mug.

Picking Daisies(CT4)

PICNIC THEME
Frank Endersby

Picnic
Style Two

Design No.: 16 Picnic
Designer: Frank Endersby
Issued: 1995 to the present

Shape	U.S. $	Can. $	U.K. £	Aust. $
Baby plate, round, small	40.00	46.00	12.00	49.00
Cereal / oatmeal bowl	25.00	33.00	9.00	39.00
Plate 6 ½"	25.00	25.00	7.00	27.00
Plate, 8"	30.00	35.00	9.00	39.00

Picnic, Style Two (16)

Playing Badminton (17)

Playing Badminton / Resting

Design No.: Front — 17 Playing Badminton
           Reverse — 18 Resting
Designer: Frank Endersby
Issued: 1995 to the present

Shape	U.S. $	Can. $	U.K. £	Aust. $
Hug-a-mug, one handle	30.00	33.00	9.00	39.00
Hug-a-mug, two handles	33.00	39.00	10.00	45.00
Money ball	35.00	40.00	13.00	45.00
Stratford straight beaker	50.00	75.00	30.00	75.00
Stratford teacup	30.00	45.00	15.00	45.00

Note: It is unusual to find the Stratford beaker with this design as this shape was officially withdrawn in 1993, two years before this Frank Endersby design was introduced.

Resting (18)

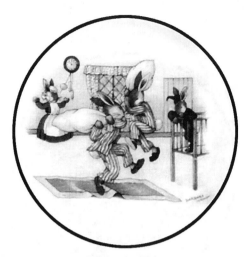

Pillow Fight (SF7)

Pillow Fight
Style One

Design No.:   SF7
Designer: Barbara Vernon
Issued: By 1940 - by 1952

Shape	U.S. $	Can. $	U.K. £	Aust. $
Baby plate, oval, small				
with signature	175.00	250.00	125.00	250.00
without signature	125.00	175.00	80.00	175.00
Cereal / oatmeal bowl				
with signature	95.00	150.00	65.00	150.00
without signature	75.00	110.00	45.00	125.00
Hot water plate				
with signature	175.00	275.00	110.00	275.00
without signature	125.00	200.00	85.00	200.00
Plate, 6 ½"				
with signature	125.00	175.00	75.00	175.00
without signature	50.00	75.00	30.00	75.00
Plate, 7 ½"				
with signature	400.00	600.00	250.00	600.00
without signature	200.00	300.00	125.00	300.00

Playing on the River

Desing No.: SF16
Designer: Walter Hayward after Barbara Vernon
Issued: By 1952 - by 1998

Shape	U.S. $	Can. $	U.K. £	Aust. $
Baby plate, round, small				
with signature	60.00	95.00	35.00	95.00
without signature	25.00	45.00	12.00	45.00
Cake stand	150.00	200.00	75.00	200.00
Casino saucer				
with signature	35.00	50.00	15.00	50.00
without signature	10.00	15.00	5.00	15.00
Casino teapot,30s				
with signature	275.00	525.00	175.00	750.00
without signature	250.00	400.00	150.00	600.00
Cereal / oatmeal bowl				
with signature	50.00	75.00	25.00	75.00
without signature	20.00	30.00	10.00	30.00
Hot water plate				
with signature	125.00	200.00	85.00	200.00
without signature	100.00	150.00	75.00	150.00
Jaffa fruit saucer (plain)				
with signature	100.00	150.00	60.00	160.00
without signature	20.00	30.00	8.00	30.00
Plate, 6 ½"				
with signature	75.00	100.00	50.00	100.00
without signature	20.00	30.00	10.00	30.00
Plate, 7 ½"				
with signature	100.00	150.00	65.00	150.00
without signature	20.00	30.00	10.00	30.00
Plate, 8"				
with signature	75.00	100.00	45.00	100.00
without signature	20.00	30.00	10.00	30.00

Playing on the River (SF16)

Playing with Cup and Spoon (EC6)

Playing with Cup and Spoon

Design No.:	EC6
Designer:	Barbara Vernon
Issued:	1937 to the present
Combined with:	*Bedtime with Dollies*, EC125
	Daisy Chains, HW25
	Drummer, EC2
	Drummer and Bugler, EC126
	Fishing the Goldfish Bowl, HW3R
	Hobby Horse, Style Two, EC121
	Holding Hat and Coat, EC4
	Playing with Doll and Pram, EC123
	Raising Hat, Style Two, EC7
	Sheltering Under an Umbrella, EC3

Shape	U.S. $	Can. $	U.K. £	Aust. $
Albion sugar bowl	40.00	60.00	25.00	65.00
Beaker cover	75.00	100.00	35.00	100.00
Casino teacup				
with signature	40.00	60.00	15.00	55.00
without signature	10.00	15.00	5.00	15.00
Egg cup				
Style One	35.00	60.00	25.00	65.00
Style Two	60.00	90.00	35.00	125.00
Style Three	**10.00**	**15.00**	**5.00**	**15.00**
Lid of hot water plate	75.00	100.00	45.00	100.00
Money ball	**35.00**	**40.00**	**13.00**	**45.00**
Night light saucer, fine china	1,500.00	2,500.00	900.00	2,500.00

Playing with Doll and Pram

Design No.:	EC123
Designer:	Walter Hayward
Issued:	1959 to the present
Combined with:	*Bedtime with Dollies*, EC125
	Building Sand Castles, HW138
	Dancing with Doll, HW115R
	Drummer, EC2
	Drummer and Bugler, EC126
	Hobby Horse, Style Two, EC121
	Holding Hat and Coat, EC4
	Playing with Cup and spoon, EC6
	Playing with Dolls and Prams, HW115
	Sailing Boats, HW138R

Playing with Doll and Pram (EC123)

Shape	U.S. $	Can. $	U.K. £	Aust. $
Albion cream jug	50.00	75.00	30.00	75.00
Albion sugar bowl	45.00	65.00	30.00	70.00
Beaker cover	75.00	100.00	35.00	100.00
Egg cup				
Style One	40.00	55.00	30.00	45.00
Style Two	60.00	95.00	35.00	100.00
Style Three	**10.00**	**15.00**	**5.00**	**15.00**
Lid of hot water plate	100.00	150.00	60.00	175.00

Playing with Dolls and Prams / Dancing with Doll

Design No.:   Front — HW115 Playing with Dolls and Prams
                   Reverse — HW115R Dancing with Doll
Designer: Walter Hayward
Issued: 1959 - by 1998
Combined with: *Disturbing Sleeping Father*, HW118
                   Ice Cream on the Beach, HW136R
                   Lunch Break, HW29R
                   Playing with Doll and Pram, EC123
                   Serving Tea, HW116R
                   Trying on Hats, HW28R

Playing with Dolls and Prams (HW115)

Shape	U.S. $	Can. $	U.K. £	Aust. $
Albion cream jug	50.00	75.00	30.00	65.00
Albion jug, ½ pint	50.00	75.00	35.00	75.00
Albion jug, 1 pint	75.00	125.00	50.00	150.00
Albion teapot	65.00	100.00	30.00	125.00
Casino saucer	20.00	30.00	10.00	50.00
Casino teacup	40.00	60.00	20.00	55.00
Divided dish	45.00	65.00	30.00	65.00
Don beaker	45.00	65.00	20.00	65.00
Don beaker, one handle	55.00	75.00	25.00	75.00
Don mug, one handle	40.00	60.00	15.00	60.00
Don mug, two handles	45.00	65.00	15.00	60.00
Egg box				
small	275.00	375.00	100.00	400.00
medium	300.00	450.00	150.00	475.00
large	350.00	525.00	200.00	550.00
Jaffa fruit saucer (plain)	20.00	30.00	10.00	30.00
Hug-a-mug, one handle	25.00	30.00	8.00	35.00
Hug-a-mug, two handles	25.00	35.00	10.00	35.00
Lamp	175.00	250.00	75.00	275.00
Lid of hot water plate	100.00	150.00	45.00	150.00
Money ball	25.00	35.00	25.00	40.00
Picture plaque, small	45.00	60.00	25.00	65.00
Plate, 6½"	20.00	30.00	10.00	30.00
Savings book	35.00	45.00	14.00	45.00
Stratford straight beaker	30.00	45.00	15.00	50.00
Stratford teacup	30.00	45.00	15.00	45.00

Dancing with Doll (HW115R)

Note: The savings book can have a combined design of *Dancing with Doll* (HW115R) and *Trying on Hats* (HW28R) or *Dancing with Doll* (HW115R) and *Lunch Break* (HW29R)

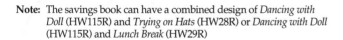

PLAYTIME THEME
Frank Endersby

See-saw (52)

See-saw
Style Two

Design No.: 52 See-saw
Designer: Frank Endersby
Issued: 1995 to the present

Shape	U.S. $	Can. $	U.K. £	Aust. $
Baby plate, round, small	40.00	46.00	12.500	49.00
Plate, 6 ½"	25.00	25.00	7.00	27.00
Plate, 8"	30.00	35.00	9.00	39.00

Pushing Swing (53)

Pushing Swing / Bunny on Swing

Design No.: Front — 53 Pushing Swing
Reverse — 54 Bunny on Swing
Designer: Frank Endersby
Issued: 1995 to the present

Shape	U.S. $	Can. $	U.K. £	Aust. $
Hug-a-mug, one handle	30.00	33.00	9.00	39.00
Hug-a-mug, two handles	33.00	39.00	10.00	45.00

Bunny on Swing (54)

Portrait Painter

Design No.: SF20
Designer: Walter Hayward
Issued: 1954 - by 1998

Shape	U.S. $	Can. $	U.K. £	Aust. $
Baby plate, round, small				
with signature	95.00	145.00	60.00	150.00
without signature	25.00	40.00	12.00	55.00
Cake stand	150.00	200.00	75.00	200.00
Casino saucer				
with signature	45.00	65.00	25.00	65.00
without signature	10.00	15.00	5.00	15.00
Casino teapot, 30s				
with signature	200.00	300.00	125.00	325.00
without signature	150.00	225.00	85.00	225.00
Cereal / oatmeal bowl				
with signature	65.00	85.00	35.00	90.00
without signature	20.00	30.00	9.00	30.00
Hot water plate				
with signature	125.00	200.00	85.00	200.00
without signature	100.00	150.00	65.00	150.00
Jaffa fruit saucer (plain)				
with signature	60.00	95.00	35.00	100.00
without signature	20.00	30.00	8.00	30.00
Plate, 6 ½"				
with signature	50.00	90.00	30.00	85.00
without signature	15.00	25.00	7.00	25.00
Plate, 7 ½"				
with signature	60.00	90.00	35.00	90.00
without signature	20.00	30.00	10.00	30.00
Plate, 8"	20.00	30.00	9.00	30.00

Portrait Painter (SF20)

POST OFFICE THEME
Frank Endersby

Posting Letters (28)

Posting Letters

Design No.: 28 Posting Letters
Designer: Frank Endersby
Issued: 1995 to the present

Shape	U.S. $	Can. $	U.K. £	Aust. $
Plate, 6 ½"	25.00	25.00	7.00	27.00
Plate, 8"	30.00	35.00	9.00	39.00

Letter Box (29)

Letter Box / Carrying Letter

Design No.: Front — 29 Letter Box
Reverse — 30 Carrying Letter
Designer: Frank Endersby
Issued: 1995 to the present

Shape	U.S. $	Can. $	U.K. £	Aust. $
Hug-a-mug, one handle	30.00	33.00	9.00	39.00
Hug-a-mug, two handles	33.00	39.00	10.00	45.00
Stratford teacup	30.00	45.00	15.00	45.00

Carrying Letter (30)

Postman Delivering Letters / Writing Letters

Design No.: Front — HW19 Postman Delivering Letters
Reverse — HW19R Writing Letters
Designer: Walter Hayward after Barbara Vernon
Issued: By 1952 - 1967

Shape	U.S. $	Can. $	U.K. £	Aust. $
Baby plate, round, small				
with signature	125.00	175.00	85.00	175.00
without signature	80.00	130.00	60.00	40.00
Casino jug, 24s				
with signature	225.00	350.00	150.00	350.00
without signature	175.00	250.00	125.00	250.00
Casino jug, 36s				
with signature	150.00	225.00	90.00	225.00
without signature	135.00	200.00	80.00	175.00
Casino jug, 42s				
with signature	135.00	200.00	85.00	200.00
without signature	125.00	175.00	175.00	150.00
Casino saucer				
with signature	75.00	100.00	45.00	100.00
without signature	50.00	75.00	35.00	75.00
Casino teacup				
with signature	100.00	150.00	60.00	150.00
without signature	50.00	75.00	30.00	75.00
Casino teapot, 24s				
with signature	325.00	500.00	185.00	550.00
without signature	275.00	400.00	165.00	500.00
Casino teapot, 30s				
with signature	375.00	575.00	225.00	650.00
without signature	300.00	450.00	175.00	575.00
Don beaker				
with signature	100.00	150.00	60.00	145.00
without signature	65.00	100.00	40.00	100.00
Don beaker, one handle				
with signature	100.00	150.00	60.00	145.00
without signature	65.00	100.00	40.00	100.00
Don mug, one handle				
with signature	75.00	100.00	45.00	110.00
without signature	40.00	60.00	30.00	65.00
Don mug, two handles				
with signature	75.00	100.00	45.00	110.00
without signature	40.00	60.00	30.00	65.00
Jaffa fruit saucer (plain)				
with signature	75.00	100.00	45.00	110.00
without signature	40.00	60.00	30.00	65.00
Lid of hot water plate				
with signature	85.00	125.00	50.00	125.00
without signature	75.00	100.00	45.00	100.00
Plate, 6 ½"				
with signature	65.00	100.00	40.00	75.00
without signature	40.00	60.00	25.00	60.00

Postman Delivering Letters (HW19)

Writing Letters (HW19R)

Pressing Trousers

Pressing Trousers (HW14)

Design No.:   HW14
Designer: Barbara Vernon
Issued: By 1937 - 1967
Combined with: *Cycling*, HW15R
                Dunce, HW1R
                Fishing in the Goldfish Bowl, HW3R
                Footballer, HW13R
                Frightening Spider, SF4

Leapfrog, HW12R
Netting a Cricket, HW6
Raising Hat, Style One, HW16R
Santa Claus, SF9
Top Hat, HW14R
Watering the Flowers, SF15
Wedding, LFd

Shape	U.S. $	Can. $	U.K. £	Aust. $
Baby bowl, fine china		Very rare		
Baby plate, round, small				
with signature	150.00	225.00	90.00	200.00
without signature	125.00	175.00	75.00	175.00
Casino jug, 24s				
with signature	250.00	375.00	150.00	350.00
without signature	200.00	300.00	125.00	275.00
Casino jug, 30s				
with signature	200.00	300.00	125.00	275.00
without signature	175.00	275.00	100.00	250.00
Casino saucer				
with signature	100.00	150.00	60.00	150.00
without signature	75.00	100.00	45.00	100.00
Casino teacup				
with signature	150.00	225.00	90.00	200.00
without signature	125.00	175.00	75.00	175.00
Casino teapot, 30s				
with signature	350.00	525.00	200.00	600.00
without signature	300.00	450.00	175.00	500.00
Casino teapot, 36s				
with signature	325.00	500.00	195.00	550.00
without signature	275.00	400.00	175.00	450.00
Don beaker				
with signature	175.00	250.00	100.00	275.00
without signature	75.00	115.00	45.00	125.00

Shape	U.S. $	Can. $	U.K. £	Aust. $
Don beaker, one handle				
with signature	185.00	275.00	125.00	100.00
without signature	85.00	130.00	50.00	60.00
Don mug, one handle				
with signature	175.00	250.00	110.00	100.00
without signature	75.00	115.00	45.00	60.00
Don mug, two handles				
with signature	185.00	275.00	125.00	100.00
without signature	85.00	130.00	50.00	60.00
Jaffa fruit saucer				
plain rim	150.00	225.00	90.00	225.00
wavy rim	200.00	300.00	125.00	300.00
Lid of hot water plate				
with signature	150.00	225.00	90.00	225.00
without signature	100.00	150.00	60.00	150.00
Plate, 6 ½"				
with signature	95.00	140.00	60.00	65.00
without signature	75.00	110.00	45.00	50.00
Saucer, fine china	400.00	600.00	250.00	600.00
Sugar bowl, fine china	400.00	600.00	250.00	600.00
Teacup, fine china	400.00	600.00	250.00	600.00

Proposal

Proposal (HW11)

Design No.: HW11
Designer: Barbara Vernon
Issued: By 1937 - by 1967
Combined with: *Cycling*, HW15R
Dunce, HW1R
Family with Pram, Style One, HW15
Footballer, HW13R

Golfer, HW4R
Kissing Under the Mistletoe, HW11R
Leapfrog, HW12R
Pulling on Trousers, HW2
Raising Hat, Style One, HW16R
Santa Claus, SF9
Wedding, LFd

Shape	U.S. $	Can. $	U.K. £	Aust. $
Baby bowl, fine china		Very rare		
Baby plate, round, small				
with signature	250.00	375.00	150.00	375.00
without signature	195.00	295.00	125.00	300.00
Beaker, fine china	350.00	525.00	200.00	500.00
Candle holder	1,500.00	2,500.00	900.00	2,500.00
Casino jug, 42s				
with signature	150.00	225.00	90.00	200.00
without signature	125.00	175.00	75.00	175.00
Casino saucer				
with signature	75.00	100.00	60.00	100.00
without signature	50.00	75.00	45.00	75.00
Casino sugar bowl, 30s				
with signature	400.00	600.00	250.00	550.00
without signature	350.00	525.00	200.00	500.00
Casino sugar bowl, 36s				
with signature	350.00	525.00	200.00	500.00
without signature	300.00	450.00	175.00	475.00
Casino teacup				
with signature	125.00	175.00	75.00	175.00
without signature	75.00	100.00	45.00	100.00
Casino teapot, 24s				
with signature	275.00	400.00	175.00	400.00
without signature	250.00	375.00	150.00	375.00
Casino teapot, 30s				
with signature	250.00	375.00	150.00	375.00
without signature	225.00	350.00	135.00	350.00

Shape	U.S. $	Can. $	U.K. £	Aust. $
Don beaker				
with signature	125.00	175.00	75.00	95.00
without signature	65.00	100.00	40.00	50.00
Don beaker, one handle				
with signature	125.00	175.00	75.00	100.00
without signature	65.00	100.00	40.00	50.00
Don mug, one handle				
with signature	125.00	175.00	75.00	95.00
without signature	65.00	100.00	40.00	50.00
Don mug, two handles				
with signature	135.00	200.00	80.00	95.00
without signature	75.00	110.00	45.00	50.00
Jaffa fruit saucer				
plain rim	100.00	150.00	60.00	150.00
wavy rim	150.00	225.00	90.00	200.00
Jam pot				
with signature	850.00	1,275.00	500.00	1,300.00
without signature	750.00	1,100.00	450.00	750.00
Lid of hot water plate				
with signature	100.00	150.00	60.00	125.00
without signature	75.00	100.00	45.00	100.00
Plate, 6 ½"				
with signature	125.00	175.00	75.00	175.00
without signature	100.00	150.00	60.00	150.00
Plate, fine china	350.00	525.00	200.00	500.00
Rex mug, fine china		Extremely rare		
Saucer, fine china	350.00	525.00	200.00	500.00
Teacup, fine china	350.00	525.00	200.00	500.00

Note: A Casino teapot (24s), combining Proposal (HW11) and Wedding (LFd), exists with a silver rimmed lid and a crackle finish, is considered extremely rare. The Rex mug combines *Proposal* (HW11) with *Cycling* (HW15R).

Pulling on Trousers (HW2)

Pulling on Trousers

Design No.:	HW2
Designer:	Barbara Vernon
Issued:	By 1937 - by 1952
Combined with:	*Artist*, HW1
	Family at Breakfast, HW12
	Fishing in the Goldfish Bowl, HW3R
	Golfer, HW4R
	Netting a Cricket, HW6
	Proposal, HW11
	Raising Hat, Style One, HW16R
	Reading the Times, HW2R

Shape	U.S. $	Can. $	U.K. £	Aust. $
Casino jug, 30s				
with signature	200.00	300.00	125.00	325.00
without signature	175.00	250.00	100.00	275.00
Casino jug, 36s				
with signature	175.00	250.00	100.00	250.00
without signature	150.00	225.00	90.00	200.00
Casino jug, 42s				
with signature	150.00	225.00	90.00	225.00
without signature	125.00	175.00	75.00	150.00
Casino saucer				
with signature	75.00	100.00	45.00	100.00
without signature	50.00	75.00	35.00	75.00
Casino sugar bowl, 30s				
with signature	250.00	375.00	175.00	400.00
without signature	200.00	300.00	125.00	300.00
Casino teacup				
with signature	125.00	175.00	70.00	150.00
without signature	75.00	125.00	45.00	125.00
Cup / mug, large	400.00	625.00	250.00	600.00
Don beaker				
with signature	175.00	225.00	100.00	200.00
without signature	90.00	135.00	55.00	120.00
Don beaker, one handle				
with signature	195.00	250.00	125.00	250.00
without signature	90.00	135.00	55.00	120.00
Don mug, one handle				
with signature	175.00	225.00	100.00	200.00
without signature	90.00	135.00	55.00	120.00
Don mug, two handles				
with signature	195.00	250.00	125.00	250.00
without signature	90.00	135.00	55.00	120.00
Jaffa fruit saucer				
plain rim	150.00	225.00	90.00	200.00
wavy rim	115.00	165.00	70.00	175.00
Jam pot	1,200.00	1,800.00	750.00	2,000.00
Lid of hot water plate				
with signature	125.00	175.00	75.00	175.00
without signature	100.00	150.00	60.00	125.00
Plate, 6½"				
with signature	100.00	150.00	60.00	150.00
without signature	75.00	100.00	45.00	100.00

Punch and Judy Show / Ice Cream on the Beach

Design No.:	Front — HW136 Punch and Judy Show
	Reverse — HW136R Ice Cream on the Beach
Designer:	Walter Hayward
Issued:	1967 - by 1998
Combined with:	*Playing with Dolls and Prams*, HW115
	Serving Tea, HW116R

Punch and Judy Show (HW136)

Shape	U.S. $	Can. $	U.K. £	Aust. $
Albion cream jug	50.00	75.00	30.00	75.00
Albion jug, ½ pint	50.00	75.00	35.00	75.00
Albion jug, 1 pint	75.00	150.00	50.00	150.00
Albion teapot	50.00	125.00	35.00	125.00
Cake stand	125.00	150.00	75.00	150.00
Casino saucer	10.00	15.00	5.00	15.00
Casino teacup	40.00	60.00	15.00	60.00
Casino teapot, 30s	275.00	400.00	125.00	425.00
Divided dish	45.00	65.00	30.00	65.00
Don beaker	40.00	60.00	20.00	65.00
Don beaker, one handle	50.00	70.00	25.00	70.00
Don mug, one handle	40.00	60.00	10.00	65.00
Don mug, two handles	45.00	65.00	15.00	65.00
Egg box				
small	250.00	350.00	125.00	375.00
medium	325.00	475.00	150.00	500.00
large	400.00	575.00	200.00	600.00
Hug-a-mug, one handle	20.00	30.00	8.00	35.00
Hug-a-mug, two handles	25.00	35.00	10.00	40.00
Jaffa fruit saucer (plain)	20.00	30.00	10.00	35.00
Lamp	175.00	250.00	75.00	275.00
Malvern beaker	30.00	45.00	15.00	50.00
Money ball	25.00	35.00	12.00	40.00
Picture plaque, small	40.00	60.00	25.00	65.00
Savings book	30.00	45.00	15.00	50.00
Stratford straight beaker	30.00	45.00	15.00	50.00
Stratford teacup	30.00	45.00	15.00	45.00

Ice Cream on the Beach (HW136R)

Note: The divided dish combines *Playing with Dolls and Prams* (HW115), *Serving Tea* (HW116R) and *Ice Cream on the Beach* (HW136R).

QUEEN OF THE MAY
Colin Twinn

Queen of the May, First Variation (CT7)

Counting Motif (CT8)

First Variation, Small Size

Design No.:   Front — CT7 Queen of the May
                Reverse — CT8 Counting Motif
Designer: Colin Twinn
Issued: 1988 - 1993
Combined with: *Picking Daisies* (CT4)

Shape	U.S. $	Can. $	U.K. £	Aust. $
Albion cream jug	50.00	75.00	30.00	55.00
Albion jug, ½ pint	50.00	75.00	30.00	75.00
Albion jug, 1 pint	75.00	150.00	50.00	150.00
Hug-a-mug, one handle	60.00	90.00	35.00	85.00
Hug-a-mug, two handles	60.00	90.00	35.00	80.00
Picture plaque, small	50.00	75.00	30.00	65.00
Money ball				
Spring 1992	60.00	90.00	40.00	100.00
Fall 1992	60.00	90.00	40.00	100.00

Note: Two money balls were issued for the U.S. Special Events Tour in 1992. This design was featured on the Spring tour with no special inscription. *Happy Birthday from Bunnykins* (CT60) was featured on the Fall tour. *Queen of the May* (CT17) is combined with *Picking Daisies* (CT4) on a one-handled, hug-a-mug.

Second Variation, Large Size

Design No.: CT13 Queen of the May
Designer: Colin Twinn
Issued: 1989 - 1993

Shape	U.S. $	Can. $	U.K. £	Aust. $
Albion jug, 1 pint	75.00	150.00	45.00	150.00
Cake stand	175.00	250.00	115.00	225.00
Cereal / oatmeal bowl	25.00	35.00	10.00	40.00
Lamp	150.00	250.00	90.00	225.00
Picture plaque, small	30.00	45.00	20.00	50.00
Picture plaque, large	45.00	70.00	30.00	75.00
Plate, 8"	25.00	35.00	15.00	40.00

Queen of the May, Second Variation (CT13)

DESIGNS BY BARBARA VERNON

Lambeth Walk, First Version (HW16)
without Barbara Vernon signature

Picnic, First Version
with Barbara Vernon signature

Santa Clause (SF9)
without Barbara Vernon signature

Visiting the Cottage, Second Version (SF6b)
with Barbara Vernon signature

Smoking in the Doorway (SF2)
with Barbara Vernon signature

Dodgem Cars (LF4)
with Barbara Vernon signature

DESIGNS BY WALTER HAYWARD
AND BARBARA VERNON

Watering the Garden (SF15)
Designed by Walter Hayward
after Barbara Vernon

Winning Post (LF106)
Designed by Walter Hayward
after Barbara Vernon

Family Cycling (LF11)
Designed by Walter Hayward

Art Class (LF107)
Designed by Walter Hayward

Breakfast Time, Bunnykins for Grown-ups Series
Designed by Walter Hayward

Tennis, Bunnykins for Grown-ups Series
Designed by Walter Hayward

DESIGNS BY COLIN TWINN
AND FRANK ENDERSBY

School Gates, Second Variation (CT22)
Designed by Colin Twinn

Bunny on Trike (CT23)
Designed by Colin Twinn

Vegetable Stall (2)
Designed by Frank Endersby

Eating Apples (3)
Designed by Frank Endersby

Picnic with Kangaroo and Koala, Second Variation
Designed by Colin Twinn

Bunnykins Celebrate Australia's Bicentenary 1788-1988
Designed by Frank Endersby

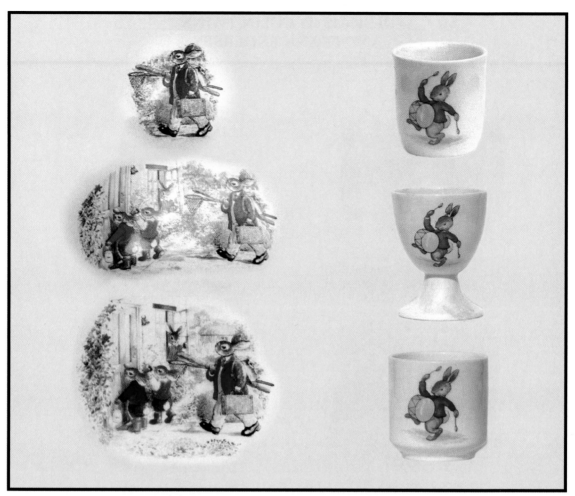

Father Bunnykins with Fishing Rod (CT27)
Home from Fishing, Second Variation (CT26)
Home from Fishing, First Variation (CT18)

Egg Cups, Drummer (EC2)
Top — Style One, Middle — Style Three
Bottom — Style Three

Pressing Trousers (HW14)

Casino Teacups
Cycling (HW15R)

Gardener with Wheelbarrow (HW9R)

COMMON DESIGNS ON VARIOUS SHAPES

Front — Daisy Chains (HW25)   Reverse — Smelling Flowers (HW25R)

Top row — Hug-a-mug, two handles
Centre row — Don mug, one handle
Bottom row — Don mug, two handles

CASINO TEAPOT SHOWING
BARBARA VERNON DESIGNS

Front — Proposal (HW11)
Reverse — Wedding (LFd)
Rare Casino Teapot with silver rimmed lid and crackle finish

BEDTIME BUNNYKINS
Colour Variations — DB63, DB103, DB79, DP55

COMMISSIONED BUNNYKINS
Mountie Bunnykins (DB135), Sergeant Mountie Bunnykins (DB136) Master Potter Bunnykins (DB131)
Uncle Sam Bunnykins (DB175), Collector Bunnykins (DB54), Ringmaster Bunnykins (DB165)

Bunnykins Royal Family, Second Variation
King John (DB91), Queen Sophie (DB92), Princess Beatrice (DB93), Prince Frederick (DB94), Harry the Herald (DB95)

School Days Bunnykins (DB57), Schoolboy Bunnykins (DB66), Schoolmaster Bunnkins (DB60)
Lollipopman Bunnykins (DB65), Brownie Bunnykins (DB61), Be Prepared Bunnykins (DB56)

Raft

Design No.: SF111
Designer: Walter Hayward after Penelope Hollinshead
Issued: 1959 - by 1998

Shape	U.S. $	Can. $	U.K. £	Aust. $
Baby plate, round, small	25.00	40.00	12.00	40.00
Casino saucer	10.00	15.00	5.00	15.00
Casino teapot, 30s	275.00	525.00	175.00	600.00
Cereal / oatmeal bowl	20.00	30.00	10.00	30.00
Hot water plate	100.00	150.00	65.00	150.00
Jaffa fruit saucer (plain)	20.00	30.00	10.00	30.00
Plate, 6 ½"	20.00	30.00	10.00	30.00
Plate, 7½"	20.00	30.00	10.00	30.00
Plate, 8"	20.00	30.00	10.00	30.00

Raft (SF111)

Raising Hat, Style One (HW16R)

Raising Hat
Style One

Design No.:   HW16R
Designer: Barbara Vernon
Issued: By 1937 - by 1952
Combined with: *Family at Breakfast*, HW12
                   Family with Pram, Style One, HW15
                   Feeding the Baby, HW13
                   Lambeth Walk, HW16
                   Pressing Trousers, HW14
                   Proposal, HW11
                   Pulling on Trousers, HW2
                   Sleeping in a Rocking Chair, EC1
                   Wedding, LFd

Shape	U.S. $	Can. $	U.K. £	Aust. $
Casino jug, 42s				
with signature	135.00	200.00	85.00	200.00
without signature	125.00	175.00	70.00	175.00
Casino teacup				
with signature	125.00	175.00	75.00	175.00
without signature	75.00	125.00	45.00	125.00
Casino teapot, 30s				
with signature	375.00	575.00	225.00	750.00
without signature	300.00	450.00	175.00	525.00
Casino teapot, 36s				
with signature	375.00	575.00	225.00	750.00
without signature	300.00	450.00	175.00	575.00
Don beaker				
with signature	125.00	175.00	75.00	175.00
without signature	75.00	125.00	45.00	125.00
Don beaker, one handle				
with signature	100.00	150.00	60.00	150.00
without signature	65.00	100.00	40.00	100.00
Don mug, one handle				
with signature	100.00	150.00	60.00	150.00
without signature	75.00	125.00	45.00	125.00
Lid of hot water plate				
with signature	85.00	125.00	50.00	125.00
without signature	75.00	100.00	45.00	100.00

Note: *Raising Hat* (HW16R) is combined with *Family with Pram*, Style One, (HW15) on a large round and an oval baby plate, and also a 7½" plate. For an illustration see page 74.

Raising Hat
Style Two

Design No.:   EC7
Designer: Barbara Vernon
Issued: 1937 to the present
Combined with: *Bedtime with Dollies*, EC125
                   Drummer, EC2
                   Engine Pulling a Carriage, HW17
                   Family with Pram, Style One, HW15
                   Hikers, EC124
                   Hobby Horse, Style One, EC21
                   Playing with Cup and Spoon, EC6
                   Sheltering Under an Umbrella, EC3
                   Sleeping in a Rocking Chair, EC1
                   To the Station, HW17R
                   Trumpeter, EC5

Raising Hat, Style Two (EC7)

Shape	U.S. $	Can. $	U.K. £	Aust. $
Albion sugar bowl	40.00	60.00	25.00	55.00
Beaker cover	75.00	95.00	40.00	100.00
Casino sugar bowl, 30s	40.00	60.00	25.00	65.00
Egg cup				
Style One	35.00	60.00	25.00	65.00
Style Two	60.00	100.00	35.00	125.00
Style Three	**10.00**	**15.00**	**5.00**	**20.00**
Lid of hot water plate	100.00	150.00	60.00	150.00

Reading (EC122)

Reading

Design No.:   EC122
Designer: Walter Hayward
Issued: 1959 to the present
Combined with: *Bedtime with Dollies*, EC125
                   The Doll's House, HW120
                   Drummer and Bugler, EC126
                   Hikers, EC124
                   Sledging, Style One, HW141

Shape	U.S. $	Can. $	U.K. £	Aust. $
Albion sugar bowl	40.00	60.00	25.00	55.00
Beaker cover	75.00	100.00	35.00	100.00
Egg cup				
Style One	35.00	60.00	25.00	65.00
Style Two	60.00	100.00	35.00	125.00
Style Three	**10.00**	**15.00**	**5.00**	**20.00**
Lid of hot water plate	100.00	150.00	60.00	150.00
Money ball	25.00	35.00	12.00	40.00

Note: *Sledging*, Style One (HW141) or *The Doll's House* (HW120) can
be combined with *Reading* (EC122) on the money ball.

Reading the Times (HW2R)

Reading the Times

Design No.:	HW2R
Designer:	Barbara Vernon
Issued:	By 1937 - by 1952
Combined with:	*Cycling*, HW15R
	Kissing under the Mistletoe, HW11R
	Netting a Cricket, HW6
	Pulling on Trousers, HW2

Shape	U.S. $	Can. $	U.K. £	Aust. $
Casino teacup	125.00	175.00	75.00	175.00
Cup / mug large	500.00	750.00	300.00	750.00
Don beaker	125.00	175.00	75.00	175.00
Don beaker, one handle	135.00	200.00	80.00	200.00
Don mug, one handle	115.00	165.00	70.00	175.00
Don mug, two handles	125.00	175.00	75.00	175.00

Note: This design should appear with the Barbara Vernon facsimile signature.

Ring-a-Ring o'Roses

Design No.:	SF21
Designer:	Walter Hayward
Issued:	1954 - by 1998

Ring-a-Ring o'Roses (SF21)

Shape	U.S. $	Can. $	U.K. £	Aust. $
Baby plate, round, small				
with signature	50.00	75.00	35.00	75.00
without signature	20.00	30.00	12.00	30.00
Cake stand	150.00	200.00	65.00	200.00
Casino saucer				
with signature	35.00	50.00	15.00	50.00
without signature	10.00	15.00	5.00	15.00
Casino teapot, 24s				
with signature	275.00	525.00	175.00	575.00
without signature	225.00	350.00	140.00	375.00
Cereal / oatmeal bowl				
with signature	50.00	75.00	25.00	75.00
without signature	20.00	30.00	9.00	30.00
Hot water plate				
with signature	125.00	200.00	85.00	200.00
without signature	100.00	150.00	65.00	150.00
Jaffa fruit saucer (plain)				
with signature	45.00	65.00	30.00	65.00
without signature	20.00	30.00	10.00	30.00
Picture plaque, large	50.00	75.00	30.00	75.00
Plate, 6 ½"				
with signature	50.00	75.00	35.00	75.00
without signature	20.00	30.00	7.00	35.00
Plate, 7½"				
with signature	50.00	75.00	35.00	75.00
without signature	20.00	30.00	10.00	30.00
Plate, 8"				
with signature	65.00	125.00	35.00	150.00
without signature	25.00	30.00	9.00	30.00

Rocking Horse / Hobby Horse, Style One

Design No.: Front — HW24 Rocking Horse
Reverse — HW24R Hobby Horse
Designer: Walter Hayward after Barbara Vernon
Issued: 1954 - 1967
Combined with: *Trumpeter*, EC5

Shape	U.S. $	Can. $	U.K. £	Aust. $
Casino teacup				
with signature	125.00	175.00	75.00	175.00
without signature	75.00	125.00	45.00	125.00
Don beaker				
with signature	125.00	175.00	75.00	175.00
without signature	75.00	125.00	45.00	125.00
Don beaker, one handle				
with signature	100.00	150.00	60.00	150.00
without signature	65.00	100.00	40.00	100.00
Don mug, one handle				
with signature	100.00	150.00	60.00	150.00
without signature	75.00	125.00	45.00	125.00
Don mug, two handles				
with signature	125.00	175.00	75.00	175.00
without signature	75.00	125.00	45.00	125.00
Jaffa fruit saucer (plain)				
with signature	125.00	175.00	75.00	175.00
without signature	75.00	125.00	45.00	125.00
Lamp	300.00	450.00	175.00	475.00
Lid of hot water plate				
with signature	85.00	125.00	50.00	125.00
without signature	75.00	100.00	45.00	100.00
Money ball	50.00	75.00	30.00	75.00
Plate, 6½"				
with signature	100.00	150.00	60.00	150.00
without signature	50.00	75.00	30.00	25.00

Rocking Horse (HW24)

Hobby Horse (HW24R)

Roller Skating Race (HW137)

Roller Skating Arm in Arm HW137R

Roller Skating Race / Roller Skating Arm in Arm

Design No.:   Front — HW137 Roller Skating Race
                  Reverse — HW137R Roller Skating Arm in Arm
Designer: Walter Hayward
Issued: 1967 - by 1998
Combined with: *Building Sand Castles*, HW138
                  Sailing Boats, HW138R

Shape	U.S. $	Can. $	U.K. £	Aust. $
Albion cream jug	50.00	75.00	25.00	80.00
Albion jug, 1 pint	75.00	150.00	50.00	150.00
Albion teapot	50.00	100.00	30.00	125.00
Cake stand	100.00	150.00	65.00	150.00
Casino teacup	40.00	60.00	20.00	55.00
Divided dish	45.00	65.00	30.00	65.00
Don beaker	45.00	65.00	20.00	65.00
Don beaker, one handle	55.00	75.00	25.00	75.00
Don mug, one handle	40.00	60.00	20.00	65.00
Don mug, two handles	45.00	65.00	15.00	65.00
Egg box				
small	250.00	350.00	125.00	375.00
medium	325.00	475.00	150.00	475.00
large	400.00	575.00	200.00	600.00
Hug-a-mug, one handle	25.00	30.00	8.00	35.00
Hug-a-mug, two handles	25.00	35.00	10.00	40.00
Jaffa fruit saucer (plain)	45.00	60.00	25.00	65.00
Lamp	175.00	250.00	75.00	275.00
Malvern beaker	60.00	90.00	35.00	100.00
Money ball	25.00	35.00	12.00	40.00
Picture plaque, small	40.00	60.00	25.00	75.00
Plate, 6½"	50.00	75.00	30.00	75.00
Savings book	30.00	40.00	14.00	45.00
Stratford straight beaker	30.00	45.00	15.00	65.00
Stratford teacup	30.00	45.00	15.00	45.00

Row Boat / Nipped by a Crab

Row Boat (HW21)

Nipped by a Crab (HW21R)

Design No.: Front — HW21 Row Boat
             Reverse — HW21R Nipped by a Crab
Designer: Walter Hayward

Issued: By 1952 - by 1998
Combined with: *Hikers*, EC124

Shape	U.S. $	Can. $	U.K. £	Aust. $
Albion jug, ½ pint	50.00	100.00	35.00	100.00
Albion jug, 1 pint	75.00	150.00	50.00	150.00
Albion teapot	50.00	100.00	30.00	125.00
Casino jug, 36s				
with signature	100.00	150.00	75.00	150.00
without signature	60.00	100.00	35.00	100.00
Casino saucer				
with signature	35.00	60.00	25.00	55.00
without signature	10.00	15.00	5.00	15.00
Casino teacup				
with signature	85.00	125.00	50.00	125.00
without signature	25.00	40.00	15.00	45.00
Casino teapot. 24s				
with signature	300.00	450.00	175.00	500.00
without signature	250.00	400.00	150.00	450.00
Don beaker				
with signature	40.00	60.00	25.00	65.00
without signature	25.00	40.00	15.00	45.00
Don beaker, one handle				
with signature	50.00	75.00	30.00	80.00
without signature	25.00	40.00	15.00	45.00
Don mug, one handle				
with signature	40.00	70.00	25.00	75.00
without signature	25.00	40.00	15.00	45.00

Shape	U.S. $	Can. $	U.K. £	Aust. $
Don mug, two handles				
with signature	50.00	75.00	30.00	85.00
without signature	25.00	40.00	15.00	45.00
Egg box				
small	250.00	350.00	100.00	400.00
medium	325.00	475.00	150.00	500.00
large	400.00	575.00	200.00	600.00
Hug-a-mug, one handle	25.00	35.00	8.00	40.00
Hug-a-mug, two handle	25.00	35.00	9.00	40.00
Jaffa fruit saucer (plain)				
with signature	45.00	65.00	25.00	70.00
without signature	25.00	40.00	15.00	45.00
Lamp	175.00	250.00	100.00	250.00
Lid of hot water plate				
with signature	85.00	125.00	50.00	125.00
without signature	75.00	100.00	45.00	100.00
Malvern beaker	30.00	45.00	20.00	50.00
Money ball	25.00	40.00	15.00	45.00
Picture plaque, small	50.00	75.00	30.00	70.00
Plate, 6 ½"				
with signature	50.00	75.00	30.00	65.00
without signature	17.00	25.00	7.00	25.00
Savings book	30.00	45.00	15.00	50.00
Stratford straight beaker	35.00	50.00	20.00	60.00
Stratford teacup	35.00	50.00	20.00	60.00

Santa Bunnykins Christmas Tree Ornament (CT68)

Santa Bunnykins
Christmas Tree Ornament

Design No.: Front — CT68 Santa Bunnykins
            Reverse — CT69 Christmas 1991
Designer: Colin Twinn
Issued: 1991 - 1991
Series: Christmas Tree Ornaments

Shape	U.S. $	Can. $	U.K. £	Aust. $
Christmas Tree Ornament	30.00	50.00	15.00	65.00

Note: For other Christmas tree ornaments in this series see pages 43, 45, 83, and 166.

Santa Bunnykins Christmas Tree Ornament (CT69)

Santa Claus

Design No.:	SF9
Designer:	Barbara Vernon
Issued:	By 1940 - by 1952
Combined with:	*Feeding the Baby*, HW13
	Pressing Trousers, HW14
	Proposal, HW11

Santa Claus (SF9)

Shape	U.S. $	Can. $	U.K. £	Aust. $
Baby plate, oval, small				
with signature	175.00	250.00	125.00	275.00
without signature	150.00	200.00	80.00	200.00
Baby plate, round, small				
with signature	150.00	225.00	90.00	225.00
without signature	125.00	175.00	70.00	175.00
Candle holder	1,500.00	2.500.00	900.00	2,500.00
Casino jug, 36s				
with signature	150.00	225.00	90.00	225.00
without signature	135.00	200.00	80.00	200.00
Casino teapot, 30s				
with signature	375.00	575.00	225.00	650.00
with signature	300.00	450.00	175.00	575.00
Cereal / oatmeal bowl				
with signature	100.00	150.00	65.00	165.00
without signature	75.00	100.00	45.00	125.00
Hot water plate				
with signature	175.00	275.00	125.00	275.00
without signature	150.00	225.00	100.00	250.00
Jaffa fruit saucer				
plain rim	150.00	225.00	100.00	250.00
wavy rim	75.00	125.00	50.00	125.00
Plate, 6 ½"				
with signature	125.00	175.00	75.00	175.00
without signature	55.00	80.00	35.00	85.00
Plate, 8½"				
with signature	125.00	200.00	75.00	185.00
without signature	75.00	100.00	40.00	100.00
Plate, 7", fine china	400.00	600.00	250.00	600.00

SCHOOL THEME
Frank Endersby

Maths Lesson (25)

Maths Lesson

Design No.: 25 Maths Lesson
Designer: Frank Endersby
Issued: 1995 to the present

Shape	U.S. $	Can. $	U.K. £	Aust. $
Baby plate, round, small	40.00	46.00	12.00	49.00
Plate, 6 ½"	25.00	25.00	7.00	27.00
Plate, 8"	30.00	35.00	9.00	39.00

Teacher Scolding (26)

Teacher Scolding / Bunny with Bag

Design No.: Front — 26 Teacher Scolding
Reverse — 27 Bunny with Bag
Designer: Frank Endersby
Issued: 1995 to the present

Shape	U.S. $	Can. $	U.K. £	Aust. $
Hug-a-mug, one handle	30.00	33.00	9.00	39.00
Hug-a-mug, two handles	33.00	39.00	10.00	45.00

Note: Bold type in the listing tables indicate a current design on a current shape.

Bunny with Bag (27)

SCHOOL DINNER THEME
Colin Twinn

First Variation, Small Size

Design No.: CT17 School Dinner
Designer: Colin Twinn
Issued: 1990 - 1993

Shape	U.S. $	Can. $	U.K. £	Aust. $
Albion jug, 1 pint	75.00	150.00	50.00	150.00
Cake stand	150.00	225.00	100.00	225.00
Cereal / oatmeal bowl	25.00	40.00	20.00	50.00
Jaffa fruit saucer (plain)	25.00	40.00	20.00	45.00
Plate, 8"	25.00	40.00	20.00	45.00

School Dinner, First Variation, (CT17)

School Dinner, Second Variation (CT30)

Second Variation, Large Size / Cook and Bunny

Design No.: Front — CT30 School Dinner
Reverse — CT31 Cook and Bunny
Designer: Colin Twinn
Issued: 1990 - 1993

Shape	U.S. $	Can. $	U.K. £	Aust. $
Albion cream jug	50.00	75.00	25.00	85.00
Albion jug, 1 pint	75.00	125.00	50.00	150.00
Albion teapot	50.00	100.00	35.00	125.00
Hug-a-mug, one handle	20.00	30.00	10.00	35.00
Lamp	125.00	175.00	75.00	175.00
Malvern beaker	30.00	45.00	70.00	50.00
Money ball	25.00	40.00	15.00	45.00
Savings book	30.00	45.00	20.00	50.00
Stratford teacup	30.00	45.00	20.00	50.00

Cook and Bunny (CT31)

SCHOOL GATES THEME
Colin Twinn

School Gates, First Variation (CT20)

First Variation, Large Size

Design No.: CT20 School Gates
Designer: Colin Twinn
Issued: 1991 - 1993

Shape	U.S. $	Can. $	U.K. £	Aust. $
Albion jug, 1 pint	75.00	125.00	50.00	150.00
Cereal / oatmeal bowl	25.00	40.00	20.00	45.00
Lamp	125.00	175.00	75.00	200.00
Picture plaque, large	50.00	75.00	30.00	75.00
Plate, 6"	20.00	30.00	15.00	35.00
Plate, 8"	25.00	40.00	20.00	45.00

School Gates, Second Variation (CT22)

School Gates
Second Variation, Small Size / Bunny on Trike

Design No.:	Front — CT22 School Gates
	Reverse — CT23 Bunny on Trike
Designer:	Colin Twinn
Issued:	1991 - 1993
Combined with:	*Bathtime Scene*, Style Two, Second Variation, CT24
	Bunnies in the Bath, First Version, CT25

Shape	U.S. $	Can. $	U.K. £	Aust. $
Albion jug, ½ pint	50.00	75.00	35.00	75.00
Albion teapot	50.00	100.00	30.00	100.00
Hug-a-mug, one handle	25.00	40.00	20.00	55.00
Hug-a-mug, two handles	25.00	40.00	20.00	55.00
Lamp	125.00	175.00	75.00	175.00
Money ball	25.00	40.00	15.00	45.00
Picture plaque, small	40.00	60.00	25.00	65.00
Stratford straight beaker	30.00	45.00	15.00	65.00

Bunny on Trike (CT23)

See-saw
Style One

Design No.: SF17
Designer: Walter Hayward
Issued: By 1952 - by 1998

Shape	U.S. $	Can. $	U.K. £	Aust. $
Albion jug, ½ pint	50.00	75.00	35.00	75.00
Albion jug, 1 pint	75.00	125.00	50.00	150.00
Baby plate, round, 6"				
with signature	50.00	75.00	45.00	85.00
without signature	25.00	40.00	12.00	45.00
Cake stand	150.00	200.00	95.00	200.00
Casino saucer				
with signature	70.00	100.00	40.00	100.00
without signature	25.00	35.00	15.00	40.00
Cereal / oatmeal bowl				
with signature	45.00	65.00	30.00	65.00
without signature	20.00	30.00	9.00	35.00
Hot water plate				
with signature	100.00	150.00	65.00	150.00
without signature	75.00	125.00	50.00	135.00
Jaffa fruit saucer (plain)				
with signature	60.00	90.00	40.00	100.00
without signature	20.00	30.00	15.00	35.00
Plate, 6 ½"				
with signature	45.00	65.00	30.00	65.00
without signature	17.00	25.00	7.00	30.00
Plate, 7 ½"				
with signature	50.00	75.00	30.00	85.00
without signature	20.00	30.00	75.00	35.00
Plate, 8"	25.00	35.00	9.00	45.00

See-saw, Style One (SF17)

Sheltering Under an Umbrella (EC3)

Sheltering Under an Umbrella

Design No.:	EC3
Designer:	Barbara Vernon
Issued:	1937 to the present
Combined with:	*Afternoon Tea*, HW116
	Bedtime with Dollies, EC125
	Drummer, EC2
	Holding Hat and Coat, EC4
	Playing with Cup and Spoon, EC6
	Raising Hat, Style Two, EC7
	Serving Tea, HW116R
	Sleeping in a Rocking Chair, EC1
	Trumpeter, EC5

Shape	U.S. $	Can. $	U.K. £	Aust. $
Albion sugar bowl	40.00	60.00	25.00	60.00
Beaker cover				
with signature	100.00	150.00	65.00	150.00
without signature	90.00	135.00	60.00	135.00
Casino sugar bowl. 30s				
with signature	125.00	175.00	75.00	175.00
without signature	100.00	150.00	60.00	150.00
Egg cup				
Style One				
with signature	95.00	150.00	60.00	150.00
without signature	85.00	150.00	50.00	150.00
Style Two	175.00	250.00	100.00	275.00
Style Three	**10.00**	**15.00**	**5.00**	**15.00**
Lid of hot water plate				
with signature	85.00	125.00	50.00	125.00
without signature	75.00	100.00	45.00	100.00

SHOPPING THEME
Frank Endersby

Shopping

Design No.: 1 Shopping
Designer: Frank Endersby
Issued: 1995 to the present

Shape	U.S. $	Can. $	U.K. £	Aust. $
Jaffa fruit saucer	25.00	30.00	9.00	35.00
Plate, 6 ½"	25.00	25.00	7.00	27.00
Plate, 8"	30.00	35.00	9.00	39.00

Shopping (1)

Vegetable Stall (2)

Vegetable Stall / Eating Apples

Design No.: Front — 2 Vegetable Stall
          Reverse — 3 Eating Apples
Designer: Frank Endersby
Issued: 1995 to the present

Shape	U.S. $	Can. $	U.K. £	Aust. $
Hug-a-mug, one handle	30.00	33.00	9.00	39.00
Hug-a-mug, two handles	33.00	39.00	10.00	45.00
Stratford teacup	30.00	45.00	15.00	45.00

Eating Apples (3)

Sledging, Style One (HW141)

Snowball Fight (HW141R)

Sledging, Style One
/ Snowball Fight

Design No.:	Front — HW141 Sledging
	Reverse — HW141R Snowball Fight
Designer:	Walter Hayward
Issued:	1967 - by 1998
Combined with:	*Engine Pulling a Carriage*, HW17
	Reading, EC122
	Serving Tea, HW116R

Shape	U.S. $	Can. $	U.K. £	Aust. $
Albion cream jug	50.00	75.00	30.00	65.00
Albion jug, ½ pint	50.00	75.00	30.00	75.00
Albion jug, 1 pint	75.00	100.00	60.00	150.00
Albion teapot	50.00	100.00	35.00	125.00
Casino teacup	50.00	75.00	30.00	75.00
Divided dish	45.00	65.00	30.00	70.00
Don beaker	40.00	60.00	20.00	65.00
Don beaker, one handle	45.00	65.00	20.00	65.00
Don mug, one handle	40.00	60.00	20.00	65.00
Don mug, two handles	40.00	60.00	20.00	65.00
Egg box				
small	250.00	375.00	100.00	400.00
medium	325.00	475.00	150.00	500.00
large	400.00	575.00	200.00	600.00
Hug-a-mug, one handle				
Christmast 1988-1991	30.00	45.00	20.00	50.00
regular issue	25.00	30.00	8.00	.3500
Hug-a-mug, two handles				
Christmas 1988-1991	30.00	45.00	20.00	50.00
regular issue	25.00	35.00	10.00	40.00
Jaffa fruit saucer (plain)	35.00	50.00	20.00	50.00
Lamp	200.00	300.00	125.00	350.00
Malvern beaker	40.00	60.00	30.00	65.00
Money ball	25.00	40.00	12.00	45.00
Picture plaque, small	40.00	60.00	20.00	65.00
Savings book	35.00	50.00	20.00	55.00
Stratford straight beaker	25.00	35.00	15.00	40.00
Stratford teacup	25.00	35.00	15.00	40.00

Note: 'A Merry Christmas from Bunnykins' was added to the hug-a-mugs as part of the Christmas set issued between 1988-1991. *Sledging*, Style One (HW141) was combined with *Reading* (EC122) on a money ball and *Engine Pulling a Carriage* (HW17) is combined with *Snowball Fight* (HW141R) on a Don mug with two handles.

Sleeping in a Rocking Chair

Design No.:	EC1
Designer:	Barbara Vernon
Issued:	1937 to the present
Combined with:	*Bugler with Toy Donkey*, HW26R
	Dress Making, HW126
	Drummer, EC2
	Feeding the Baby, HW13
	Footballer, HW13R
	Haymaking, HW29
	Hikers, EC124
	Lambeth Walk, Secod Version, HW16
	Lunch Break, HW29R
	Raising Hat, Style One, HW16R
	Raising Hat, Style Two, EC7
	Sheltering Under an Umbrella, EC3

Sleeping in a Rocking Chair (EC1)

Shape	U.S. $	Can. $	U.K. £	Aust. $
Albion sugar bowl	40.00	60.00	30.00	70.00
Beaker cover				
with signature	100.00	150.00	65.00	150.00
without signature	90.00	135.00	60.00	135.00
Egg cup				
Style One				
with signature	150.00	225.00	90.00	250.00
without signature	100.00	150.00	65.00	100.00
Style Two	75.00	100.00	45.00	100.00
Style Three	**10.00**	**15.00**	**5.00**	**15.00**
Lid of hot water plate				
with signature	85.00	125.00	60.00	125.00
without signature	75.00	100.00	45.00	100.00

Smoking in the Doorway (SF2)

Smoking in the Doorway

Design No.:	SF2
Designer:	Barbara Vernon
Issued:	1937 - by 1952
Combined with:	*Family at Breakfast*, HW12
	Fixing Braces, HW3

Shape	U.S. $	Can. $	U.K. £	Aust. $
Baby plate, oval, small	150.00	225.00	90.00	225.00
Baby plate, round, small	100.00	150.00	60.00	150.00
Candle holder	1,500.00	2,500.00	1,000.00	2,500.00
Casino saucer	75.00	100.00	45.00	100.00
Casino teapot	375.00	575.00	225.00	650.00
Cereal / oatmeal bowl	95.00	135.00	60.00	150.00
Don beaker, one handle	135.00	200.00	80.00	200.00
Hot water plate	500.00	750.00	300.00	750.00
Jaffa fruit saucer				
plain rim	150.00	225.00	85.00	225.00
wavy rim	125.00	175.00	75.00	150.00
Plate, 6 ½"	100.00	150.00	60.00	150.00
Plate, 7 ½"	100.00	150.00	60.00	150.00
Plate, 7½", fine china	Very rare			
Porridge bowl	150.00	225.00	70.00	225.00

Note: This design should appear with the Barbara Vernon facsimile signature.

SNOW SCENES THEME
Frank Endersby

Snow Scene

Design No.: 58 Snow Scene
Designer: Frank Endersby
Issued: 1995 to the present

Shape	U.S. $	Can. $	U.K. £	Aust. $
Jaffa fruit saucer	25.00	30.00	9.00	35.00
Plate, 6 ½"	25.00	25.00	7.00	27.00
Plate, 8"	30.00	35.00	9.00	35.00

Snow Scenes First Version (58)

Building Snowman (59)

Building Snowman /
Sledging, Style Two

Design No.: Front — 59 Building Snowman
             Reverse — 60 Sledging
Designer: Frank Endersby
Issued: 1995 to the present

Shape	U.S. $	Can. $	U.K. £	Aust. $
Hug-a-mug, one handle	30.00	33.00	9.00	39.00
Hug-a-mug, two handles	33.00	39.00	10.00	45.00
Malvern beaker	30.00	45.00	15.00	50.00
Money ball	35.00	40.00	13.00	45.00
Stratford teacup	30.00	45.00	15.00	45.00

Sledging, Style Two (60)

Soldiers Marching to the Music (HW18)

Soldier Marching (HW18R)

Soldiers Marching to the Music / Soldier Marching

Design No.: Front — HW18 Soldiers Marching to the Music
Reverse — HW18R Soldier Marching
Designer: Walter Hayward after Barbara Vernon
Issued: By 1952 - 1967
Combined with: *Convalescing*, SF5

Shape	U.S. $	Can. $	U.K. £	Aust. $
Casino jug, 30s				
with signature	175.00	250.00	125.00	250.00
without signature	150.00	200.00	80.00	200.00
Casino saucer				
with signature	50.00	75.00	35.00	75.00
without signature	30.00	45.00	20.00	50.00
Casino teacup				
with signature	75.00	100.00	50.00	100.00
without signature	50.00	75.00	30.00	75.00
Casino teapot, 36s				
with signature	375.00	575.00	225.00	650.00
without signature	300.00	450.00	175.00	575.00
Don beaker				
with signature	75.00	100.00	45.00	95.00
without signature	50.00	75.00	30.00	75.00
Don beaker, one handle				
with signature	75.00	100.00	45.00	95.00
without signature	50.00	75.00	30.00	75.00
Don mug, one handle				
with signature	70.00	100.00	45.00	95.00
without signature	50.00	75.00	30.00	75.00
Don mug, two handles				
with signature	65.00	100.00	45.00	95.00
without signature	50.00	75.00	30.00	75.00
Jaffa fruit saucer (plain)				
with signature	75.00	100.00	45.00	100.00
without signature	50.00	75.00	30.00	75.00
Lid of hot water plate				
with signature	85.00	125.00	50.00	125.00
without signature	75.00	100.00	45.00	100.00
Plate, 6½"				
with signature	75.00	100.00	45.00	100.00
without signature	50.00	75.00	30.00	75.00

Space Rocket Launch

Design No.: SF132
Designer: Walter Hayward
Issued: 1967 - by 1998

Shape	U.S. $	Can. $	U.K. £	Aust. $
Albion cream jug	75.00	125.00	50.00	125.00
Baby plate, round, small	25.00	40.00	12.00	45.00
Cake stand	150.00	225.00	100.00	225.00
Casino saucer	35.00	50.00	20.00	35.00
Cereal / oatmeal bowl	20.00	30.00	9.00	35.00
Hot water plate	100.00	150.00	65.00	150.00
Jaffa fruit saucer (plain)	20.00	30.00	8.00	50.00
Plate, 6 ½"	20.00	30.00	7.00	55.00
Plate, 7 ½"	40.00	60.00	10.00	70.00
Plate, 8"	40.00	60.00	10.00	70.00

Space Rocket Launch (SF132)

Spring Cleaning (LF14)

Spring Cleaning

Design No.: LF14
Designer: Walter Hayward
Issued: By 1952 - 1970

Shape	U.S. $	Can. $	U.K. £	Aust. $
Baby plate, oval, large				
with signature	225.00	325.00	135.00	350.00
without signature	125.00	200.00	80.00	225.00
Baby plate, round, large				
with signature	250.00	350.00	150.00	350.00
without signature	150.00	200.00	100.00	225.00
Bread / butter plate, handles				
with signature	200.00	295.00	125.00	300.00
without signature	150.00	225.00	100.00	250.00
Cereal / oatmeal bowl				
with signature	85.00	125.00	50.00	125.00
without signature	75.00	100.00	45.00	125.00
Hot water plate				
with signature	100.00	150.00	65.00	125.00
without signature	75.00	100.00	45.00	100.00
Plate, 8 ½"				
with signature	90.00	140.00	55.00	175.00
without signature	75.00	100.00	50.00	100.00
Porridge bowl				
with signature	135.00	175.00	85.00	175.00
without signature	100.00	145.00	75.00	150.00

SPRING CLEANING THEME
Frank Endersby

Dusting (19)

Dusting

Design No.:	19 Dusting			
Designer:	Frank Endersby			
Issued:	1995 to the present			

Shape	U.S. $	Can. $	U.K. £	Aust. $
Baby plate, round, small	40.00	46.00	12.00	49.00
Plate, 6 ½"	25.00	25.00	7.00	27.00
Plate, 8"	30.00	35.00	9.00	39.00

Beating Carpet (20)

Beating Carpet / Resting

Design No.:	Front — 20 Beating Carpet			
	Reverse — 21 Resting			
Designer:	Frank Endersby			
Issued:	1995 to the present			

Shape	U.S. $	Can. $	U.K. £	Aust. $
Hug-a-mug, one handle	30.00	33.00	9.00	39.00
Hug-a-mug, two handles	33.00	39.00	10.00	45.00

Resting (21)

Storytime

Design No.: SF110
Designer: Walter Hayward
Issued: 1959 - 1967

Shape	U.S. $	Can. $	U.K. £	Aust. $
Baby plate, round, small	150.00	225.00	85.00	250.00
Casino saucer	50.00	75.00	35.00	85.00
Cereal / oatmeal bowl	75.00	100.00	50.00	100.00
Hot water plate	100.00	150.00	60.00	150.00
Plate, 6 ½"	65.00	100.00	40.00	100.00
Plate, 7 ½"	85.00	125.00	50.00	125.00
Plate, 8"	90.00	135.00	55.00	135.00

Storytime (SF110)

Swinging (HW20)

Skipping (HW20R)

Swinging / Skipping

Design No.:	Front — HW20 Swinging
	Reverse — HW20R Skipping
Designer:	Walter Hayward
Issued:	By 1952 - 1967
Combined with:	*Holding Hat and Coat*, EC4

Shape	U.S. $	Can. $	U.K. £	Aust. $
Casino saucer				
with signature	50.00	75.00	30.00	75.00
without signature	35.00	50.00	25.00	50.00
Casino sugar bowl, 36s				
with signature	175.00	250.00	125.00	250.00
without signature	125.00	175.00	75.00	175.00
Casino teacup				
with signature	60.00	90.00	45.00	95.00
without signature	50.00	75.00	30.00	75.00
Casino teapot, 36s				
with signature	375.00	575.00	225.00	600.00
without signature	325.00	475.00	200.00	500.00
Divided dish	75.00	100.00	45.00	100.00
Don beaker				
with signature	75.00	100.00	45.00	95.00
without signature	60.00	90.00	35.00	85.00
Don beaker, one handle				
with signature	60.00	90.00	35.00	95.00
without signature	45.00	65.00	30.00	85.00
Don mug, one handle				
with signature	40.00	60.00	25.00	95.00
without signature	35.00	50.00	20.00	85.00
Don mug, two handles				
with signature	50.00	75.00	30.00	95.00
without signature	40.00	60.00	25.00	85.00
Egg box				
small	275.00	375.00	125.00	400.00
Jaffa fruit saucer (plain)				
with signature	75.00	100.00	45.00	100.00
without signature	50.00	75.00	30.00	75.00
Lid of hot water plate				
with signature	85.00	125.00	50.00	125.00
without signature	75.00	100.00	45.00	100.00
Plate, 6 ½"				
with signature	65.00	100.00	40.00	100.00
without signature	50.00	75.00	30.00	85.00

Note: *Holding Hat and Coat* (EC4) is combined with *Swinging* (HW20) and *Skipping* (HW20R) on the casino sugar bowl.

Television Time

Design No.: SF112
Designer: Walter Hayward
Issued: 1959 - by 1998

Shape	U.S. $	Can. $	U.K. £	Aust. $
Baby plate, round, small	20.00	30.00	15.00	35.00
Cake stand	100.00	150.00	65.00	150.00
Casino saucer	20.00	30.00	10.00	45.00
Cereal / oatmeal bowl	25.00	35.00	15.00	40.00
Hot water plate	100.00	150.00	65.00	150.00
Jaffa fruit saucer (plain)	20.00	30.00	10.00	35.00
Plate, 6 ½"	25.00	40.00	15.00	55.00
Plate, 7 ½"	30.00	45.00	20.00	55.00

Television Time (SF112)

Tennis

Tennis

A boxed Bunnykins for Grown Ups Set containing a cereal bowl and a hug-a-mug with one handle with the *Aerobics/Jogging* design, a 6" plate with the *Aeroplane* design, an 8" plate with the *Breakfast Time* design and a cereal bowl with the *Tennis* design was distributed mainly in the U.S.A.

Design No.: None
Designer: Walter Hayward
Issued: 1986 - 1988 (U.S.A.)
Series: Bunnykins for Grown-Ups

Shape	U.S. $	Can. $	U.K. £	Aust. $
Cereal / oatmeal bowl	45.00	65.00	35.00	65.00
Complete set (M.I.B.)	200.00	300.00	125.00	300.00

Note: See also *Aerobics / Jogging* and *Aeroplane* page 14 and *Breakfast Time* page 30.

Ticket Queue (SF109)

Ticket Queue

Design No.: SF109
Designer: Walter Hayward
Issued: 1959 - by 1998

Shape	U.S. $	Can. $	U.K. £	Aust. $
Baby plate, round, small	20.00	30.00	15.00	35.00
Casino saucer	10.00	15.00	5.00	15.00
Cereal / oatmeal bowl	25.00	35.00	10.00	35.00
Hot water plate	100.00	150.00	65.00	150.00
Plate, 6 ½"	20.00	30.00	10.00	45.00
Plate, 7 ½"	20.00	30.00	10.00	55.00
Plate, 8"	30.00	45.00	15.00	55.00
Plate, 10"	30.00	45.00	15.00	55.00

Toast for Tea Today

Design No.:   SF23
Designer: Walter Hayward
Issued: 1954 - 1967
Combined with: *Dress Making*, HW26
                Windy Day, HW27

Toast for Tea Today (SF23)

Shape	U.S. $	Can. $	U.K. £	Aust. $
Baby plate, round, small				
with signature	150.00	225.00	85.00	200.00
without signature	100.00	150.00	65.00	150.00
Casino saucer				
with signature	75.00	100.00	45.00	100.00
without signature	50.00	75.00	35.00	75.00
Casino teapot, 24s				
with signature	300.00	450.00	175.00	500.00
without signature	250.00	400.00	150.00	450.00
Casino teapot, 30s				
with signature	325.00	500.00	200.00	600.00
without signature	275.00	425.00	175.00	500.00
Cereal / oatmeal bowl				
with signature	100.00	150.00	65.00	100.00
without signature	75.00	100.00	45.00	75.00
Hot water plate				
with signature	175.00	275.00	100.00	275.00
without signature	125.00	200.00	90.00	175.00
Jaffa fruit saucer (plain)				
with signature	75.00	100.00	45.00	100.00
without signature	50.00	75.00	35.00	75.00
Plate, 6 ½"				
with signature	90.00	135.00	55.00	150.00
without signature	75.00	100.00	45.00	100.00

Note: *Toast for Tea Today* (SF23) is combined with *Dress Making* (HW26) and *Windy Day* (HW27) on the casino teapot (24s).

Top Hat

Desing No.:	HW14R
Designer:	Barbara Vernon
Issued:	By 1937 -1967
Combined with:	*Embracing at a Window*, HW5
	Feeding the Baby, HW13
	Lambeth Walk, HW16
	Pressing Trousers, HW14

Shape	U.S. $	Can. $	U.K. £	Aust. $
Casino jug, 36s				
with signature	150.00	225.00	90.00	225.00
without signature	125.00	175.00	80.00	200.00
Casino jug, 42s				
with signature	135.00	200.00	85.00	175.00
without signature	100.00	150.00	65.00	150.00
Casino teacup				
with signature	95.00	145.00	60.00	150.00
without signature	75.00	100.00	45.00	100.00
Don beaker				
with signature	95.00	145.00	60.00	150.00
without signature	75.00	100.00	45.00	100.00
Don beaker, one handle				
with signature	95.00	145.00	60.00	150.00
without signature	75.00	100.00	45.00	100.00
Don mug, one handle				
with signature	80.00	125.00	50.00	125.00
without signature	65.00	95.00	40.00	100.00
Don mug, two handles				
with signature	80.00	125.00	50.00	125.00
without signature	65.00	95.00	40.00	100.00
Teacup, fine china		Very rare		

Top Hat (HW14R)

Toppling the Fruit Cart

Design No.:	SF134
Designer:	Walter Hayward
Issued:	1967 - by 1998

Shape	U.S. $	Can. $	U.K. £	Aust. $
Albion jug, 1 pint	75.00	100.00	50.00	150.00
Baby plate, round, small	20.00	30.00	12.00	35.00
Cake stand	150.00	225.00	90.00	250.00
Casino saucer	10.00	15.00	5.00	15.00
Cereal / oatmeal bowl	25.00	35.00	15.00	40.00
Hot water plate	100.00	150.00	65.00	150.00
Jaffa fruit saucer (plain)	30.00	45.00	20.00	50.00
Picture plaque, large	30.00	45.00	20.00	50.00
Plate, 6 ½"	50.00	75.00	30.00	80.00
Plate, 7½"	50.00	75.00	30.00	80.00
Plate, 8"	25.00	35.00	20.00	40.00

Toppling the Fruit Cart (SF134)

Toy Shop (SF114)

Toy Shop

Design No.: SF114
Designer: Walter Hayward after Barbara Vernon
Issued: 1959 - 1967

Shape	U.S. $	Can. $	U.K. £	Aust. $
Baby plate, round, small	150.00	225.00	100.00	250.00
Casino saucer	100.00	150.00	60.00	150.00
Cereal / oatmeal bowl	100.00	150.00	65.00	150.00
Hot water plate	175.00	275.00	100.00	250.00
Jaffa fruit saucer (plain)	150.00	225.00	100.00	250.00
Plate, 6 ½"	90.00	135.00	55.00	125.00
Plate, 7 ½"	100.00	150.00	60.00	150.00

TRAIN STATION THEME
Frank Endersby

Waiting for Train

Design No.: 49 Waiting for Train
Designer: Frank Endersby
Issued: 1995 to the present

Shape	U.S. $	Can. $	U.K. £	Aust. $
Baby plate, round, small	40.00	46.00	12.00	49.00
Jaffa fruit saucer	25.00	30.00	9.00	35.00
Plate, 6 ½"	15.00	25.00	7.00	27.00
Plate, 8"	30.00	35.00	9.00	39.00

Waiting for Train (49)

Ticket Office (50)

Ticket Office / Sitting on Suitcase

Design No.: Front — 50 Ticket Office
             Reverse — 51 Sitting on Suitcase
Designer: Frank Endersby
Issued: 1995 to the present

Shape	U.S. $	Can. $	U.K. £	Aust. $
Hug-a-mug, one handle	30.00	33.00	9.00	39.00
Hug-a-mug, two handles	33.00	39.00	10.00	45.00

Note: Bold type in the listing tables indicate a current design on a current shape.

Sitting on Suitcase (51)

Trimming the Tree (CT80)

Trimming the Tree
Christmas Tree Ornament

Design No.: Front — CT80 Trimming the Tree
          Reverse — CT81 Christmas 1994
Designer: Colin Twinn
Issued: 1994 - 1994
Series: Christmas Tree Ornaments

Shape	U.S. $	Can. $	U.K. £	Aust. $
Christmas tree ornament	30.00	50.00	15.00	55.00

Note: For other Christmas tree ornaments in this series see pages 43, 45, 83, and 144.

Trimming the Tree (CT81)

Trumpeter

Design No.:	EC5
Designer:	Barbara Vernon
Issued:	1937 to the present
Combined with:	*Drummer*, EC2
	Drummer and Bugler, EC126
	Family Going out on Washing Day, HW8
	Hikers, EC124
	Hobby Horse, Style One, HW24R
	Holding Hat and Coat, EC4
	Raising Hat, Style Two, EC7
	Rocking Horse, HW24
	Sheltering Under an Umbrella, EC3
	Washing Day, HW8R

Trumpeter (EC5)

Shape	U.S. $	Can. $	U.K. £	Aust. $
Albion sugar bowl, ¼ pint	50.00	75.00	35.00	85.00
Beaker cover				
with signature	100.00	150.00	65.00	150.00
without signature	75.00	100.00	45.00	100.00
Casino sugar bowl, 36s				
with signature	100.00	150.00	65.00	150.00
without signature	75.00	100.00	45.00	100.00
Egg cup				
Style One				
with signature	100.00	150.00	65.00	150.00
wihtout signature	50.00	75.00	30.00	75.00
Style Two				
with signature	150.00	225.00	90.00	250.00
without signature	60.00	90.00	35.00	100.00
Style Three	**15.00**	**15.00**	**5.00**	**14.00**
Lid of hot water plate				
with signature	85.00	120.00	50.00	125.00
without signature	75.00	100.00	45.00	100.00

Tug of War (LF1)

Tug of War

Design No.:	LF1
Designer:	Barbara Vernon
Issued:	By 1937 - by 1952

Shape	U.S. $	Can. $	U.K. £	Aust. $
Bread / butter plate, handles				
with signature	400.00	600.00	250.00	650.00
without signature	325.00	500.00	200.00	500.00
Plate, 8 ½"				
with signature	100.00	150.00	65.00	135.00
without signature	75.00	100.00	45.00	100.00
Porridge bowl				
with signature	250.00	375.00	150.00	400.00
without signature	200.00	300.00	125.00	300.00

Unravelling the Knitting (HW119)

Trying on Knitting (HW119R)

Unravelling the Knitting / Trying on Knitting

Design No.:	Front — HW119 Unravelling the Knitting
	Reverse — HW119R Trying on Knitting
Designer:	Walter Hayward
Issued:	1959 - 1992
Combined with:	*Bedtime with Dollies*, EC125

Shape	U.S. $	Can. $	U.K. £	Aust. $
Albion cream jug	50.00	75.00	30.00	75.00
Albion jug, ½ pint	50.00	75.00	30.00	75.00
Albion jug, 1 pint	100.00	150.00	65.00	150.00
Albion teapot	85.00	130.00	60.00	125.00
Cake stand	100.00	150.00	65.00	150.00
Casino jug, 30s	150.00	200.00	90.00	200.00
Casino jug, 36s	125.00	175.00	80.00	175.00
Casino jug, 42s	100.00	150.00	65.00	150.00
Casino saucer	20.00	30.00	10.00	35.00
Casino sugar bowl, 36s	35.00	50.00	20.00	60.00
Casino teacup	40.00	60.00	25.00	65.00
Casino teapot, 30s	275.00	400.00	125.00	425.00
Don beaker	45.00	60.00	25.00	65.00
Don beaker, one handle	60.00	90.00	35.00	100.00
Don mug, one handle	40.00	60.00	25.00	65.00
Don mug, two handles	45.00	70.00	30.00	75.00
Egg box				
small	250.00	375.00	125.00	400.00
medium	325.00	475.00	200.00	500.00
large	400.00	575.00	300.00	600.00
Hug-a-mug, one handle	25.00	40.00	15.00	45.00
Hug-a-mug, two handles	30.00	45.00	20.00	50.00
Jaffa fruit saucer (plain)	30.00	45.00	20.00	50.00
Lamp	175.00	250.00	125.00	250.00
Lid of hot water plate	100.00	150.00	60.00	150.00
Malvern beaker / mug	35.00	50.00	20.00	60.00
Money ball	35.00	50.00	20.00	60.00
Picture plaque, small	40.00	60.00	25.00	75.00
Plate, 6 ½ "	55.00	75.00	35.00	75.00
Savings book	45.00	65.00	25.00	65.00
Stratford straight beaker	40.00	60.00	25.00	65.00
Stratford teacup	40.00	60.00	25.00	65.00

Visiting the Cottage
First Version

Design No.: SF6a
Designer: Barbara Vernon
Issued: By 1940 - c.1949

Shape	U.S. $	Can. $	U.K. £	Aust. $
Baby plate, round, small	250.00	375.00	150.00	375.00
Baby plate, round, large	325.00	500.00	200.00	500.00
Bread / butter plate	500.00	750.00	300.00	750.00
Hot water plate	500.00	750.00	300.00	750.00
Plate, 6 ½"	200.00	300.00	125.00	300.00
Plate, 7 ½"	250.00	375.00	150.00	375.00
Plate 8½"	300.00	450.00	175.00	450.00

Note: This design should appear with the Barbara Vernon facsimile
signature.

Visiting the Cottage, First Version, (SF6a)

Visiting the Cottage, Second Version (SF6b)

Visiting the Cottage
Second Version

Design No.: SF6b
Designer: Barbara Vernon
Issued: c.1949 - 1952

Shape	U.S. $	Can. $	U.K. £	Aust. $
Baby plate, round, small	325.00	500.00	200.00	500.00
Baby plate, round, large	400.00	600.00	250.00	600.00
Bread and butter plate	575.00	850.00	350.00	800.00
Casino jug, 24s	575.00	850.00	350.00	800.00
Cereal / oatmeal bowl	175.00	250.00	100.00	250.00
Jaffa fruit saucer				
plain rim	325.00	500.00	200.00	500.00
wavy rim	175.00	250.00	100.00	250.00
Plate, 6 ½"	250.00	375.00	150.00	400.00
Plate, 7 ½"	300.00	450.00	175.00	450.00
Plate 8½"	350.00	525.00	200.00	500.00
Porridge plate	250.00	375.00	150.00	400.00

Note: This design should appear with the Barbara Vernon facsimile
signature.

Washing Day (HW8R)

Washing Day

Design No.:	HW8R
Designer:	Barbara Vernon
Issued:	By 1937 - by 1967
Combined with:	*Family at Breakfast*, HW12
	Family Going out on Washing Day, HW8
	Trumpeter, EC5

Shape	U.S. $	Can. $	U.K. £	Aust. $
Casino sugar bowl, 36s				
with signature	150.00	225.00	90.00	200.00
without signature	125.00	175.00	75.00	150.00
Casino teacup				
with signature	125.00	175.00	75.00	165.00
without signature	80.00	125.00	50.00	100.00
Casino teapot, 36s				
with signature	275.00	400.00	175.00	425.00
without signature	250.00	375.00	165.00	400.00
Don beaker, one handle				
with signature	95.00	150.00	60.00	150.00
without signature	75.00	100.00	45.00	100.00
Don mug, one handle				
with signature	90.00	140.00	60.00	150.00
without signature	75.00	100.00	45.00	100.00
Don mug, two handles				
with signature	95.00	150.00	60.00	150.00
without signature	75.00	100.00	45.00	100.00

Washing in the Open Air

Design No.: HW10R
Designer: Barbara Vernon
By 1937 - by 1967
Combined with: *Asleep in the Open Air*, HW10
Convalescing, SF5
Family with Pram, Style One, HW15
Feeding the Baby, HW13
Gardening, Style One, HW9
Leapfrog, HW12R

Washing in the Open Air (HW10R)

Shape	U.S. $	Can. $	U.K. £	Aust. $
Casino jug, 30s				
with signature	150.00	225.00	100.00	200.00
without signature	125.00	200.00	75.00	175.00
Casino jug, 36s				
with signature	150.00	225.00	100.00	200.00
without signature	125.00	200.00	75.00	175.00
Casino sugar bowl, 30s				
with signature	200.00	300.00	125.00	325.00
without signature	150.00	225.00	85.00	250.00
Casino teacup				
with signature	75.00	125.00	45.00	125.00
without signature	50.00	75.00	30.00	65.00
Don beaker, one handle				
with signature	100.00	150.00	60.00	125.00
without signature	75.00	100.00	45.00	100.00
Don mug, one handle				
with signature	100.00	150.00	60.00	125.00
without signature	75.00	100.00	45.00	100.00
Don mug, two handles				
with signature	100.00	150.00	60.00	125.00
without signature	75.00	100.00	45.00	100.00

WASHING UP THEME
Colin Twinn

Washing Up, First Variation (CT15)

First Variation, Large Size

Design No.: CT15 Washing Up
Designer: Colin Twinn
Issued: 1990 - 1993

Shape	U.S. $	Can. $	U.K. £	Aust. $
Albion jug, 1 pint	75.00	125.00	45.00	150.00
Baby bowl, round, small	25.00	35.00	15.00	40.00
Cake stand	150.00	225.00	100.00	200.00
Picture plaque, large	50.00	75.00	30.00	75.00
Plate, 8"	60.00	90.00	40.00	75.00

Washing Up, Second Variation (CT32)

Second Variation, Small Size
/ Splashing at Sink

Design No.: Front — CT32 Washing Up
Reverse — CT33 Splashing at Sink
Designer: Colin Twinn
Issued: 1990 - 1993
Combined with: *Ice Cream Seller*, CT5
Pushing the Wheelbarrow, CT3

Shape	U.S. $	Can. $	U.K. £	Aust. $
Albion teapot	50.00	75.00	30.00	80.00
Divided plate	45.00	65.00	25.00	70.00
Hug-a-mug, two handles	25.00	35.00	15.00	40.00
Lamp	125.00	200.00	75.00	225.00
Malvern beaker	30.00	45.00	20.00	50.00
Money ball	25.00	35.00	15.00	40.00
Savings book	35.00	50.00	20.00	60.00

Splashing at Sink (CT33)

Watering the Flowers

Design No.:	SF15
Designer:	Walter Hayward after Barbara Vernon
Issued:	By 1952 - 1967
Combined with:	*Pressing Trousers*, HW14

Shape	U.S. $	Can. $	U.K. £	Aust. $
Baby plate, round, small				
with signature	75.00	100.00	45.00	100.00
without signature	60.00	90.00	35.00	90.00
Casino jug, 30s				
with signature	275.00	400.00	165.00	350.00
without signature	225.00	325.00	135.00	300.00
Casino saucer				
with signature	75.00	100.00	45.00	100.00
without signature	50.00	75.00	35.00	75.00
Casino teapot, 24s				
with signature	350.00	525.00	200.00	500.00
without signature	300.00	450.00	175.00	425.00
Cereal / oatmeal bowl				
with signature	75.00	100.00	45.00	100.00
without signature	60.00	90.00	35.00	95.00
Hot water plate				
with signature	175.00	275.00	100.00	250.00
without signature	125.00	200.00	85.00	200.00
Jaffa fruit saucer (plain)				
with signature	75.00	100.00	45.00	100.00
without signature	60.00	90.00	35.00	95.00
Plate, 6 ½"				
with signature	85.00	125.00	50.00	125.00
without signature	65.00	100.00	40.00	100.00
Plate, 7 ½"				
with signature	85.00	125.00	50.00	125.00
without signature	65.00	100.00	40.00	100.00

Watering the Flowers (SF15)

Note: *Pressing Trousers* (HW14) is combined with *Watering the Flowers* (SF15) on the casino teapot.

Wedding (LFd)

Wedding

Design No.:	LFd
Designer:	Barbara Vernon
Issued:	1937 - by 1952
Combined with:	*Pressing Trousers*, HW14
	Proposal, HW11
	Raising Hat, Style One, HW16R

Shape	U.S. $	Can. $	U.K. £	Aust. $
Baby plate, round, large	300.00	450.00	200.00	475.00
Casino teapot, 24s	300.00	450.00	200.00	475.00
Hot water plate	300.00	450.00	200.00	475.00
Plate, 7 ½"	225.00	350.00	130.00	375.00
Plate, 8"	250.00	375.00	150.00	400.00
Plate, 8 ½"	250.00	375.00	150.00	400.00
Porridge bowl	200.00	275.00	125.00	300.00

Note: The Casino teapot (24s), combining *Proposal* (HW11) and *Wedding* (LFd), exists with a silver rimmed lid and a crackle finish, this is considered extremely rare.

Wheelbarrow Race, Style One / Cricketer

Wheelbarrow Race, Style One (HW22)   Cricketer (HW22R)

Design No.:   Front — HW22 Wheelbarrow Race
             Reverse — HW22R Cricketer
Designer: Walter Hayward
Issued: By 1952 - by 1998

Combined with: *Bedtime with Dollies*, EC125
                 Drummer, EC2
                 Holding Hat and Coat, EC4

Shape	U.S. $	Can. $	U.K. £	Aust. $
Albion cream jug	50.00	75.00	30.00	75.00
Albion jug, 1 pint	75.00	100.00	60.00	100.00
Albion teapot	50.00	75.00	30.00	75.00
Casino jug, 30s				
with signature	150.00	225.00	90.00	225.00
without signature	125.00	175.00	80.00	175.00
Casino saucer				
with signature	35.00	50.00	20.00	60.00
without signature	10.00	15.00	5.00	15.00
Casino sugar bowl, 30s				
with signature	175.00	250.00	100.00	250.00
without signature	150.00	225.00	90.00	200.00
Casino teacup				
with signature	50.00	75.00	30.00	75.00
without signature	25.00	35.00	15.00	40.00
Casino teapot, 30s				
with signature	275.00	400.00	175.00	450.00
without signature	250.00	375.00	150.00	400.00
Casino teapot, 36s				
with signature	225.00	375.00	150.00	350.00
without signature	200.00	300.00	125.00	300.00
Divided dish	45.00	65.00	30.00	65.00
Don beaker				
with signature	40.00	60.00	30.00	70.00
without signature	30.00	45.00	20.00	50.00

Shape	U.S. $	Can. $	U.K. £	Aust. $
Don beaker, one handle				
with signature	45.00	65.00	30.00	70.00
without signature	30.00	45.00	20.00	50.00
Don mug, one handle				
with signature	40.00	60.00	30.00	70.00
without signature	30.00	45.00	20.00	50.00
Don mug, two handles				
with signature	45.00	65.00	30.00	70.00
without signature	30.00	45.00	20.00	50.00
Egg box				
small	250.00	375.00	100.00	400.00
medium	325.00	475.00	150.00	500.00
large	400.00	575.00	200.00	600.00
Hug-a-mug, one handle	25.00	35.00	10.00	40.00
Hug-a-mug, two handles	25.00	35.00	10.00	40.00
Jaffa fruit saucer (plain)	40.00	60.00	25.00	65.00
Lamp	150.00	225.00	90.00	200.00
Lid of hot water plate	75.00	100.00	45.00	100.00
Malvern beaker	30.00	45.00	20.00	50.00
Money ball	25.00	35.00	15.00	40.00
Picture plaque, small	40.00	60.00	25.00	65.00
Plate, 6½"				
with signature	50.00	75.00	30.00	75.00
without signature	20.00	30.00	10.00	35.00
Savings book	30.00	45.00	20.00	50.00
Stratford teacup	30.00	45.00	20.00	50.00

Note: *Drummer* (EC2) is combine with *Wheelbarrow Race* (HW22) on the casino sugar bowl and *Holding Hat and Coat* (EC4) is combined wtih *Wheelbarrow Race* (HW22) on the money ball.

Wheelbarrow Race, Style Two (CT1)

Wheelbarrow Race
Style Two

Design No.: CT1
Designer: Colin Twinn
Issued: 1988 - 1993

Shape	U.S. $	Can. $	U.K. £	Aust. $
Albion jug, 1 pint	125.00	175.00	90.00	150.00
Baby plate, round, small	25.00	35.00	15.00	45.00
Cake stand	150.00	225.00	90.00	200.00
Cereal / oatmeal bowl	25.00	35.00	15.00	40.00
Jaffa fruit saucer	25.00	35.00	15.00	40.00
Picture plaque, large	50.00	75.00	35.00	85.00
Plate, 6 ½"	20.00	30.00	10.00	35.00
Plate, 8"	25.00	35.00	15.00	40.00

Pushing the Wheelbarrow

Design No.: CT3
Designer: Colin Twinn
Issued: 1988 - 1993
Combined with: *Bunnies in the Bath, Second Version*, CT34
Ice Cream Seller, CT5
Picking Daisies, CT4
Splashing at Sink, CT33
Washing Up, CT32

Shape	U.S. $	Can. $	U.K. £	Aust. $
Albion sugar bowl	40.00	60.00	25.00	50.00
Albion teapot	50.00	75.00	35.00	100.00
Egg cup				
Style Three	40.00	60.00	25.00	65.00
Hug-a-mug, one handle	25.00	35.00	15.00	40.00
Lamp	175.00	250.00	100.00	200.00
Malvern beaker	30.00	45.00	15.00	50.00
Stratford teacup	30.00	45.00	15.00	50.00

Pushing the Wheelbarrow (CT3)

Windy Day / Broken Umbrella

Windy Day (HW27)

Broken Umbrella (HW27R)

Design No.:	Front — HW27 Windy Day
	Reverse — HW27R Broken Umbrella
Designer:	Walter Hayward

Issued:	1952 - by 1998
Combined with:	*Dress Making*, HW26
	Toast fot Tea Today, SF23

Shape	U.S. $	Can. $	U.K. £	Aust. $
Albion cream jug	50.00	75.00	30.00	75.00
Albion jug, ½ pint	50.00	75.00	30.00	75.00
Albion teapot	50.00	75.00	30.00	100.00
Casino jug, 42s				
with signature	100.00	150.00	60.00	150.00
without signature	75.00	100.00	40.00	100.00
Casino saucer				
with signature	35.00	50.00	25.00	50.00
without signature	10.00	15.00	5.00	15.00
Casino teacup				
with signature	50.00	75.00	45.00	75.00
without signature	25.00	35.00	15.00	35.00
Casino teapot, 24s				
with signature	300.00	450.00	175.00	550.00
without signature	275.00	400.00	150.00	500.00
Divided dish	45.00	65.00	30.00	65.00
Don beaker				
with signature	50.00	75.00	30.00	85.00
without signature	35.00	50.00	20.00	60.00
Don beaker, one handle				
with signature	50.00	75.00	30.00	85.00
without signature	35.00	50.00	20.00	60.00
Don mug, one handle				
with signature	50.00	75.00	30.00	85.00
without signature	35.00	50.00	20.00	60.00

Shape	U.S. $	Can. $	U.K. £	Aust. $
Don mug, two handles				
with signature	50.00	75.00	30.00	85.00
without signature	35.00	50.00	20.00	60.00
Egg box				
small	250.00	350.00	100.00	400.00
medium	325.00	475.00	150.00	500.00
large	400.00	575.00	200.00	600.00
Hug-a-mug, one handle	23.00	30.00	8.00	30.00
Hug-a-mug, two handles	25.00	35.00	10.00	35.00
Jaffa fruit saucer (plain)				
with signature	75.00	100.00	60.00	100.00
without signature	25.00	35.00	15.00	40.00
Lamp	150.00	225.00	100.00	225.00
Malvern beaker	30.00	45.00	20.00	50.00
Money ball	25.00	40.00	12.00	45.00
Picture plaque, small	40.00	60.00	25.00	65.00
Plate, 6 ½"				
with signature	90.00	135.00	60.00	125.00
without signature	20.00	30.00	10.00	35.00
Savings book	35.00	50.00	20.00	50.00
Stratford straight beaker	40.00	60.00	25.00	65.00
Stratford teacup	40.00	60.00	25.00	65.00

Note: *Toast for Tea Today* (SF23) and *Dress Making* (HW25) are combined with *Windy Day* (HW27) on the Casino teapot.

Winning Post (LF106)

Winning Post

Design No.: LF106
Designer: Walter Hayward after Barbara Vernon
Issued: 1959 - 1970

Shape	U.S. $	Can. $	U.K. £	Aust. $
Baby plate, round, small	125.00	175.00	70.00	200.00
Baby plate, round, large	150.00	225.00	90.00	175.00
Plate, 8 ½"	75.00	100.00	45.00	175.00
Porridge bowl	150.00	225.00	90.00	200.00

XMAS MENU

Design No.: LF8
Designer: Barbara Vernon
Issued: 1940 - by 1952

Shape	U.S. $	Can. $	U.K. £	Aust. $
Baby plate, oval, large				
with signature	225.00	325.00	135.00	350.00
without signature	125.00	200.00	80.00	225.00
Baby plate, round, large				
with signature	275.00	400.00	175.00	400.00
without signature	175.00	250.00	100.00	250.00
Brean / butter plate, handles				
with signature	300.00	450.00	200.00	500.00
without signature	125.00	250.00	75.00	250.00
Cereal / oatmeal bowl				
with signature	125.00	175.00	75.00	200.00
without signature	75.00	125.00	45.00	150.00
Plate, 8 ½"				
with signature	200.00	300.00	125.00	325.00
without signature	150.00	235.00	90.00	250.00
Porridge bowl				
with signature	175.00	275.00	100.00	250.00
without signature	125.00	200.00	80.00	225.00

Xmas Menu (LF8)

BUNNYKINS BREAKFAST SET
CHARLES NOKE

Designed by Charles Noke in 1939, this breakfast set comprises six pieces. Production started in 1940 but was soon halted due to wartime needs for material elsewhere.

Charles Noke designer of the Bunnykins Breakfast Set

D6010
TEAPOT

Designer: Charles Noke
Height: 4¾", 12.1 cm
Colour: Brown rabbit; green leaves
Issued: 1939 - by 1945

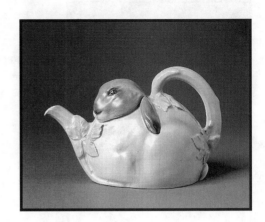

Doulton	Price			
Number	U.S. $	Can. $	U.K. £	Aust. $
D6010	Sold at auction for £1,000.00 (1998).			

D6034
EGG CUP
Style One

Designer: Charles Noke
Height: 1¾", 4.5 cm
Colour: Brown rabbit
Issued: 1939 - by1939

Doulton	Price			
Number	U.S. $	Can. $	U.K. £	Aust. $
D6034			Sold at auction for £2,250.00 (1998.)	

D6040
SUGAR SIFTER

Designer: Charles Noke
Height: 2¾", 7.0 cm
Colour: Brown rabbit, blue sweater, red trousers
Issued: 1939 - by 1945

Doulton	Price			
Number	U.S. $	Can. $	U.K. £	Aust. $
D6040			Sold at auction for £6,000.00 (1998.)	

D6056
SUGAR BOWL

Designer: Charles Noke
Height: 1¾", 4.5 cm
Colour: Brown rabbit, green leaves
Issued: 1939 - by 1945

Doulton	*Price*			
Number	*U.S. $*	*Can. $*	*U.K. £*	*Aust. $*
D6056	Sold at auction for £1,300.00 (1998).			

D6057
CREAM JUG

Designer: Charles Noke
Height: 2¾", 7.0 cm
Colour: Brown rabbit, green leaves
Issued: 1939 - by 1945

Doulton	*Price*			
Number	*U.S. $*	*Can. $*	*U.K. £*	*Aust. $*
D6057	Sold at auction for £3,000.00 (October 1998).			

BUNNYKINS BANKS
Issue of 1967 - 1991

D6615A
BUNNYBANK™
First Version

Designer:	Unknown
Modeller:	Unknown
Height:	8 ½", 21.6 cm
Colour:	Grey rabbit, green coat and hat, maroon drum
Issued:	1967 - 1977

Doulton	Price			
Number	U.S. $	Can. $	U.K. £	Aust. $
D6615A	450.00	550.00	225.00	500.00

D6615B
BUNNYBANK™
Second Version

Designer:	Unknown
Modeller:	Unknown
Height:	9 ¼", 23.5 cm
Colour:	Brown rabbit, green coat and hat, maroon drum
Issued:	1979 - 1991

Doulton	Price			
Number	U.S. $	Can. $	U.K. £	Aust. $
D6615B	375.00	450.00	200.00	475.00

Note: This model is ¾" taller and the coin slot is altered.

BUNNYKINS TEAPOTS
ISSUES of 1994 - 1998

Aussie Explorer Bunnkins Teapot (D7027) London City Gent Teapot (D6966) U.S.A. President Bunnykins Teapot (D6996)

D6966
LONDON CITY GENT
BUNNYKINS™ TEAPOT

Designer:	Unknown
Modeller:	Martyn Alcock
Height:	8", 20.3 cm
Colour:	Brown and black
Issued:	1994 in a special edition of 2,500
Series:	Bunnykins Teapots of the World

Doulton Number	Price			
	U.S. $	Can. $	U.K. £	Aust. $
D6966	150.00	175.00	60.00	175.00

BUNNYKINS TEAPOTS OF THE WORLD
Hand made and hand decorated
Royal Doulton®
BUNNYKINS®
LONDON CITY GENT
D 6966
© 1994 ROYAL DOULTON
SPECIAL EDITION OF 2,500

D6996
U.S.A. PRESIDENT BUNNYKINS™ TEAPOT

Designer:	Unknown
Modeller:	Shane Ridge
Height:	8", 20.3 cm
Colour:	Red, white and blue
Issued:	1995 in a special edition of 2,500
Series:	Bunnykins Teapots of the World

Doulton Number	Price			
	U.S. $	Can. $	U.K. £	Aust. $
D6996	150.00	175.00	60.00	175.00

BUNNYKINS TEAPOTS OF THE WORLD
Hand made and hand decorated
Royal Doulton®
BUNNYKINS®
U.S.A. PRESIDENT
D 6996
© 1995 ROYAL DOULTON
SPECIAL EDITION OF 2,500

D7027
AUSSIE EXPLORER BUNNYKINS™ TEAPOT

Designer:	Unknown
Modeller:	Shane Ridge
Height:	7 ¾", 19.5 cm
Colour:	Brown bunny, yellow waistcoat, green hat, orange boomerang
Issued:	1996 in a special edition of 2,500
Series:	Bunnykins Teapots of the World

Doulton Number	Price			
	U.S. $	Can. $	U.K. £	Aust. $
D7027	150.00	175.00	60.00	175.00

D7126
JAPANESE BUNNYKINS™ TEAPOT
GEISHA GIRL

Designer:	Caroline Dadd
Modeller:	Martyn Alcock
Height:	7 ¾", 20.0 cm
Colour:	Brown bunny, lilac kimono with green and yellow sash, black hat, cream fan with red flowers
Issued:	1998 in a special edition of 2,500
Series:	Bunnykins Teapots of the World. The last of four.

Doulton Number	Price			
	U.S. $	Can. $	U.K. £	Aust. $
D7126	125.00	175.00	69.00	180.00

BUNNYKINS CHINA TEASET
Issues of 1998

COOKIE JAR

Designer:	Unknown
Modeller:	Unknown
Height:	13 ½", 34.3 cm
Colour:	Brown bunny, blue dress, white collar and apron, pink hat, red flowers in brown basket
Issued:	1998 to the present

		Price		
Description	*U.S. $*	*Can. $*	*U.K. £*	*Aust. $*
Cookie jar	40.00	—	—	—

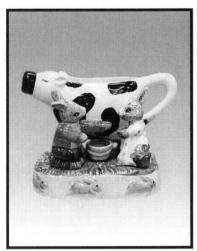

CREAMER

Designer:	Unknown
Modeller:	Unknown
Height:	4 ½", 11.9 cm
Colour:	Girl bunny - white dress with blue polka dots
	Boy bunny - deep pink jacket, pale pink jumper, brown trouser; white cow with black markings
Issued:	1998 to the present

		Price		
Description	*U.S. $*	*Can. $*	*U.K. £*	*Aust. $*
Creamer	20.00	—	—	—

SALT AND PEPPER SET

Designer:	Unknown
Modeller:	Unknown
Height:	Salt — 5 ¾", 14.16 cm
	Pepper — 6", 15.0 cm
Colour:	Salt — Girl bunny wearing white dress with blue polka dots
	Pepper — Boy bunny wearing deep pink jacket, pink jumper, brown trousers
Issued:	1998 to the present

		Price		
Description	*U.S. $*	*Can. $*	*U.K. £*	*Aust. $*
Salt and pepper set	23.00	—	—	—

SUGAR DISH

Designer:	Unknown
Modeller:	Unknown
Height:	5 ½", 14.0 cm
Colour:	Brown bunny, blue dress, white collar and apron; brown sugar dish with white lid and spoon
Issued:	1998 to the present

	Price			
Description	*U.S. $*	*Can. $*	*U.K. £*	*Aust. $*
Sugar dish	20.00	—	—	—

TEAPOT

Designer:	Unknown
Modeller:	Unknown
Height:	9 ½", 24.0 cm
Colour:	Brown bunny, green jacket, yellow shirt, deep pink bow tie, black belt and spectacles
Issued:	1998 to the present

	Price			
Description	*U.S. $*	*Can. $*	*U.K. £*	*Aust. $*
Teapot	35.00	—	—	—

Note: This set was released through Royal Doulton stores in the U.S.A.

PART TWO
BUNNYKINS FIGURINES

Earthenware Issues of 1939 - 1940
Earthenware Issues of 1972 to the present

Mother Bunnykin, Farmer Bunnykin,
Bunnykins Breakfast Set Teapot
Mary Bunnykin, Reggie Bunnykin, Freddie Bunnykin, Billy Bunnykin

BUNNYKINS BACKSTAMPS

BK-1. DOULTON & CO. LIMITED, 1972 - 1976

These backstamps were used on all figurines introduced between 1972 and 1976.

BK-2. ROYAL DOULTON TABLEWARE LTD, 1976 - 1984

The name Doulton & Co. Limited was changed to Royal Doulton Tableware Ltd., and this backstamp was used on all new figurines introduced between 1976 and 1984. It was also used on all models that had been in production previously, updating the older backstamp (BK-1). In these instances the copyright year on the stamps was kept the same as that of the original backstamp (BK-1).

BK-3. GOLDEN JUBILEE CELEBRATION, 1984

All models manufactured during 1984 carried the words "Golden Jubilee Celebration 1984", which were added to the 1976-1984 backstamp (BK-2).

BK-4. ROYAL DOULTON (U.K.), 1985 - 1986

The backstamp of 1976-1984 was modified to Royal Doulton (U.K.). All items introduced between 1985 and 1986 carry this backstamp.

BK-5. ROYAL DOULTON, 1987 TO DATE

The backstamp of 1985 - 1986 was again modified by removing the (U.K.). All new figurines introduced since 1987 carry this backstamp.

BK-SPECIALS. SPECIAL COMMISSION BACKSTAMPS

Many figurines are issued for special events, anniversaries, promotions, etc. All these carry a special stamp.

YEAR CYPHER

All Bunnykins figurines produced from 1998 forward will carry the new year cypher mark.

The cypher for 1998 was an umbrella.

The new year cypher mark for 1999 is the Top Hat as worn by Sir Henry Doulton,

EARTHENWARE ISSUES
1939 - 1940

D6001
BILLY BUNNYKIN™
Designer: Charles Noke
Height: 4 ½", 11.4 cm
Colour: Red trousers, blue jacket,
            white bowtie with blue spots
Issued: 1939-c.1940

Doulton	Price			
Number	U.S. $	Can. $	U.K. £	Aust. $
D6001	2,500.00	3,250.00	1,500.00	3,000.00

D6002
MARY BUNNYKIN™
Designer: Charles Noke
Height: 6 ½", 16.5 cm
Colour: Red bodice, dark blue collar;
            pale blue skirt, white apron
Issued: 1939-c.1940

Doulton	Price			
Number	U.S. $	Can. $	U.K. £	Aust. $
D6002	3,000.00	3,500.00	1,600.00	3,000.00

D6003
FARMER BUNNYKIN™
Designer: Charles Noke
Height: 7 ½", 19 cm
Colour: Green coat, blue and white smock, yellow bowtie,
            red handkerchief with white dots
Issued: 1939-c.1940

Doulton	Price			
Number	U.S. $	Can. $	U.K. £	Aust. $
D6003	2,750.00	3,250.00	1,500.00	3,250.00

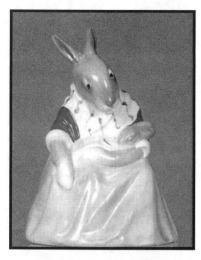

D6004
MOTHER BUNNYKIN™

Designer: Charles Noke
Height: 7", 17.5 cm
Colour: Blue skirt, red jacket, white shawl with blue stripes
Issued: 1939-c.1940

| Doulton | Price | | | |
Number	U.S. $	Can. $	U.K. £	Aust. $
D6004	3,000.00	3,500.00	1,600.00	3,000.00

D6024
FREDDIE BUNNYKIN™

Designer: Charles Noke
Height: 3 ¾", 9.5 cm
Colour: Green trousers, red jacket
    and yellow bowtie
Issued: 1939-c.1940

| Doulton | Price | | | |
Number	U.S. $	Can. $	U.K. £	Aust. $
D6024	3,500.00	5,000.00	2,000.00	5,000.00

D6025
REGGIE BUNNYKIN™

Designer: Charles Noke
Height: 3 ¾", 9.5 cm
Colour: Blue smock; red bow tie
Issued: 1939-c.1940

| Doulton | Price | | | |
Number	U.S. $	Can. $	U.K. £	Aust. $
D6025	3,250.00	4,250.00	1,750.00	4,000.00

EARTHENWARE ISSUES
1972 to the present

DB1
FAMILY PHOTOGRAPH BUNNYKINS™
First Variation

Designer:	Based on a design by Walter Hayward
Modeller:	Albert Hallam
Height:	4 ½", 11.4 cm
Colour:	Blue, white, burgundy and grey
Issued:	1972 - 1988
Varieties:	DB67; also called Father, Mother and Victoria Bunnykins, DB68

BUNNYKINS ®
"Family Photograph"
DB1
© ROYAL DOULTON
TABLEWARE LTD 1972

Back Stamp	Price			
	U.S. $	Can. $	U.K. £	Aust. $
BK-1	165.00	185.00	90.00	200.00
BK-2	165.00	185.00	90.00	200.00
BK-3	175.00	225.00	125.00	225.00

DB2
BUNTIE BUNNYKINS HELPING MOTHER™

Designer:	Based on a design by Walter Hayward
Modeller:	Albert Hallam
Height:	3 ½", 8.9 cm
Colour:	Rose-pink and yellow
Issued:	1972 - 1993

BUNTIE BUNNYKINS
"Helping Mother"
DB2
COPR. 1972
DOULTON & CO. LIMITED
Rd. No. 956234
Rd. No. 12900
R.S.A Rd. No. 193/72

Back Stamp	Price			
	U.S. $	Can. $	U.K. £	Aust. $
BK-1	85.00	100.00	45.00	80.00
BK-2	85.00	100.00	45.00	80.00
BK-3	115.00	125.00	85.00	100.00

DB3
BILLIE BUNNYKINS COOLING OFF™

Designer:	Based on a design by Walter Hayward
Modeller:	Albert Hallam
Height:	3 ¾", 9.5 cm
Colour:	Burgundy, yellow and green-grey
Issued:	1972 - 1987

BILLIE BUNNYKINS
"Cooling Off"
DB3
© ROYAL DOULTON
TABLEWARE LTD 1972

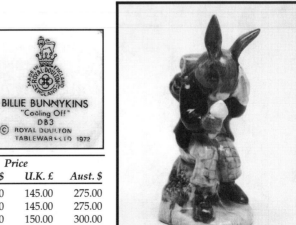

Back Stamp	Price			
	U.S. $	Can. $	U.K. £	Aust. $
BK-1	250.00	300.00	145.00	275.00
BK-2	250.00	300.00	145.00	275.00
BK-3	275.00	350.00	150.00	300.00

DB4
BILLIE AND BUNTIE BUNNYKINS
SLEIGH RIDE™
First Variation

Designer:	Based on a design by Walter Hayward
Modeller:	Albert Hallam
Height:	3 ¼", 8.3 cm
Colour:	Blue, maroon and yellow
Issued:	1972 - 1997
Varieties:	DB81

Back	Price			
Stamp	U.S. $	Can. $	U.K. £	Aust. $
BK-1	50.00	60.00	35.00	65.00
BK-2	50.00	60.00	30.00	65.00
BK-3	125.00	150.00	70.00	125.00

DB5
MR. BUNNYKINS AUTUMN DAYS™

Designer:	Based on a design by Walter Hayward
Modeller:	Albert Hallam
Height:	4", 10.1 cm
Colour:	Maroon, yellow and blue
Issued:	1972 - 1982

Back	Price			
Stamp	U.S. $	Can. $	U.K. £	Aust. $
BK-1	475.00	550.00	250.00	500.00
BK-2	475.00	550.00	250.00	500.00

DB6
MRS. BUNNYKINS CLEAN SWEEP™

Designer:	Based on a design by Walter Hayward
Modeller:	Albert Hallam
Height:	4", 10.1 cm
Colour:	Blue and white
Issued:	1972 - 1991

Back	Price			
Stamp	U.S. $	Can. $	U.K. £	Aust. $
BK-1	100.00	135.00	60.00	125.00
BK-2	100.00	135.00	60.00	125.00
BK-3	125.00	150.00	85.00	150.00

DB7
DAISIE BUNNYKINS SPRING TIME™

Designer:	Based on a design by Walter Hayward
Modeller:	Albert Hallam
Height:	3 ½", 8.9 cm
Colour:	Blue, white and yellow
Issued:	1972 - 1983

DAISIE BUNNYKINS
"Spring Time"
DB7
COPR. 1972
DOULTON & CO. LIMITED
Rd. No. 956231
Rd. No. 12906
R.S.A. Rd. No. 186/72

Back Stamp	Price			
	U.S. $	Can. $	U.K. £	Aust. $
BK-1	500.00	650.00	275.00	600.00
BK-2	500.00	650.00	275.00	600.00

DB8
DOLLIE BUNNYKINS PLAYTIME™
First Variation

Designer:	Based on a design by Walter Hayward
Modeller:	Albert Hallam
Height:	4", 10.1 cm
Colour:	White dress with pink design, blue dress
Issued:	1972 - 1993
Varieties:	DB80

DOLLIE BUNNYKINS
"Playtime"
DB8
COPR. 1972
DOULTON & CO. LIMITED
Rd. No. 956229
Rd. No. 12906
R.S.A. Rd. No. 187/72

Back Stamp	Price			
	U.S. $	Can. $	U.K. £	Aust. $
BK-1	75.00	100.00	40.00	75.00
BK-2	75.00	100.00	40.00	75.00
BK-3	100.00	125.00	60.00	100.00

DB9
STORYTIME BUNNYKINS™
First Variation

Designer:	Based on a design by Walter Hayward
Modeller:	Albert Hallam
Height:	3", 7.6 cm
Colour:	White dress with blue design, pink dress
Issued:	1972 - 1997
Varieties:	DB59; also called Partners in Collecting, DB151

BUNNYKINS ®
Storytime
DB9
© ROYAL DOULTON
TABLEWARE LTD 1974

Back Stamp	Price			
	U.S. $	Can. $	U.K. £	Aust. $
BK-1	50.00	60.00	35.00	65.00
BK-2	50.00	60.00	25.00	65.00
BK-3	75.00	100.00	75.00	100.00

DB10
BUSY NEEDLES BUNNYKINS™

Designer:	Based on a design by Walter Hayward
Modeller:	Albert Hallam
Height:	3 ¼", 8.3 cm
Colour:	White, green and maroon
Issued:	1973 - 1988
Varieties:	DB70

Back Stamp	Price			
	U.S. $	Can. $	U.K. £	Aust. $
BK-1	125.00	150.00	85.00	165.00
BK-2	125.00	150.00	85.00	165.00
BK-3	150.00	225.00	125.00	225.00

DB11
RISE AND SHINE BUNNYKINS™

Designer:	Based on a design by Walter Hayward
Modeller:	Albert Hallam
Height:	3 ¾", 9.5 cm
Colour:	Maroon, yellow and blue
Issued:	1973 - 1988

Back Stamp	Price			
	U.S. $	Can. $	U.K. £	Aust. $
BK-1	175.00	200.00	95.00	200.00
BK-2	175.00	200.00	95.00	200.00
BK-3	200.00	250.00	125.00	225.00

DB12
TALLY HO! BUNNYKINS™
First Variation

Designer:	Based on a design by Walter Hayward
Modeller:	Albert Hallam
Height:	3 ¾", 9.5 cm
Colour:	Burgundy, yellow, blue, white and green
Issued:	1973 - 1988
Varieties:	DB78; also called William Bunnykins, DB69

Back Stamp	Price			
	U.S. $	Can. $	U.K. £	Aust. $
BK-1	150.00	200.00	80.00	200.00
BK-2	150.00	200.00	80.00	200.00
BK-3	200.00	225.00	125.00	225.00

DB13
THE ARTIST BUNNYKINS™

Designer:	Based on a design by Walter Hayward
Modeller:	Alan Maslankowski
Height:	3 ¾", 9.5 cm
Colour:	Burgundy, yellow and blue
Issued:	1975 - 1982

Back Stamp	Price			
	U.S. $	Can. $	U.K. £	Aust. $
BK-1	500.00	600.00	275.00	600.00
BK-2	500.00	600.00	275.00	600.00

DB14
GRANDPA'S STORY BUNNYKINS™

Designer:	Based on a design by Walter Hayward
Modeller:	Alan Maslankowski
Height:	4", 10.1 cm
Colour:	Burgundy, grey, yellow, blue and green
Issued:	1975 - 1983

Back Stamp	Price			
	U.S. $	Can. $	U.K. £	Aust. $
BK-1	550.00	600.00	300.00	575.00
BK-2	550.00	600.00	300.00	575.00

DB15
SLEEPYTIME BUNNYKINS™

Designer:	Based on a design by Walter Hayward
Modeller:	Alan Maslankowski
Height:	1 ¾", 4.7 cm
Colour:	Brown, white, yellow, blue and red
Issued:	1975 - 1993

Back Stamp	Price			
	U.S. $	Can. $	U.K. £	Aust. $
BK-1	95.00	110.00	40.00	75.00
BK-2	95.00	110.00	40.00	75.00
BK-3	125.00	150.00	75.00	100.00

DB16
MR. BUNNYBEAT STRUMMING™

Designer:	Harry Sales
Modeller:	David Lyttleton
Height:	4 ½", 11.4 cm
Colour:	Pink and yellow coat, blue and white striped trousers, white with blue polka-dot neck bow
Issued:	1982 - 1988
Varieties:	Also called Rock and Roll Bunnykins, DB124

Back Stamp	Price			
	U.S. $	Can. $	U.K. £	Aust. $
BK-2	250.00	325.00	150.00	275.00
BK-3	300.00	350.00	200.00	300.00

DB17
SANTA BUNNYKINS HAPPY CHRISTMAS™

Designer:	Harry Sales
Modeller:	David Lyttleton
Height:	4 ½", 11.4 cm
Colour:	Red, white and brown
Issued:	1981 - 1996

Back Stamp	Price			
	U.S. $	Can. $	U.K. £	Aust. $
BK-2	50.00	65.00	35.00	60.00
BK-3	100.00	125.00	65.00	125.00

DB18
MR BUNNYKINS AT THE EASTER PARADE™
First Variation

Designer:	Harry Sales
Modeller:	David Lyttleton
Height:	5", 12.7 cm
Colour:	Red, yellow and brown
Issued:	1982 - 1993
Varieties:	DB51

Back Stamp	Price			
	U.S. $	Can. $	U.K. £	Aust. $
BK-2	125.00	150.00	70.00	125.00
BK-3	135.00	150.00	95.00	135.00

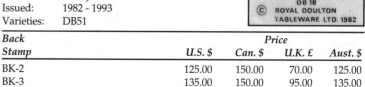

DB19
MRS BUNNYKINS
AT THE EASTER PARADE™
First Variation

Designer:	Harry Sales
Modeller:	David Lyttleton
Height:	4 ½", 11.4 cm
Colour:	Pale blue and maroon
Issued:	1982 - 1996
Varieties:	DB52

Back	Price			
Stamp	U.S. $	Can. $	U.K. £	Aust. $
BK-2	100.00	135.00	35.00	100.00
BK-3	135.00	175.00	75.00	135.00

DB20
ASTRO BUNNYKINS ROCKET MAN™

Designer:	Harry Sales
Modeller:	David Lyttleton
Height:	4 ¼", 10.8 cm
Colour:	White, red, blue and yellow
Issued:	1983 - 1988

Back	Price			
Stamp	U.S. $	Can. $	U.K. £	Aust. $
BK-2	200.00	250.00	100.00	175.00
BK-3	225.00	250.00	125.00	200.00

DB21
HAPPY BIRTHDAY BUNNYKINS™

Designer:	Harry Sales
Modeller:	Graham Tongue
Height:	3 ¾", 9.5 cm
Colour:	Red and blue
Issued:	1983 - 1997

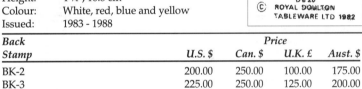

Back	Price			
Stamp	U.S. $	Can. $	U.K. £	Aust. $
BK-2	50.00	70.00	25.00	75.00
BK-3	95.00	125.00	75.00	125.00

DB22
JOGGING BUNNYKINS™

Designer:	Harry Sales
Modeller:	David Lyttleton
Height:	2 ½", 6.4 cm
Colour:	Yellow, blue and white
Issued:	1983 - 1989

Back	Price			
Stamp	U.S. $	Can. $	U.K. £	Aust. $
BK-2	150.00	175.00	80.00	165.00
BK-3	175.00	200.00	100.00	200.00

DB23
SOUSAPHONE BUNNYKINS™
First Variation

Designer:	Harry Sales
Modeller:	David Lyttleton
Height:	3 ½", 8.9 cm
Colour:	Red, blue and yellow
Issued:	1984 - 1990
Varieties:	DB86, DB105
Series:	Bunnykins Oompah Band

Back	Price			
Stamp	U.S. $	Can. $	U.K. £	Aust. $
BK-3	175.00	250.00	125.00	225.00
BK-4	175.00	250.00	125.00	225.00
Set DB23 - 27 (5 pcs.)	1,100.00	1,300.00	650.00	1,200.00

DB24
TRUMPETER BUNNYKINS™
First Variation

Designer:	Harry Sales
Modeller:	David Lyttleton
Height:	3 ½", 8.9 cm
Colour:	Red, blue and yellow
Issued:	1984 - 1990
Varieties:	DB87, DB106
Series:	Bunnykins Oompah Band

Back	Price			
Stamp	U.S. $	Can. $	U.K. £	Aust. $
BK-3	175.00	250.00	125.00	225.00
BK-4	175.00	250.00	125.00	225.00

DB25
CYMBALS BUNNYKINS™
First Variation

Designer:	Harry Sales
Modeller:	David Lyttleton
Height:	3 ½", 8.9 cm
Colour:	Red, blue and yellow
Issued:	1984 - 1990
Varieties:	DB88, DB107
Series:	Bunnykins Oompah Band

Back Stamp	Price			
	U.S. $	Can. $	U.K. £	Aust. $
BK-3	175.00	250.00	125.00	225.00
BK-4	175.00	250.00	125.00	250.00

DB26A
DRUMMER BUNNYKINS™
First Variation, 50th Anniversary Edition

Designer:	Harry Sales
Modeller:	David Lyttleton
Height:	3 ½", 8.9 cm
Colour:	Blue, yellow, red and cream
Issued:	1984 - 1984
Series:	Bunnykins Oompah Band

Back Stamp	Price			
	U.S. $	Can. $	U.K. £	Aust. $
BK-3	175.00	300.00	175.00	275.00

DB26B
DRUMMER BUNNYKINS™
Second Variation, Bunnykins Oompah Band Edition

Designer:	Harry Sales
Modeller:	David Lyttleton
Height:	3 ¾", 9.5 cm
Colour:	Blue, yellow, red and cream
Issued:	1984 - 1990
Varieties:	DB89, DB108
Series:	Bunnykins Oompah Band

Back Stamp	Price			
	U.S. $	Can. $	U.K £	Aust. $
BK-4	150.00	250.00	125.00	225.00

DB27
DRUM-MAJOR BUNNYKINS™
First Variation

Designer:	Harry Sales		
Modeller:	David Lyttleton		
Height:	3 ½", 8.9 cm		
Colour:	Red, blue and yellow		
Issued:	1984 - 1990		
Varieties:	DB90, DB109		
Series:	Bunnykins Oompah Band		

Back	Price			
Stamp	U.S. $	Can. $	U.K. £	Aust. $
BK-3	175.00	250.00	125.00	225.00
BK-4	175.00	250.00	125.00	225.00

DB28A
OLYMPIC BUNNYKINS™
First Variation

Designer:	Harry Sales
Modeller:	David Lyttleton
Height:	3 ¾", 9.4 cm
Colour:	White and blue
Issued:	1984 - 1988

Back	Price			
Stamp	U.S. $	Can. $	U.K. £	Aust. $
BK-2	275.00	325.00	150.00	375.00
BK-3	250.00	300.00	125.00	350.00
BK-4	225.00	275.00	100.00	300.00

DB28B
OLYMPIC BUNNYKINS™
Second Variation

Designer:	Harry Sales
Modeller:	David Lyttleton
Height:	3 ½", 8.9 cm
Colour:	Gold and green
Issued:	1984 - 1984

Back	Price			
Stamp	U.S. $	Can. $	U.K. £	Aust. $
BK-Special	800.00	1,000.00	450.00	1,000.00

DB29A
TOUCHDOWN BUNNYKINS™
First Variation

Designer:	Harry Sales
Modeller:	David Lyttleton
Height:	3 ¼", 8.3 cm
Colour:	Blue and white
Issued:	1985 - 1988
Varieties:	DB29B, 96, 97, 98, 99, 100

Back Stamp	Price			
	U.S. $	Can. $	U.K. £	Aust. $
BK-3	175.00	200.00	65.00	225.00
BK-4	175.00	200.00	65.00	225.00
BK-5	175.00	200.00	65.00	225.00

DB29B
TOUCHDOWN BUNNYKINS™
Second Variation (Boston College)

Designer:	Harry Sales
Modeller:	David Lyttleton
Height:	3 ¼", 8.3 cm
Colour:	Maroon and gold
Issued:	1985 in a limited edition of 50
Varieties:	DB29B, 96, 97, 98, 99, 100

Back Stamp	Price			
	U.S. $	Can. $	U.K. £	Aust. $
BK-4	2,500.00	3,000.00	1,250.00	3,000.00

DB30
KNOCKOUT BUNNYKINS™

Designer:	Harry Sales
Modeller:	David Lyttleton
Height:	4", 10.1 cm
Colour:	Yellow, green and white
Issued:	1984 - 1988

Back Stamp	Price			
	U.S. $	Can. $	U.K. £	Aust. $
BK-3	400.00	450.00	185.00	475.00
BK-4	350.00	425.00	175.00	450.00
BK-5	325.00	375.00	150.00	400.00

DB31
DOWNHILL BUNNYKINS™

Designer:	Harry Sales
Modeller:	Graham Tongue
Height:	2 ½", 6.4 cm
Colour:	Yellow, green, maroon and grey
Issued:	1985 - 1988

Back Stamp	Price			
	U.S. $	Can. $	U.K. £	Aust. $
BK-3	300.00	375.00	150.00	350.00
BK-4	275.00	325.00	125.00	300.00
BK-5	275.00	325.00	125.00	300.00

DB32
BOGEY BUNNYKINS™

Designer:	Harry Sales
Modeller:	David Lyttleton
Height:	4", 10.1 cm
Colour:	Green, brown and yellow
Issued:	1984 - 1992

Back Stamp	Price			
	U.S. $	Can. $	U.K. £	Aust. $
BK-3	250.00	250.00	100.00	250.00
BK-4	200.00	200.00	85.00	225.00
BK-5	200.00	200.00	80.00	200.00

DB33A
TALLY HO!™
Music Box
First Variation, "Tally-Ho!" Figurine

Designer:	Walter Hayward
Modeller:	Albert Hallam
Height:	7", 17.8 cm
Colour:	Red coat, yellow jumper
Issued:	1984 - 1993
Tune:	Rock A Bye Baby

Back Stamp	Price			
	U.S. $	Can. $	U.K. £	Aust. $
BK-3	300.00	250.00	125.00	300.00
BK-4	300.00	250.00	125.00	300.00
BK-5	300.00	250.00	125.00	300.00

DB33B
TALLY HO!™
Music Box
Second Variation, "William Bunnykins" Figurine

Designer:	Walter Hayward
Modeller:	Albert Hallam
Height:	7", 17.8 cm
Colour:	Brown trousers, red coat and maroon tie
Issued:	1988 - 1991
Tune:	Rock A Bye Baby

Back	Price			
Stamp	U.S. $	Can. $	U.K. £	Aust. $
BK-4	300.00	250.00	100.00	300.00
BK-5	300.00	250.00	100.00	300.00

DB34
SANTA BUNNYKINS™
Music Box

Designer:	Harry Sales
Modeller:	David Lyttleton
Height:	7 ¼", 18.4 cm
Colour:	Red, white and brown
Issued:	1984 - 1991
Tune:	White Christmas

Back	Price			
Stamp	U.S. $	Can. $	U.K. £	Aust. $
BK-3	300.00	275.00	110.00	325.00
BK-4	275.00	250.00	100.00	300.00
BK-5	275.00	250.00	100.00	300.00

DB35
ASTRO BUNNYKINS ROCKET MAN™
Music Box

Designer:	Harry Sales
Modeller:	David Lyttleton
Height:	7", 17.8 cm
Colour:	White, red and blue
Issued:	1984 - 1989
Tune:	Fly Me To The Moon

Back	Price			
Stamp	U.S. $	Can. $	U.K. £	Aust. $
BK-3	425.00	450.00	125.00	425.00
BK-4	425.00	450.00	125.00	425.00
BK-5	425.00	450.00	125.00	425.00

DB36
HAPPY BIRTHDAY BUNNYKINS™
Music Box

Designer:	Harry Sales
Modeller:	Graham Tongue
Height:	7", 17.8 cm
Colour:	Red and white
Issued:	1984 - 1993
Tune:	Happy Birthday To You

Back	Price			
Stamp	U.S. $	Can. $	U.K. £	Aust. $
BK-3	250.00	275.00	100.00	300.00
BK-4	250.00	275.00	100.00	300.00
BK-5	250.00	275.00	100.00	300.00

DB37
JOGGING BUNNYKINS™
Music Box

Designer:	Harry Sales
Modeller:	David Lyttleton
Height:	5 ½", 14.0 cm
Colour:	Yellow and blue
Issued:	1987 - 1989
Tune:	King of the Road

Back	Price			
Stamp	U.S. $	Can. $	U.K. £	Aust. $
BK-5	400.00	450.00	150.00	450.00

DB38
MR. BUNNYBEAT STRUMMING™
Music Box

Designer:	Harry Sales
Modeller:	David Lyttleton
Height:	7 ½", 19.1 cm
Colour:	Pink, white and yellow
Issued:	1987 - 1989
Tune:	Hey Jude

Back	Price			
Stamp	U.S. $	Can. $	U.K. £	Aust. $
BK-5	450.00	475.00	200.00	500.00

DB39
MRS. BUNNYKINS
AT THE EASTER PARADE™
Music Box

Designer:	Harry Sales
Modeller:	David Lyttleton
Height:	7", 17.8 cm
Colour:	Blue, yellow and maroon
Issued:	1987 - 1991
Tune:	Easter Parade

Back Stamp	Price			
	U.S. $	Can. $	U.K. £	Aust. $
BK-5	400.00	450.00	100.00	475.00

DB40
AEROBIC BUNNYKINS™

Designer:	Harry Sales
Modeller:	David Lyttleton
Height:	2 ¾", 7.0 cm
Colour:	Yellow and pale blue
Issued:	1985 - 1988

Back Stamp	Price			
	U.S. $	Can. $	U.K. £	Aust. $
BK-4	275.00	325.00	125.00	300.00
BK-5	275.00	325.00	125.00	300.00

DB41
FREEFALL BUNNYKINS™

Designer:	Harry Sales
Modeller:	David Lyttleton
Height:	2 ¼", 5.7 cm
Colour:	Grey, yellow and white
Issued:	1986 - 1989

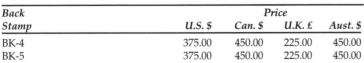

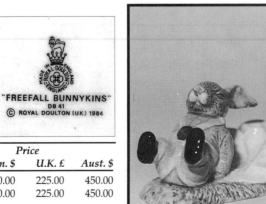

Back Stamp	Price			
	U.S. $	Can. $	U.K. £	Aust. $
BK-4	375.00	450.00	225.00	450.00
BK-5	375.00	450.00	225.00	450.00

DB42
ACE BUNNYKINS™

Designer:	Harry Sales
Modeller:	David Lyttleton
Height:	3 ¾", 9.5 cm
Colour:	White and blue
Issued:	1986 - 1989

Back Stamp	Price			
	U.S. $	Can. $	U.K. £	Aust. $
BK-4	275.00	325.00	165.00	300.00
BK-5	275.00	325.00	165.00	300.00

DB43
HOME RUN BUNNYKINS™
(1 on Back of Jersey)

Designer:	Harry Sales
Modeller:	David Lyttleton
Height:	4", 10.1 cm
Colour:	Blue, yellow and white
Issued:	1986 - 1993

Back Stamp	Price			
	U.S. $	Can. $	U.K. £	Aust. $
BK-4	125.00	150.00	65.00	150.00
BK-5	125.00	150.00	65.00	150.00

DB44: Assigned to Ballet Bunnykins but not issued.

DB45
KING JOHN™
First Variation

Designer:	Harry Sales
Modeller:	David Lyttleton
Height:	4", 10.1 cm
Colour:	Red, yellow and blue
Issued:	1986 - 1990
Varieties:	DB91
Series:	Bunnykins Royal Family

Back Stamp	Price			
	U.S. $	Can. $	U.K. £	Aust. $
BK-4	150.00	200.00	95.00	225.00
BK-5	150.00	200.00	95.00	225.00
Set DB45 - 49 (5 pcs.)	650.00	1,000.00	500.00	1,100.00

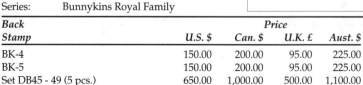

DB46
QUEEN SOPHIE™
First Variation

Designer:	Harry Sales
Modeller:	David Lyttleton
Height:	4 ½", 11.4 cm
Colour:	Blue and red
Issued:	1986 - 1990
Varieties:	DB92
Series:	Bunnykins Royal Family

Back Stamp	Price			
	U.S. $	Can. $	U.K. £	Aust. $
BK-4	175.00	200.00	95.00	225.00
BK-5	150.00	200.00	95.00	225.00

DB47
PRINCESS BEATRICE™
First Variation

Designer:	Harry Sales
Modeller:	David Lyttleton
Height:	3 ½", 8.9 cm
Colour:	Pale green
Issued:	1986 - 1990
Varieties:	DB93
Series:	Bunnykins Royal Family

Back Stamp	Price			
	U.S. $	Can. $	U.K. £	Aust. $
BK-4	150.00	200.00	95.00	225.00
BK-5	150.00	200.00	95.00	225.00

DB48
PRINCE FREDERICK™
First Variation

Designer:	Harry Sales
Modeller:	David Lyttleton
Height:	3 ½", 8.9 cm
Colour:	Green, white and red
Issued:	1986 - 1990
Varieties:	DB94
Series:	Bunnykins Royal Family

Back Stamp	Price			
	U.S. $	Can. $	U.K. £	Aust. $
BK-4	150.00	200.00	95.00	225.00
BK-5	150.00	200.00	95.00	225.00

DB49
HARRY THE HERALD™
First Variation

Designer:	Harry Sales
Modeller:	David Lyttleton
Height:	3 ½", 8.9 cm
Colour:	Maroon, white and tan
Issued:	1986 - 1990
Varieties:	DB95, DB115
Series:	Bunnykins Royal Family

Back Stamp	Price			
	U.S. $	Can. $	U.K. £	Aust. $
BK-4	200.00	250.00	100.00	235.00
BK-5	200.00	250.00	100.00	235.00

DB50
UNCLE SAM BUNNYKINS™
First Variation

Designer:	Harry Sales
Modeller:	David Lyttleton
Height:	4 ½", 11 cm
Colour:	Blue, red and white
Issued:	1986 to the present
Varieties:	DB175

Back Stamp	Price			
	U.S. $	Can. $	U.K. £	Aust. $
BK-4	45.00	65.00	35.00	75.00
BK-5	45.00	65.00	35.00	75.00

DB51
MR. BUNNYKINS AT THE EASTER PARADE™
Second Variation

Designer:	Harry Sales
Modeller:	David Lyttleton
Height:	5", 12.7 cm
Colour:	Blue tie and hat band, maroon coat, light grey trousers, pink ribbon on package
Issued:	1986 - 1986
Varieties:	DB18

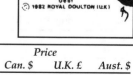

Back Stamp	Price			
	U.S. $	Can. $	U.K. £	Aust. $
BK-4	1,350.00	2,000.00	800.00	1,900.00

Colonial House of Collectibles
& Santa's North Pole World

ROYAL DOULTON IS OUR SPECIALTY!

We Buy ♦ We Sell ♦ We Appraise

Colonial House Features the Largest Selection of Current and Discontinued Items in the Following Lines:

- ♦ OLD & NEW ROYAL DOULTON FIGURES & CHARACTER JUGS
- ♦ HUMMELS
- ♦ DAVID WINTER COTTAGES
- ♦ DEPT. 56 COTTAGES AND SNOWBABIES

- ♦ ROYAL WORCESTER
- ♦ WEE FOREST FOLK
- ♦ WALT DISNEY CLASSICS
- ♦ SWAROVSKI CRYSTAL
- ♦ LLADRÓ
- ♦ LILLIPUT LANE

Send for our latest product catalogue!

Colonial House of Collectibles

We Carry Current and Discontinued Beanie Babies!

WE DO MAIL ORDER

Monday to Saturday
10 a.m. to 5 p.m.
or by appointment

182 Front Street,
Berea, OH 44017
Tel.: (440) 826-4169 or
(800) 344-9299
Fax: (440) 826-0839
E-mail: yworrey@aol.com

DB52
MRS. BUNNYKINS AT THE
EASTER PARADE™
Second Variation

Designer:	Harry Sales
Modeller:	David Lyttleton
Height:	4 ½", 11.4 cm
Colour:	Maroon dress, white collar, blue bow on bonnet, multi-coloured bows on packages
Issued:	1986 - 1986
Varieties:	DB19

Back Stamp	Price			
	U.S. $	Can. $	U.K. £	Aust. $
BK-4	1,200.00	1,500.00	750.00	1,500.00

DB53
CAROL SINGER™
Music Box

Designer:	Harry Sales
Modeller:	David Lyttleton
Height:	7", 17.8 cm
Colour:	Red, yellow and green
Issued:	1986 - 1989
Tune:	Silent Night

Back Stamp	Price			
	U.S. $	Can. $	U.K. £	Aust. $
BK-4	450.00	500.00	175.00	475.00
BK-5	450.00	500.00	175.00	475.00

DB54
COLLECTOR BUNNYKINS™

Designer:	Harry Sales
Modeller:	David Lyttleton
Height:	4 ¼", 10.8 cm
Colour:	Brown, blue and grey
Issued:	1987 - 1987
Series:	R.D.I.C.C.

COLLECTOR BUNNYKINS
DB54
EXCLUSIVELY FOR
COLLECTORS CLUB
© 1986 ROYAL DOULTON
MODELLED BY
D. Lyttleton

Back Stamp	Price			
	U.S. $	Can. $	U.K. £	Aust. $
BK-Special	900.00	1,200.00	475.00	1,200.00

DB55
BEDTIME BUNNYKINS™
First Variation

Designer:	Graham Tongue
Modeller:	David Lyttleton
Height:	3 ¼", 8.3 cm
Colour:	Blue and white striped pyjamas, brown teddy bear
Issued:	1987 - 1998
Varieties:	DB63, 79, 103

Back Stamp	Price			
	U.S. $	Can. $	U.K. £	Aust. $
BK-5	40.00	65.00	18.00	65.00

DB56
BE PREPARED BUNNYKINS™

Designer:	Graham Tongue
Modeller:	David Lyttleton
Height:	4", 10.1 cm
Colour:	Dark green and grey
Issued:	1987 - 1996

Back Stamp	Price			
	U.S. $	Can. $	U.K. £	Aust. $
BK-5	75.00	95.00	35.00	75.00

DB57
SCHOOL DAYS BUNNYKINS™

Designer:	Graham Tongue
Modeller:	David Lyttleton
Height:	3 ½", 8.9 cm
Colour:	Dark green, white and yellow
Issued:	1987 - 1994

Back Stamp	Price			
	U.S. $	Can. $	U.K. £	Aust. $
BK-5	95.00	125.00	35.00	115.00

DB58
AUSTRALIAN BUNNYKINS™

Designer:	Harry Sales
Modeller:	Warren Platt
Height:	4", 10.1 cm
Colour:	Gold and green
Issued:	1988 - 1988

Back Stamp	Price			
	U.S. $	Can. $	U.K. £	Aust. $
BK-Special	750.00	900.00	450.00	600.00

DB59
STORYTIME BUNNYKINS™
Second Variation

Designer:	Walter Hayward
Modeller:	Albert Hallam
Height:	3", 7.6 cm
Colour:	Left - green polka dots on white dress, yellow shoes Right - yellow dress, green shoes
Issued:	1987 - 1987
Varieties:	DB9; also called Partners in Collecting, DB151

Back Stamp	Price			
	U.S. $	Can. $	U.K. £	Aust. $
BK-5	600.00	700.00	375.00	700.00

Note: Produced for distribution at special events in the U.S.A.

DB60
SCHOOLMASTER BUNNYKINS™

Designer:	Graham Tongue
Modeller:	Warren Platt
Height:	4", 10.1 cm
Colour:	Black, green and white
Issued:	1987 - 1996

Back Stamp	Price			
	U.S. $	Can. $	U.K. £	Aust. $
BK-5	75.00	85.00	35.00	90.00

DB61
BROWNIE BUNNYKINS™

Designer: Graham Tongue
Modeller: Warren Platt
Height: 4", 10.1 cm
Colour: Brown uniform, yellow neck-tie
Issued: 1987 - 1993

Back Stamp	Price			
	U.S. $	Can. $	U.K. £	Aust. $
BK-5	95.00	115.00	75.00	115.00

DB62
SANTA BUNNYKINS HAPPY CHRISTMAS™
Christmas Tree Ornament

Designer: Harry Sales
Modeller: David Lyttleton
Height: 3 ¾", 9.5 cm
Colour: Red and white
Issued: 1987 in a limited edition

Back Stamp	Price			
	U.S. $	Can. $	U.K. £	Aust. $
BK-5	1,750.00	2,500.00	850.00	2,500.00

DB63
BEDTIME BUNNYKINS™
Second Variation

Designer: Graham Tongue
Modeller: David Lyttleton
Height: 3 ¼", 8.3 cm
Colour: Red and white striped
             pyjamas, white teddy bear
Issued: 1987 - 1987
Varieties: DB55, 79, 103

Back Stamp	Price			
	U.S. $	Can. $	U.K. £	Aust. $
BK-Special	525.00	600.00	175.00	600.00

DB64
POLICEMAN BUNNYKINS™

Designer:	Graham Tongue
Modeller:	Martyn Alcock
Height:	4 ¼", 10.8 cm
Colour:	Dark blue uniform
Issued:	1988 to the present

Back Stamp	Price			
	U.S. $	Can. $	U.K. £	Aust. $
BK-5	45.00	60.00	17.00	70.00

DB65
LOLLIPOPMAN BUNNYKINS™

Designer:	Graham Tongue
Modeller:	Martyn Alcock
Height:	3 ¾", 9.5 cm
Colour:	White and yellow
Issued:	1988 - 1991

Back Stamp	Price			
	U.S. $	Can. $	U.K. £	Aust. $
BK-5	175.00	200.00	125.00	225.00

DB66
SCHOOLBOY BUNNYKINS™

Designer:	Graham Tongue
Modeller:	Martyn Alcock
Height:	4", 10.1 cm
Colour:	Blue, white and grey
Issued:	1988 - 1991

Back Stamp	Price			
	U.S. $	Can. $	U.K. £	Aust. $
BK-5	200.00	250.00	115.00	275.00

DB67
FAMILY PHOTOGRAPH BUNNYKINS™
Second Variation

Designer:	Based on a design by Walter Hayward
Modeller:	Albert Hallam
Height:	4 ½", 11.4 cm
Colour:	Pink, black and white
Issued:	1988 - 1988
Varieties:	DB1; also called Father, Mother and Victoria Bunnykins, DB68

Back Stamp	Price			
	U.S. $	Can. $	U.K. £	Aust. $
BK-Special	250.00	325.00	175.00	300.00

DB68
FATHER, MOTHER AND VICTORIA BUNNYKINS™

Designer:	Based on design Family Photograph by Walter Hayward
Modeller:	Martyn Alcock
Height:	4 ½", 11.4 cm
Colour:	Blue, grey, maroon and yellow
Issued:	1988 - 1996
Varieties:	Also called Family Photograph, DB1, 67

Back Stamp	Price			
	U.S. $	Can. $	U.K. £	Aust. $
BK-5	65.00	95.00	35.00	90.00

DB69
WILLIAM BUNNYKINS™

Designer:	Based on a design by Walter Hayward
Modeller:	Martyn Alcock
Height:	4", 10.1 cm
Colour:	Red and white
Issued:	1988 - 1993
Varieties:	Also called Tally Ho! Bunnykins, DB12, 78

Back Stamp	Price			
	U.S. $	Can. $	U.K. £	Aust. $
BK-5	100.00	100.00	45.00	100.00

DB70
SUSAN BUNNYKINS™

Designer:	Based on a design by Walter Hayward
Modeller:	Martyn Alcock
Height:	3 ¼", 8.3 cm
Colour:	White, blue and yellow
Issued:	1988 - 1993

Back Stamp	Price			
	U.S. $	Can. $	U.K. £	Aust. $
BK-5	100.00	110.00	55.00	100.00

DB71
POLLY BUNNYKINS™

Designer:	Graham Tongue
Modeller:	Martyn Alcock
Height:	3 ½", 8.7 cm
Colour:	Pink
Issued:	1988 - 1993

Back Stamp	Price			
	U.S. $	Can. $	U.K. £	Aust. $
BK-5	100.00	110.00	55.00	100.00

DB72
TOM BUNNYKINS™

Designer:	Graham Tongue
Modeller:	Martyn Alcock
Height:	3", 7.6 cm
Colour:	Browns, white and blue
Issued:	1988 - 1993

Back Stamp	Price			
	U.S. $	Can. $	U.K. £	Aust. $
BK-5	100.00	110.00	45.00	100.00

DB73
HARRY BUNNYKINS™

Designer:	Graham Tongue
Modeller:	Martyn Alcock
Height:	3", 7.9 cm
Colour:	Blue, brown, white and yellow
Issued:	1988 - 1993

Back	Price			
Stamp	U.S. $	Can. $	U.K. £	Aust. $
BK-5	100.00	110.00	55.00	100.00

DB74A
NURSE BUNNYKINS™
First Variation (Red Cross)

Designer:	Graham Tongue
Modeller:	Martyn Alcock
Height:	4 ¼", 10.8 cm
Colour:	Dark and light blue and white, red cross
Issued:	1989 - 1994
Varieties:	DB74B

Back	Price			
Stamp	U.S. $	Can. $	U.K. £	Aust. $
BK-5	350.00	400.00	160.00	400.00

DB74B
NURSE BUNNYKINS™
Second Variation (Green Cross)

Designer:	Graham Tongue
Modeller:	Martyn Alcock
Height:	4 ¼", 10.8 cm
Colour:	Dark and light blue and white, green cross
Issued:	1994 to the present
Varieties:	DB74A

Back	Price			
Stamp	U.S. $	Can. $	U.K. £	Aust. $
BK-5	45.00	65.00	17.00	80.00

DB75
FIREMAN BUNNYKINS™
First Variation

Designer:	Graham Tongue
Modeller:	Martyn Alcock
Height:	4 ¼", 10.8 cm
Colour:	Dark blue and yellow
Issued:	1989 to the present
Varieties:	DB183

Back Stamp	Price			
	U.S. $	*Can. $*	*U.K. £*	*Aust. $*
BK-5	45.00	70.00	18.00	80.00

DB76
POSTMAN BUNNYKINS™

Designer:	Graham Tongue
Modeller:	Martyn Alcock
Height:	4 ½", 11.4 cm
Colour:	Dark blue and red
Issued:	1989 - 1993

Back Stamp	Price			
	U.S. $	*Can. $*	*U.K. £*	*Aust. $*
BK-5	125.00	150.00	85.00	125.00

DB77
PAPERBOY BUNNYKINS™

Designer:	Graham Tongue
Modeller:	Martyn Alcock
Height:	4", 10.4 cm
Colour:	Green, yellow, red and white
Issued:	1989 - 1993

Back Stamp	Price			
	U.S. $	*Can. $*	*U.K. £*	*Aust. $*
BK-5	125.00	150.00	70.00	125.00

DB78
TALLY HO! BUNNYKINS™
Second Variation

Designer:	Based on a design
	by Walter Hayward
Modeller:	Albert Hallam
Height:	4", 10.1 cm
Colour:	Light blue coat and white rocking
	horse, yellow sweater
Issued:	1988 - 1988
Varieties:	DB12; also called William
	Bunnykins, DB69

Back Stamp	Price			
	U.S. $	Can. $	U.K. £	Aust. $
BK-Special	275.00	325.00	125.00	300.00

DB79
BEDTIME BUNNYKINS™
Third Variation

Designer:	Graham Tongue
Modeller:	David Lyttleton
Height:	3 ¼", 8.3 cm
Colour:	Light blue and white
Issued:	1988 - 1988
Varieties:	DB55, 63, 103

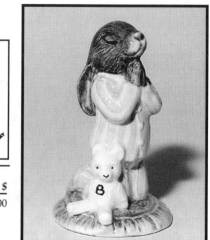

Back Stamp	Price			
	U.S. $	Can. $	U.K. £	Aust. $
BK-Special	1,200.00	1,500.00	600.00	1,500.00

DB80
DOLLIE BUNNYKINS PLAYTIME™
Second Variation

Designer:	Based on a design
	by Walter Hayward
Modeller:	Albert Hallam
Height:	4", 10.1 cm
Colour:	White and yellow
Issued:	1988 in a limited edition of 250
Varieties:	DB8

Back Stamp	Company	Price			
		U.S. $	Can. $	U.K. £	Aust. $
BK-Special	Higbee	295.00	350.00	85.00	375.00
BK-Special	Holmes	295.00	350.00	85.00	375.00
BK-Special	Hornes	295.00	350.00	85.00	375.00
BK-Special	Strawbridge	295.00	350.00	85.00	375.00

DB81
BILLIE AND BUNTIE BUNNYKINS
SLEIGH RIDE™
Second Variation

Designer:	Based on a design by Walter Hayward
Modeller:	Albert Hallam
Height:	3 ½", 8.9 cm
Colour:	Green, yellow and red
Issued:	1989 - 1989
Varieties:	DB4
Series:	Special Events 1989

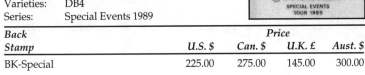

Back Stamp	Price			
	U.S. $	*Can. $*	*U.K. £*	*Aust. $*
BK-Special	225.00	275.00	145.00	300.00

DB82
ICE CREAM BUNNYKINS™

Designer:	Graham Tongue
Modeller:	Warren Platt
Height:	4 ½", 11.4 cm
Colour:	White, blue and green
Issued:	1990 - 1993

Back Stamp	Price			
	U.S. $	*Can. $*	*U.K. £*	*Aust. $*
BK-5	225.00	250.00	85.00	275.00

DB83
SUSAN BUNNYKINS AS
QUEEN OF THE MAY™

Designer:	Graham Tongue
Modeller:	Martyn Alcock
Height:	4", 10.2 cm
Colour:	White polka-dot dress, blue and brown chair
Issued:	1990 - 1991

Back Stamp	Price			
	U.S. $	*Can. $*	*U.K. £*	*Aust. $*
BK-5	225.00	250.00	85.00	275.00

DB84
FISHERMAN BUNNYKINS™
Style One

Designer:	Graham Tongue
Modeller:	Warren Platt
Height:	4 ¼", 10.8 cm
Colour:	Maroon, yellow and grey
Issued:	1990 - 1993

Back	Price			
Stamp	U.S. $	Can. $	U.K. £	Aust. $
BK-5	175.00	225.00	85.00	200.00

DB85
COOK BUNNYKINS™

Designer:	Graham Tongue
Modeller:	Warren Platt
Height:	4 ¼", 10.8 cm
Colour:	White and green
Issued:	1990 - 1994

Back	Price			
Stamp	U.S. $	Can. $	U.K. £	Aust. $
BK-5	85.00	115.00	60.00	125.00

DB86
SOUSAPHONE BUNNYKINS™
From the Oompah Band - Second Variation

Designer:	Harry Sales
Modeller:	David Lyttleton
Height:	3 ½", 8.9 cm
Colour:	Blue uniform and yellow sousaphone
Issued:	1990 in a limited edition of 250
Varieties:	DB23, 105
Series:	Royal Doulton Collectors Band

Back	Price			
Stamp	U.S. $	Can. $	U.K. £	Aust. $
BK-5	600.00	700.00	300.00	650.00
DB86 to 90 (5 pcs.)	3,000.00	3,500.00	1,500.00	3,250.00

DB87
TRUMPETER BUNNYKINS™
From the Oompah Band - Second Variation

Designer:	Harry Sales
Modeller:	David Lyttleton
Height:	3 ¾", 9.5 cm
Colour:	Blue uniform and yellow trumpet
Issued:	1990 in a limited edition of 250
Varieties:	DB24, 106
Series:	Royal Doulton Collectors Band

Back Stamp	Price			
	U.S. $	Can. $	U.K. £	Aust. $
BK-5	600.00	700.00	300.00	650.00

DB88
CYMBALS BUNNYKINS™
From the Oompah Band - Second Variation

Designer:	Harry Sales
Modeller:	David Lyttleton
Height:	3 ½", 8.9 cm
Colour:	Blue uniform and yellow cymbals
Issued:	1990 in a limited edition of 250
Varieties:	DB25, 107
Series:	Royal Doulton Collectors Band

Back Stamp	Price			
	U.S. $	Can. $	U.K. £	Aust. $
BK-5	600.00	700.00	300.00	650.00

DB89
DRUMMER BUNNYKINS™
Third Variation

Designer:	Harry Sales
Modeller:	David Lyttleton
Height:	3 ¾", 9.5 cm
Colour:	Blue trousers and sleeves, yellow vest, cream and red drum
Issued:	1990 in a limited edition of 250
Varieties:	DB26, 26A, 26B, 108
Series:	Royal Doulton Collectors Band

Back Stamp	Price			
	U.S. $	Can. $	U.K. £	Aust. $
BK-Special	600.00	700.00	300.00	650.00

DB90
DRUM-MAJOR BUNNYKINS™
Second Variation

Designer:	Harry Sales
Modeller:	David Lyttleton
Height:	3 ¾", 9.5 cm
Colour:	Blue and yellow uniform
Issued:	1990 in a limited edition of 250
Varieties:	DB27, 109
Series:	Royal Doulton Collectors Band

Back Stamp	Price			
	U.S. $	*Can. $*	*U.K. £*	*Aust. $*
BK-5	600.00	700.00	300.00	650.00

DB91
KING JOHN™
Second Variation

Designer:	Harry Sales
Modeller:	David Lyttleton
Height:	4", 10.1 cm
Colour:	Purple, yellow and white
Issued:	1990 in a limited edition of 250
Varieties:	DB45
Series:	Bunnykins Royal Family

Back Stamp	Price			
	U.S. $	*Can. $*	*U.K. £*	*Aust. $*
BK-Special	600.00	700.00	300.00	650.00
Set DB91 - 95 (5 pcs.)	3,000.00	3,500.00	1,500.00	3,250.00

DB92
QUEEN SOPHIE™
Second Variation

Designer:	Harry Sales
Modeller:	David Lyttleton
Height:	4 ½", 11.4 cm
Colour:	Pink and purple
Issued:	1990 in a limited edition of 250
Varieties:	DB46
Series:	Bunnykins Royal Family

Back Stamp	Price			
	U.S. $	*Can. $*	*U.K. £*	*Aust. $*
BK-5	600.00	700.00	300.00	650.00

DB93
PRINCESS BEATRICE™
Second Variation

Designer:	Harry Sales
Modeller:	David Lyttleton
Height:	3 ½", 8.9 cm
Colour:	Yellow and gold
Issued:	1990 in a limited edition of 250
Varieties:	DB47
Series:	Bunnykins Royal Family

Back	*Price*			
Stamp	*U.S. $*	*Can. $*	*U.K. £*	*Aust. $*
BK-5	600.00	700.00	300.00	650.00

DB94
PRINCE FREDERICK™
Second Variation

Designer:	Harry Sales
Modeller:	David Lyttleton
Height:	3 ½", 8.9 cm
Colour:	Red, blue and yellow
Issued:	1990 in a limited edition of 250
Varieties:	DB48
Series:	Bunnykins Royal Family

Back	*Price*			
Stamp	*U.S. $*	*Can. $*	*U.K. £*	*Aust. $*
BK-5	600.00	700.00	300.00	650.00

DB95
HARRY THE HERALD™
Second Variation

Designer:	Harry Sales
Modeller:	David Lyttleton
Height:	3 ½", 8.9 cm
Colour:	Blue, red and yellow
Issued:	1990 in a limited edition of 250
Varieties:	DB49, 115
Series:	Bunnykins Royal Family

Back	*Price*			
Stamp	*U.S. $*	*Can. $*	*U.K. £*	*Aust. $*
BK-5	600.00	700.00	300.00	650.00

DB96
TOUCHDOWN BUNNYKINS™
Third Variation (Ohio State University)

Designer:	Harry Sales
Modeller:	David Lyttleton
Height:	3 ¼", 8.3 cm
Colour:	Grey and orange
Issued:	1990 in a limited edition of 200
Varieties:	DB29A, 29B, 97, 98, 99, 100

Back	Price			
Stamp	U.S. $	Can. $	U.K. £	Aust. $
BK-5	900.00	1,250.00	500.00	1,100.00
Set DB96-100 (5 pcs.)	4,500.00	6,250.00	2,500.00	5,500.00

DB97
TOUCHDOWN BUNNYKINS™
Fourth Variation (University of Michigan)

Designer:	Harry Sales
Modeller:	David Lyttleton
Height:	3 ¼", 8.3 cm
Colour:	Yellow and blue
Issued:	1990 in a limited edition of 200
Varieties:	DB29A, 29B, 96, 98, 99, 100

Back	Price			
Stamp	U.S. $	Can. $	U.K. £	Aust. $
BK-5	900.00	1,250.00	500.00	1,100.00

DB98
TOUCHDOWN BUNNYKINS™
Fifth Variation (Cincinnati Bengals)

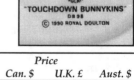

Designer:	Harry Sales
Modeller:	David Lyttleton
Height:	3 ½", 8.3 cm
Colour:	Orange and black
Issued:	1990 in a limited edition of 200
Varieties:	DB29A, 29B, 96, 97, 99, 100

Back	Price			
Stamp	U.S. $	Can. $	U.K. £	Aust. $
BK-5	900.00	1,250.00	500.00	1,100.00

DB99
TOUCHDOWN BUNNYKINS™
Sixth Variation (Notre Dame College)

Designer:	Harry Sales
Modeller:	David Lyttleton
Height:	3 ½", 8.3 cm
Colour:	Green and yellow
Issued:	1990 in a limited edition of 200
Varieties:	DB29A, 29B, 96, 97, 98, 100

Back Stamp	Price			
	U.S. $	Can. $	U.K. £	Aust. $
BK-5	900.00	1,250.00	500.00	1,100.00

DB100
TOUCHDOWN BUNNYKINS™
Seventh Variation (University of Indiana)

Designer:	Harry Sales
Modeller:	David Lyttleton
Height:	3 ½", 8.3 cm
Colour:	White and red
Issued:	1990 in a limited edition of 200
Varieties:	DB29A, 29B, 96, 97, 98, 99

Back Stamp	Price			
	U.S. $	Can. $	U.K. £	Aust. $
BK-5	900.00	1,250.00	500.00	1,100.00

DB101
BRIDE BUNNYKINS™

Designer:	Graham Tongue
Modeller:	Amanda Hughes-Lubeck
Height:	4", 10.1 cm
Colour:	Cream dress, grey, blue and white train
Issued:	1991 to the present

Back Stamp	Price			
	U.S. $	Can. $	U.K. £	Aust. $
BK-5	45.00	75.00	20.00	95.00

DB102
GROOM BUNNYKINS™

Designer:	Graham Tongue
Modeller:	Martyn Alcock
Height:	4 ½", 11.4 cm
Colour:	Grey and burgundy
Issued:	1991 to the present

Back Stamp	Price			
	U.S. $	Can. $	U.K. £	Aust. $
BK-5	45.00	75.00	20.00	95.00

DB103
BEDTIME BUNNYKINS™
Fourth Variation

Designer:	Graham Tongue
Modeller:	David Lyttleton
Height:	3 ¼", 8.3 cm
Colour:	Yellow and green striped pyjamas, brown teddy bear
Issued:	1991 - 1991
Varieties:	DB55, 63, 79
Series:	Special Events Tour 1991

Back Stamp	Colour	Price			
		U.S. $	Can. $	U.K. £	Aust. $
BK-Special	Pale yellow	300.00	350.00	125.00	300.00
BK-Special	Daffodil yellow	300.00	350.00	125.00	300.00

DB104
CAROL SINGER BUNNYKINS™

Designer:	Harry Sales
Modeller:	David Lyttleton
Height:	4", 10.1 cm
Colour:	Dark green, red, yellow and white
Issued:	1991 in a special edition of 1,000

Back Stamp	Price			
	U.S. $	Can. $	U.K.£	Aust. $
BK-Special, UK Backstamp - 700	300.00	450.00	200.00	500.00
BK-Special, USA Backstamp - 300	600.00	750.00	300.00	800.00

DB105
SOUSAPHONE BUNNYKINS™
From the Oompah Band - Third Variation

Designer:	Harry Sales
Modeller:	David Lyttleton
Height:	4", 10.1 cm
Colour:	Dark green, red and yellow
Issued:	1991 in a limited edition of 200
Varieties:	DB23, 86
Series:	Royal Doulton Collectors Band

Back Stamp	Price			
	U.S. $	*Can. $*	*U.K. £*	*Aust. $*
BK-5	600.00	700.00	300.00	650.00
Set DB 105 to 109 (5 pcs.)	3,000.00	3,500.00	1,500.00	3,250.00

DB106
TRUMPETER BUNNYKINS™
From the Oompah Band - Third Variation

Designer:	Harry Sales
Modeller:	David Lyttleton
Height:	3 ¾", 9.5 cm
Colour:	Dark green, red and yellow
Issued:	1991 in a limited edition of 250
Varieties:	DB24, 87
Series:	Royal Doulton Collectors Band

Back Stamp	Price			
	U.S. $	*Can. $*	*U.K. £*	*Aust. $*
BK-5	600.00	700.00	300.00	650.00

DB107
CYMBALS BUNNYKINS™
From the Oompah Band - Third Variation

Designer:	Harry Sales
Modeller:	David Lyttleton
Height:	4", 10.1 cm
Colour:	Dark green, red and yellow
Issued:	1991 in a limited edition of 250
Varieties:	DB25, 88
Series:	Royal Doulton Collectors Band

Back Stamp	Price			
	U.S. $	*Can. $*	*U.K. £*	*Aust. $*
BK-5	600.00	700.00	300.00	650.00

DB108
DRUMMER BUNNYKINS™
From the Oompah Band - Fourth Variation

Designer:	Harry Sales
Modeller:	David Lyttleton
Height:	3 ½", 8.9 cm
Colour:	Dark green, red and white
Issued:	1991 in a special edition of 250
Varieties:	DB26, 26A, 26B, 89
Series:	Royal Doulton Collectors Band

Back Stamp	Price			
	U.S. $	Can. $	U.K. £	Aust. $
BK-Special	600.00	700.00	300.00	650.00

DB109
DRUM-MAJOR BUNNYKINS™
From the Oompah Band - Third Variation

Designer:	Harry Sales
Modeller:	David Lyttleton
Height:	3 ½", 8.9 cm
Colour:	Dark green, red and yellow
Issued:	1991 in a limited edition of 250
Varieties:	DB27, 90
Series:	Royal Doulton Collectors Band

Back Stamp	Price			
	U.S. $	Can. $	U.K. £	Aust. $
BK-5	600.00	700.00	300.00	650.00

DB 110 TO DB 114 — Not issued

DB115
HARRY THE HERALD™
Third Variation

Designer:	Harry Sales
Modeller:	David Lyttleton
Height:	3 ½", 8.9 cm
Colour:	Yellow and dark green
Issued:	1991 in a special edition of 300
Varieties:	DB49, 95
Series:	Bunnykins Royal Family

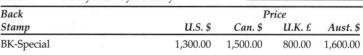

Back Stamp	Price			
	U.S. $	Can. $	U.K. £	Aust. $
BK-Special	1,300.00	1,500.00	800.00	1,600.00

DB116
GOALKEEPER BUNNYKINS™
First Variation

Designer:	Denise Andrews
Modeller:	Warren Platt
Height:	4 ½", 11.4 cm
Colour:	Green and black
Issued:	1991 in a special edition of 250
Varieties:	DB118, 120, 122
Series:	Footballers

Back Stamp	Price			
	U.S. $	Can. $	U.K. £	Aust. $
BK-Special	750.00	1,000.00	450.00	1,000.00

DB117
FOOTBALLER BUNNYKINS™
First Variation

Designer:	Denise Andrews
Modeller:	Warren Platt
Height:	4 ½", 11.4 cm
Colour:	Green and white
Issued:	1991 in a special edition of 250
Varieties:	DB119, 121; also called Soccer Player, DB123
Series:	Footballers

Back Stamp	Price			
	U.S. $	Can. $	U.K. £	Aust. $
BK-Special	750.00	1,000.00	450.00	1,000.00

DB118
GOALKEEPER BUNNYKINS™
Second Variation

Designer:	Denise Andrews
Modeller:	Warren Platt
Height:	4 ½", 11.4 cm
Colour:	Red and black
Issued:	1991 in a special edition of 250
Varieties:	DB116, 120, 122
Series:	Footballers

Back Stamp	Price			
	U.S. $	Can. $	U.K. £	Aust. $
BK-Special	750.00	1,000.00	450.00	1,000.00

DB119
FOOTBALLER BUNNYKINS™
Second Variation

Designer:	Denise Andrews
Modeller:	Warren Platt
Height:	4 ½", 11.4 cm
Colour:	Red
Issued:	1991 in a special edition of 250
Varieties:	DB117, 121; also called Soccer Player, DB123
Series:	Footballers

Back Stamp	Price			
	U.S. $	Can. $	U.K. £	Aust. $
BK-Special	750.00	1,000.00	450.00	1,000.00

DB120
GOALKEEPER BUNNYKINS™
Third Variation

Designer:	Denise Andrews
Modeller:	Warren Platt
Height:	4 ½", 11.4 cm
Colour:	Yellow and black
Issued:	1991 in a special edition of 250
Varieties:	DB116, 118, 122
Series:	Footballers

Back Stamp	Price			
	U.S. $	Can. $	U.K. £	Aust. $
BK-Special	750.00	1,000.00	450.00	1,000.00

DB121
FOOTBALLER BUNNYKINS™
Third Variation

Designer:	Denise Andrews
Modeller:	Warren Platt
Height:	4 ½", 11.4 cm
Colour:	White and blue
Issued:	1991 in a special edition of 250
Varieties:	DB117, 119; also called Soccer Player, DB123
Series:	Footballers

Back Stamp	Price			
	U.S. $	Can. $	U.K. £	Aust. $
BK-Special	750.00	1,000.00	450.00	1,000.00

DB122
GOALKEEPER BUNNYKINS™
Fourth Variation

Designer:	Denise Andrews
Modeller:	Warren Platt
Height:	4 ½", 1.4 cm
Colour:	Grey and black
Issued:	1991 in a special edition of 250
Varieties:	DB116, 118, 120
Series:	Footballers

Back Stamp	Price			
	U.S. $	Can. $	U.K. £	Aust. $
BK-Special	750.00	1,000.00	450.00	1,000.00

DB123
SOCCER PLAYER BUNNYKINS™
Fourth Variation

Designer:	Denise Andrews
Modeller:	Warren Platt
Height:	4 ½", 11.4 cm
Colour:	Dark blue and white
Issued:	1991 in a special edition of 250
Varieties:	Also called Footballer Bunnykins, DB117, 119, 121
Series:	Footballers

Back Stamp	Price			
	U.S. $	Can. $	U.K. £	Aust. $
BK-Special	750.00	1,000.00	450.00	1,000.00

DB124
ROCK AND ROLL BUNNYKINS™

Designer:	Harry Sales
Modeller:	David Lyttleton
Height:	4 ½", 11.4 cm
Colour:	White, blue and red
Issued:	1991 in a limited edition of 1,000
Varieties:	Also called Mr. Bunnybeat Strumming, DB16

Back Stamp	Price			
	U.S. $	Can. $	U.K. £	Aust. $
BK-Special	500.00	700.00	375.00	650.00

DB125
MILKMAN BUNNYKINS™

Designer:	Graham Tongue
Modeller:	Amanda Hughes-Lubeck
Height:	4 ½", 11.4 cm
Colour:	White, green and grey
Issued:	1992 in a special edition of 1,000

MILKMAN BUNNYKINS
DB 125
© 1991 ROYAL DOULTON
EXCLUSIVELY PRODUCED FOR
U.K. INTERNATIONAL CERAMICS LTD
SPECIAL EDITION OF 1,000 PIECES

Back Stamp	Price			
	U.S. $	Can. $	U.K. £	Aust. $
BK-Special	600.00	700.00	300.00	700.00

DB126
MAGICIAN BUNNYKINS™
First Variation

Designer:	Graham Tongue
Modeller:	Warren Platt
Height:	4 ½", 11.4 cm
Colour:	Black suit, yellow shirt, yellow table cloth with deeper yellow border
Issued:	1992 in a limited edition of 1,500
Varieites:	DB159

MAGICIAN BUNNYKINS
DB 126
© 1992 ROYAL DOULTON

Back Stamp	Price			
	U.S. $	Can. $	U.K. £	Aust. $
BK-5	400.00	475.00	235.00	450.00

DB127
GUARDSMAN BUNNYKINS™

Designer:	Denise Andrews
Modeller:	Warren Platt
Height:	4 ½", 11.4 cm
Colour:	Scarlet jacket, black trousers and bearskin hat
Issued:	1992 in a special edition of 1,000

GUARDSMAN BUNNYKINS
DB 127
PRODUCED EXCLUSIVELY
FOR U.K.I. CERAMICS LTD.
IN A SPECIAL EDITION OF 1,000
© 1992 ROYAL DOULTON

Back Stamp	Price			
	U.S. $	Can. $	U.K. £	Aust. $
BK-Special	475.00	500.00	200.00	500.00

DB128
CLOWN BUNNYKINS™
First Variation

Designer:	Denise Andrews
Modeller:	Warren Platt
Height:	4 ¼", 10.8 cm
Colour:	White costume with black stars and pompons, red square on trousers and red ruff at neck
Issued:	1992 in a special edition of 750
Varieties:	DB129

Back Stamp	Price			
	U.S. $	Can. $	U.K. £	Aust. $
BK-Special	750.00	900.00	400.00	900.00

DB129
CLOWN BUNNYKINS™
Second Variation

Designer:	Denise Andrews
Modeller:	Warren Platt
Height:	4 ¼", 10.8 cm
Colour:	White costume with red stars and black pompons, black ruff around neck
Issued:	1992 in a special edition of 250
Varieties:	DB128

Back Stamp	Price			
	U.S. $	Can. $	U.K. £	Aust. $
BK-Special	1,250.00	1,800.00	700.00	2,000.00

DB130
SWEETHEART BUNNYKINS™
First Variation

Designer:	Graham Tongue
Modeller:	Warren Platt
Height:	3 ¾", 9.5 cm
Colour:	Yellow sweater, blue trousers, red heart
Issued:	1992 - 1997
Varieties:	DB174

Back Stamp	Price			
	U.S. $	Can. $	U.K. £	Aust. $
BK-5	45.00	60.00	25.00	65.00

DB131
MASTER POTTER BUNNYKINS™

Designer:	Graham Tongue
Modeller:	Warren Platt
Height:	3 ¾", 9.3 cm
Colour:	Blue, white, green and brown
Issued:	1992 - 1993
Series:	R.D.I.C.C.

Back Stamp	Price			
	U.S. $	Can. $	U.K. £	Aust. $
BK-Special	295.00	350.00	165.00	325.00

DB132
HALLOWEEN BUNNYKINS™

Designer:	Graham Tongue
Modeller:	Martyn Alcock
Height:	3 ¼", 8.3 cm
Colour:	Orange and yellow pumpkin
Issued:	1993 - 1997

Back Stamp	Price			
	U.S. $	Can.$	U.K. £	Aust. $
BK-5	50.00	75.00	30.00	80.00

DB133
AUSSIE SURFER BUNNYKINS™

Designer:	Graham Tongue
Modeller:	Martyn Alcock
Height:	4", 10.1 cm
Colour:	Gold and green outfit, white and blue base
Issued:	1994 - 1994

Back Stamp	Price			
	U.S. $	Can. $	U.K. £	Aust. $
BK-Special	150.00	200.00	75.00	200.00

DB134
JOHN BULL BUNNYKINS™

Designer:	Denise Andrews
Modeller:	Amanda Hughes-Lubeck
Height:	4 ½", 11.4 cm
Colour:	Grey, yellow, red, white and blue Union Jack waistcoat
Issued:	1993 in a special edition of 1,000

Back Stamp	Price			
	U.S. $	Can. $	U.K. £	Aust. $
BK-Special	425.00	500.00	250.00	475.00

DB135
MOUNTIE BUNNYKINS™

Designer:	Graham Tongue
Modeller:	Warren Platt
Height:	4", 10.1 cm
Colour:	Red jacket, dark blue trousers and brown hat
Issued:	1993 in a special edition of 750

Back Stamp	Price			
	U.S. $	Can. $	U.K. £	Aust. $
BK-Special	850.00	1,250.00	425.00	1,300.00

DB136
SERGEANT MOUNTIE BUNNYKINS™

Designer:	Graham Tongue
Modeller:	Warren Platt
Height:	4", 10.1 cm
Colour:	Red jacket, yellow stripes on sleeve, dark blue trousers, brown hat
Issued:	1993 in a special edition of 250

Back Stamp	Price			
	U.S. $	Can. $	U.K. £	Aust. $
BK-Special	1,750.00	2,000.00	1,000.00	2,000.00

DB137
60th ANNIVERSARY BUNNYKINS™

Designer:	Graham Tongue
Modeller:	Martyn Alcock
Height:	4 ½", 11.4 cm
Colour:	Lemon, yellow and white
Issued:	1994 - 1994

Back Stamp	Price			
	U.S. $	Can. $	U.K. £	Aust. $
BK-5	85.00	125.00	45.00	100.00

Note: Numbers DB138 to DB141 not issued.

DB142
CHEERLEADER BUNNYKINS™
First Variation

Designer:	Denise Andrews
Modeller:	Warren Platt
Height:	4 ½", 11.4 cm
Colour:	Red
Issued:	1994 in a special edition of 1,000

Back Stamp	Price			
	U.S. $	Can. $	U.K. £	Aust. $
BK-Special	325.00	375.00	140.00	350.00

DB143
CHEERLEADER BUNNYKINS™
Second Variation

Designer:	Denise Andrews
Modeller:	Warren Platt
Height:	4 ½", 11.4 cm
Colour:	Yellow
Issued:	1994 in a special edition of 1,000

Back Stamp	Price			
	U.S. $	Can. $	U.K. £	Aust. $
BK-Special	300.00	350.00	140.00	300.00

DB144
BATSMAN BUNNYKINS™

Designer:	Denise Andrews
Modeller:	Amanda Hughes-Lubeck
Height:	4", 10.1 cm
Colour:	White, beige and black
Issued:	1994 in a special edition of 1,000

Back Stamp	Price			
	U.S. $	Can. $	U.K. £	Aust. $
BK-Special	350.00	450.00	195.00	400.00

DB145
BOWLER BUNNYKINS™

Designer:	Denise Andrews
Modeller:	Warren Platt
Height:	4", 10.1 cm
Colour:	White, beige and black
Issued:	1994 in a special edition of 1,000

Back Stamp	Price			
	U.S. $	Can. $	U.K. £	Aust. $
BK-Special	350.00	450.00	195.00	400.00

DB146
CHRISTMAS SURPRISE BUNNYKINS™

Designer:	Graham Tongue
Modeller:	Warren Platt
Height:	3 ½", 8.9 cm
Colour:	Cream and red
Issued:	1994 to the present

Back Stamp	Price			
	U.S. $	Can. $	U.K. £	Aust. $
BK-5	55.00	90.00	20.00	105.00

DB147
RAINY DAY BUNNYKINS™

Designer:	Graham Tongue
Modeller:	Warren Platt
Height:	4", 10.1 cm
Colour:	Yellow coat and hat, blue trousers, black boots
Issued:	1994 - 1997

RAINY DAY
BUNNYKINS
DB 147
© 1994 ROYAL DOULTON

Back	Price			
Stamp	U.S. $	Can. $	U.K. £	Aust. $
BK-5	50.00	65.00	30.00	70.00

DB148
BATHTIME BUNNYKINS™

Designer:	Graham Tongue
Modeller:	Warren Platt
Height:	4", 10.1 cm
Colour:	White bathrobe with grey trim, yellow towel and duck
Issued:	1994 - 1997

BATHTIME BUNNYKINS
DB 148
© 1994 ROYAL DOULTON

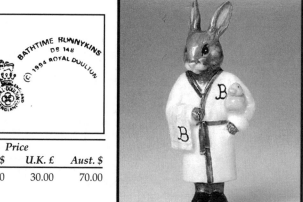

Back	Price			
Stamp	U.S. $	Can. $	U.K. £	Aust. $
BK-5	50.00	65.00	30.00	70.00

DB149
EASTER GREETINGS BUNNYKINS™

Designer:	Graham Tongue
Modeller:	Warren Platt
Height:	4 ½", 11.4 cm
Colour:	Yellow, white and green
Issued:	1995 to the present

EASTER GREETINGS
BUNNYKINS
DB 149
© 1994 ROYAL DOULTON

Back	Price			
Stamp	U.S. $	Can. $	U.K. £	Aust. $
BK-5	55.00	90.00	20.00	90.00

DB150
WICKETKEEPER BUNNYKINS™

Designer:	Denise Andrews
Modeller:	Amanda Hughes-Lubeck
Height:	3 ½", 8.9 cm
Colour:	White, beige and black
Issued:	1995 in a special edition of 1,000

| Back | Price | | | |
Stamp	U.S. $	Can. $	U.K. £	Aust. $
BK-Special	375.00	450.00	195.00	425.00

DB151
PARTNERS IN COLLECTING™

Designer:	Walter Hayward
Modeller:	Albert Hallam
Height:	3", 7.6 cm
Colour:	Red, white and blue
Issued:	1995 - 1995
Varieties:	Also called Storytime Bunnykins, DB9, DB59
Series:	RDICC (15th anniversary of RDICC)

| Back | Price | | | |
Stamp	U.S. $	Can. $	U.K. £	Aust. $
BK-Special	175.00	225.00	85.00	175.00

DB152
BOY SKATER BUNNYKINS™
First Variation

Designer:	Graham Tongue
Modeller:	Martyn Alcock
Height:	4 ¼", 10.8 cm
Colour:	Blue coat, brown pants, yellow hat, green boots and black skates
Issued:	1995 - 1998
Varieties:	DB187

| Back | Price | | | |
Stamp	U.S. $	Can. $	U.K. £	Aust. $
BK-5	50.00	75.00	25.00	80.00

DB153
GIRL SKATER BUNNYKINS™

Designer:	Graham Tongue
Modeller:	Martyn Alcock
Height:	3 ½", 8.9 cm
Colour:	Green coat with white trim, pink dress, blue books, yellow skates
Issued:	1995 - 1997

Back Stamp	Price			
	U.S. $	Can. $	U.K. £	Aust. $
BK-5	50.00	75.00	25.00	80.00

DB154
FATHER BUNNYKINS™

Designer:	Graham Tongue
Modeller:	Martyn Alcock
Height:	4", 10.1 cm
Colour:	Red and white striped blazer, creamy yellow trousers
Issued:	1996 - 1996
Series:	1. Bunnykins of the Year, 1996
	2. Holiday Outing

Back Stamp	Price			
	U.S. $	Can. $	U.K. £	Aust. $
BK-5	75.00	90.00	35.00	75.00

DB155
MOTHER'S DAY BUNNYKINS™

Designer:	Graham Tongue
Modeller:	Shane Ridge
Height:	3 ½", 8.9 cm
Colour:	Brown and blue
Issued:	1995 to the present

Back Stamp	Price			
	U.S. $	Can. $	U.K. £	Aust. $
BK-5	55.00	90.00	20.00	99.00

DB156
GARDENER BUNNYKINS™

Designer:	Graham Tongue
Modeller:	Warren Platt
Height:	4 ¼", 10.8 cm
Colour:	Brown jacket, white shirt, grey trousers, light green wheelbarrow
Issued:	1996 - 1998

Back Stamp	Price			
	U.S. $	Can. $	U.K. £	Aust. $
BK-5	50.00	75.00	25.00	75.00

DB157
GOODNIGHT BUNNYKINS™

Designer:	Graham Tongue
Modeller:	Shane Ridge
Height:	3 ¾", 9.5 cm
Colour:	Pink nightgown, reddish brown teddy, blue and white base
Issued:	1995 to the present

Back Stamp	Price			
	U.S. $	Can. $	U.K. £	Aust. $
BK-5	45.00	75.00	17.00	79.00

DB158
NEW BABY BUNNYKINS™

Designer:	Graham Tongue
Modeller:	Graham Tongue
Height:	3 ¾", 9.5 cm
Colour:	Blue dress with white trim, white cradle, pink pillow, yellow blanket
Issued:	1995 to the present

Back Stamp	Price			
	U.S. $	Can. $	U.K. £	Aust. $
BK-5	45.00	75.00	20.00	90.00

DB159
MAGICIAN BUNNYKINS™
Second Variation

Designer:	Graham Tongue
Modeller:	Warren Platt
Height:	4½", 11.4 cm
Colour:	Black suit, yellow shirt, yellow table cloth with red border
Issued:	1998 in a special edition of 1,000
Varieties:	DB126

Back Stamp	Price			
	U.S. $	Can. $	U.K. £	Aust. $
BK-Special	525.00	600.00	300.00	600.00

DB160
OUT FOR A DUCK BUNNYKINS™

Designer:	Denise Andrews
Modeller:	Amanda Hughes-Lubeck
Height:	4", 10.1 cm
Colour:	White, beige and green
Issued:	1995 in a special edition of 1,250

Back Stamp	Price			
	U.S. $	Can. $	U.K. £	Aust. $
BK-Special	350.00	425.00	200.00	400.00

DB161
JESTER BUNNYKINS™

Designer:	Denise Andrews
Modeller:	Shane Ridge
Height:	4 ½", 11.9 cm
Colour:	Red, green and yellow
Issued:	1995 in a special edition of 1,500

Back Stamp	Price			
	U.S. $	Can. $	U.K. £	Aust. $
BK-Special	575.00	700.00	225.00	675.00

DB162
TRICK OR TREAT BUNNYKINS™

Designer:	Denise Andrews
Modeller:	Amanda Hughes-Lubeck
Height:	4 ½", 11.4 cm
Colour:	Red dress, black hat, shoes and cloak, white moons and stars
Issued:	1995 in a special edition of 1,500

Back Stamp	Price			
	U.S. $	Can. $	U.K. £	Aust. $
BK-Special	675.00	800.00	350.00	850.00

DB163
BEEFEATER BUNNYKINS™

Designer:	Denise Andrews
Modeller:	Amanda Hughes-Lubeck
Height:	4 ½", 11.4 cm
Colour:	Red, gold, black and white livery, black hat with red, blue and white band
Issued:	1996 in a special edition of 1,500

Back Stamp	Price			
	U.S. $	Can. $	U.K. £	Aust. $
BK-Special	475.00	500.00	225.00	475.00

DB164
JUGGLER BUNNYKINS™

Designer:	Denise Andrews
Modeller:	Warren Platt
Height:	4 ½", 11.4 cm
Colour:	Blue suit, black pompons, white ruff
Issued:	1996 in a special edition of 1,500

Back Stamp	Price			
	U.S. $	Can. $	U.K. £	Aust. $
BK-Special	475.00	500.00	175.00	475.00

DB165
RINGMASTER BUNNYKINS™

Designer:	Denise Andrews
Modeller:	Warren Platt
Height:	4 ½", 11.4 cm
Colour:	Black hat and trousers, red jacket, white waistcoat and shirt, black bowtie
Issued:	1996 in a special edition of 1,500

RINGMASTER BUNNYKINS
DB 165
PRODUCED EXCLUSIVELY
FOR U.K.I. CERAMICS LTD
IN A SPECIAL EDITION OF 1,500
© 1996 ROYAL DOULTON

Back Stamp	Price			
	U.S. $	Can. $	U.K. £	Aust. $
BK-Special	450.00	500.00	175.00	475.00

DB166
SAILOR BUNNYKINS™

Designer:	Graham Tongue
Modeller:	Shane Ridge
Height:	2 ½", 6.4 cm
Colour:	White and blue
Issued:	1997 - 1997
Series:	1. Bunnykins of the Year, 1997
	2. Holiday Outing

SAILOR BUNNYKINS
DB 166
BUNNYKINS OF THE YEAR 1997
© 1996 ROYAL DOULTON

Back Stamp	Price			
	U.S. $	Can. $	U.K. £	Aust. $
BK-Special	50.00	75.00	25.00	70.00

DB167
MOTHER AND BABY BUNNYKINS™

Designer:	Shane Ridge
Modeller:	Shane Ridge
Height:	4 ½", 11.4 cm
Colour:	Brown, light pink dress, red shoes, yellow blanket
Issued:	1997 to the present

MOTHER AND
BABY BUNNYKINS
DB 167
© 1996 ROYAL DOULTON

Back Stamp	Price			
	U.S. $	Can. $	U.K. £	Aust. $
BK-5	45.00	90.00	18.00	90.00

DB168
WIZARD BUNNYKINS™

Designer: Denise Andrews
Modeller: Shane Ridge
Height: 5", 12.7 cm
Colour: Brown rabbit, purple robes and hat
Issued: 1997 in a special edition of 2,000

Back Stamp	Price			
	U.S. $	Can. $	U.K. £	Aust. $
BK-Special	500.00	575.00	265.00	575.00

DB169
JOCKEY BUNNYKINS™

Designer: Denise Andrews
Modeller: Martyn Alcock
Height: 4 ½", 11.4 cm
Colour: Green, white and yellow jockey suit, black shoes
Issued: 1997 in a special edition of 2,000

Back Stamp	Price			
	U.S. $	Can. $	U.K. £	Aust. $
BK-5	275.00	425.00	165.00	450.00

DB170
FISHERMAN BUNNYKINS™
Style Two

Designer: Graham Tongue
Modeller: Shane Ridge
Height: 4", 10.1 cm
Colour: Blue hat and trousers, light yellow sweater, black wellingtons
Issued: 1997 to the present

Back Stamp	Price			
	U.S. $	Can. $	U.K. £	Aust. $
BK-5	55.00	90.00	20.00	125.00

DB171
JOKER BUNNYKINS™

Designer: Denise Andrews
Modeller: Martyn Alcock
Height: 5", 12.7 cm
Colour: Yellow jacket, orange and white trousers, black hat
Issued: 1997 in a special edition of 2,500

Back Stamp	Price			
	U.S. $	Can. $	U.K. £	Aust. $
BK-Special	225.00	350.00	150.00	375.00

DB172
WELSH LADY BUNNYKINS™

Designer: Denise Andrews
Modeller: Warren Platt
Height: 5", 12.7 cm
Colour: Light pink and yellow dress, black hat
Issued: 1997 in a special edition of 2,500

Back Stamp	Price			
	U.S. $	Can. $	U.K. £	Aust. $
BK-Special	275.00	425.00	150.00	450.00

DB173
BRIDESMAID BUNNYKINS™

Designer: Graham Tongue
Modeller: Amanda Hughes-Lubeck
Height: 3 ¾", 9.5 cm
Colour: Light yellow dress, darker yellow flowers
Issued: 1997 to the present

Back Stamp	Price			
	U.S. $	Can. $	U.K. £	Aust. $
BK-5	44.00	90.00	20.00	105.00

DB174
SWEETHEART BUNNYKINS™
Second Variation - I Love Bunnykins

Designer:	Graham Tongue
Modeller:	Warren Platt
Height:	3 ¾", 9.5 cm
Colour:	White and blue, pink heart
Issued:	1997 in a special edition of 2,500
Varieties:	DB130

Back Stamp	Price			
	U.S. $	Can. $	U.K. £	Aust. $
BK-Special	225.00	350.00	150.00	375.00

DB175
UNCLE SAM BUNNYKINS™
Second Variation

Designer:	Harry Sales
Modeller:	David Lyttleton
Height:	4 ½", 11.4 cm
Colour:	Red jacket, yellow shirt, blue and white striped trousers, red white and blue hat, platinum bowtie
Issued:	1997 in a special edition of 1,500
Varieties:	DB50

Back Stamp	Price			
	U.S. $	Can. $	U.K. £	Aust. $
BK-Special	225.00	350.00	150.00	375.00

DB176
BALLERINA BUNNYKINS™

Designer:	Graham Tongue
Modeller:	Graham Tongue
Height:	3 ½", 8.9 cm
Colour:	Pink dress, yellow footstool
Issued:	1998 to the present

Back Stamp	Price			
	U.S. $	Can. $	U.K. £	Aust. $
BK-5	55.00	90.00	20.00	110.00

DB177
SEASIDE BUNNYKINS

Designer:	Martyn Alcock
Modeller:	Martyn Alcock
Height:	3", 7.6 cm
Colour:	Blue bathing costume, white and blue bathing cap, yellow sandy base
Issued:	1998 - 1998
Series:	1. Bunnykins of the Year, 1998
	2. Holiday Outing

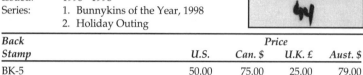

Back	Price			
Stamp	U.S.	Can. $	U.K. £	Aust. $
BK-5	50.00	75.00	25.00	79.00

DB178
IRISHMAN BUNNYKINS™

Designer:	Denise Andrews
Modeller:	Martyn Alcock
Height:	5", 12.7 cm
Colour:	Green waistcoat with shamrocks, white shirt, tan hat and trousers, white socks and black shoes
Issued:	1998 in an special edition of 2,500

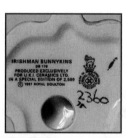

Back	Price			
Stamp	U.S. $	Can. $	U.K. £	Aust. $
BK-Special	225.00	300.00	150.00	375.00

DB179
CAVALIER BUNNYKINS™

Designer:	Graham Tongue
Modeller:	Graham Tongue
Height:	4 ½", 11.4 cm
Colour:	Red tunic, white collar, black trousers and hat, yellow cape, light brown boots
Issued:	1998 in an special edition of 2,500

Back	Price			
Stamp	U.S. $	Can. $	U.K. £	Aust. $
BK-Special	225.00	300.00	150.00	375.00

DB180
THE SCOTSMAN BUNNYKINS™

Designer:	Denise Andrews
Modeller:	Graham Tongue
Height:	5", 12.7 cm
Colour:	Dark blue jacket and hat, red-yellow kilt, white shirt, sporran and socks, black shoes
Issued:	1998 in a special edition of 2,500

Back Stamp	Price			
	U.S. $	Can. $	U.K. £	Aust. $
BK-Special	100.00	150.00	58.00	160.00

DB181
DOCTOR BUNNYKINS™

Designer:	Martyn Alcock
Modeller:	Martyn Alcock
Height:	4 ¼, 10.8 cm
Colour:	White lab coat and shirt, dark blue trousers, black shoes, white and blue striped tie
Issued:	1998 to the present

Back Stamp	Price			
	U.S. $	Can. $	U.K. £	Aust. $
	50.00	75.00	20.00	65.00

DB182
BANJO BUNNYKINS™

Designer:	Kim Curtis
Modeller:	Shane Ridge
Height:	5", 12.7 cm
Colour:	White and red striped blazer, black trousers, yellow straw hat
Issued:	1999 in a limited edition of 2,500
Series:	Bunnykins Jazz Band

Back Stamp	Price			
	U.S. $	Can. $	U.K. £	Aust. $
BK-Special	100.00	150.00	58.00	160.00

DB183
FIREMAN BUNNYKINS™
Second Variation

Designer:	Graham Tongue
Modeller:	Martyn Alcock
Height:	4 ¼", 10.8 cm
Colour:	Red jacket and helmet, black trousers, yellow boots
Issued:	1998 in a special edition of 3,500
Varieties:	DB75

Back Stamp	Price			
	U.S. $	Can. $	U.K. £	Aust. $
BK-Special	95.00	150.00	60.00	160.00

DB184
CLARINET PLAYER BUNNYKINS™

Designer:	Kim Curtis
Modeller:	Shane Ridge
Height:	5", 12.7 cm
Colour:	Blue and white striped jacket, grey trousers, yellow straw hat
Issued:	1999 in a limited edition of 2,500
Series:	Bunnykins Jazz Band

Back Stamp	Price			
	U.S. $	Can. $	U.K. £	Aust. $
BK-Special	100.00	150.00	58.00	160.00

DB185
DOUBLE BASS PLAYER BUNNYKINS™

Designer:	Kim Curtis
Modeller:	Shane Ridge
Height:	5", 12.7 cm
Colour:	Green and yellow striped jacket, green trousers, yellow straw hat
Issued:	1999 in a limited edition of 2,500
Series:	Bunnykins Jazz Band

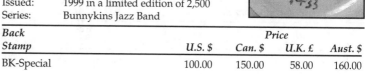

Back Stamp	Price			
	U.S. $	Can. $	U.K. £	Aust. $
BK-Special	100.00	150.00	58.00	160.00

DB186
SAXAPHONE PLAYER BUNNYKINS™

Designer:	Kim Curtis
Modeller:	Shane Ridge
Height:	5", 12.7 cm
Colour:	Navy and white striped shirt, blue vest, black trousers
Issued:	1999 in a limited edition of 2,500
Series:	Bunnykins Jazz Band

Back Stamp	Price			
	U.S. $	Can. $	U.K. £	Aust. $
BK-Special	100.00	150.00	58.00	160.00

DB187
BOY SKATER BUNNYKINS™
Second Variation

Designer:	Graham Tongue
Modeller:	Martyn Alcock
Height:	4 ¼", 10.8 cm
Colour:	Blue jacket, white trouser, red boots
Issued:	1998 in a special edition of 2,500
Varieties:	DB152

Back Stamp	Price			
	U.S. $	Can. $	U.K. £	Aust. $
BK-Special	95.00	150.00	60.00	160.00

DB188
JUDGE BUNNYKINS™

Designer:	Caroline Dadd
Modeller:	Shane Ridge
Height:	4 ¼", 10.8 cm
Colour:	Red and white
Issued:	1999 - 1999
Series:	RDICC (Member package)

Back Stamp	Price			
	U.S. $	Can. $	U.K. £	Aust. $
BK-Special	50.00	75.00	18.00	80.00

DB189
MOTHER BUNNYKINS™

Designer:	Caroline Dadd
Modeller:	Martyn Alcock
Height:	4", 10.1 cm
Colour:	Blue, white and red
Issued:	1999 - 1999
Series:	1. Bunnykins Figure of the Year
	2. Holiday Outing

Back	Price			
Stamp	U.S. $	Can. $	U.K. £	Aust. $
BK-Special	55.00	80.00	20.00	80.00

DB190
TOURIST BUNNYKINS™

Designer:	Caroline Dadd
Modeller:	Martyn Alcock
Height:	5", 12.7 cm
Colour:	Blue, yellow, ICC on hat
Issued:	1999 in a limited time offer.
	Order final date April 11, 1999
Series:	1. Holiday Outing
	2. RDICC

Back	Price			
Stamp	U.S. $	Can. $	U.K. £	Aust. $
BK-Special	55.00	90.00	20.00	90.00

DB191
PIPER BUNNYKINS™

Designer:	Martyn Alcock
Modeller:	Martyn Alcock
Height:	4 ¼", 10.8 cm
Colour:	Green, brown and black
Issued:	1999 in a special edition of 3,000

Back	Price			
Stamp	U.S. $	Can. $	U.K. £	Aust. $
BK-Special	150.00	225.00	90.00	250.00

DB195
SYDNEY BUNNYKINS™

Designers:	Dalglish, Bryant, Bartholomeucz
Modeller:	Amanda Hughes-Lubeck
Height:	5", 12.7 cm
Colour:	Blue, white, black and brown
Issued:	1999 in a special numbered edition of 2,500

Back Stamp	Price			
	U.S. $	Can. $	U.K. £	Aust. $
BK-Special	110.00	170.00	65.00	180.00

DB198
STATUE OF LIBERTY BUNNYKINS™

Designer:	Caroline Dadd
Modeller:	Amanda Hughes-Lubeck
Height:	5", 12.7 cm
Colour:	Red, white and blue
Issued:	1999 in a special edition of 3,000

Back Stamp	Price			
	U.S. $	Can. $	U.K. £	Aust. $
BK-Special	150.00	225.00	90.00	250.00

Australian Bunnykins (DB58), Aussie Surfer Bunnykins (DB133), Olympic Bunnykins (DB28B)

RESIN ISSUE 1996 - 1997

Father Bunnykins and Harry Decorating the Tree

BUNNYKINS
Resin Issue 1996-1997

DBR1
HARRY BUNNYKINS
A LITTLE BUNNY AT PLAY™

Designer:	Unknown
Modeller:	Unknown
Height:	1 ¾", 4.5 cm
Colour:	Pale blue pyjamas, red and dark blue toys
Issued:	1996 - 1997

Royal Doulton
Harry Bunnykins
"a little bunny at play"
DBR1/ **491**
© 1996 Royal Doulton
Made in China

Doulton Number	Price			
	U.S. $	*Can. $*	*U.K. £*	*Aust. $*
DBR1	15.00	20.00	10.00	20.00

DBR2
HARRY BUNNYKINS
PLAYTIME™

Designer:	Unknown
Modeller:	Unknown
Height:	2", 5.0 cm
Colour:	Pale blue pyjamas, yellow toy, pink, yellow and green pillow
Issued:	1996 - 1997

Royal Doulton
Harry Bunnykins
Playtime
DBR2/ **3605**
© 1996 Royal Doulton
Made in China

Doulton Number	Price			
	U.S. $	*Can. $*	*U.K. £*	*Aust. $*
DBR2	15.00	20.00	10.00	20.00

DBR3
REGINALD RATLEY
UP TO NO GOOD™

Designer:	Unknown
Modeller:	Unknown
Height:	2 ¼", 5.7 cm
Colour:	Black jacket, hat and shoes, yellow shirt, red tie
Issued:	1996 - 1997

Royal Doulton
Reginald Ratley
Up to no good
DBR3/ **3530**
© 1996 Royal Doulton
Made in China

Doulton Number	Price			
	U.S. $	*Can. $*	*U.K. £*	*Aust. $*
DBR3	15.00	20.00	10.00	20.00

DBR4
SUSAN BUNNYKINS
THE HELPER™

Designer:	Unknown
Modeller:	Unknown
Height:	3", 7.6 cm
Colour:	White and blue dress
Issued:	1996 - 1997

Doulton	Price			
Number	U.S. $	Can. $	U.K. £	Aust. $
DBR4	15.00	20.00	10.00	20.00

DBR5
WILLIAM BUNNYKINS
ASLEEP IN THE SUN™

Designer:	Unknown
Modeller:	Unknown
Height:	2 ¼", 5.7 cm
Colour:	White shirt, red jacket, brown trousers
Issued:	1996 - 1997

Doulton	Price			
Number	U.S. $	Can. $	U.K. £	Aust. $
DBR5	15.00	20.00	10.00	20.00

DBR6
LADY RATLEY
HER LADYSHIP EXPLAINS™

Designer:	Unknown
Modeller:	Unknown
Height:	3 ¼", 8.3 cm
Colour:	Light and dark purple dress black shoes and handbag
Issued:	1996 - 1997

Doulton	Price			
Number	U.S. $	Can. $	U.K. £	Aust. $
DBR6	20.00	30.00	15.00	30.00

DBR7
MRS. BUNNYKINS
A BUSY MORNING SHOPPING™

Designer:	Unknown
Modeller:	Unknown
Height:	3 ½", 8.9 cm
Colour:	White dress with blue flowers, pale yellow apron and hat, brown basket
Issued:	1996 - 1997

Royal Doulton
Mrs Bunnykins
A busy morning
shopping
DBR7/ *186*
© 1996 Royal Doulton
Made in China

Doulton	Price			
Number	U.S. $	Can. $	U.K. £	Aust. $
DBR7	20.00	30.00	15.00	30.00

DBR8
FATHER BUNNYKINS
HOME FROM WORK™

Designer:	Unknown
Modeller:	Unknown
Height:	3 ¾", 9.5 cm
Colour:	Cream trousers, green jacket and black shoes
Issued:	1996 - 1997

Royal Doulton
Father Bunnykins
Home from work
DBR8/ *1036*
© 1996 Royal Doulton
Made in China

Doulton	Price			
Number	U.S. $	Can. $	U.K. £	Aust. $
DBR8	20.00	30.00	15.00	30.00

DBR9
WILLIAM BUNNYKINS
A BUNNY IN A HURRY™

Designer:	Unknown
Modeller:	Unknown
Height:	2 ¼", 5.7 cm
Colour:	Brown trousers, white shirt and red jacket
Issued:	1996 - 1997

Royal Doulton
William Bunnykins
A bunny in a hurry
DBR9/ *186*
© 1996 Royal Doulton
Made in China

Doulton	Price			
Number	U.S. $	Can. $	U.K. £	Aust. $
DBR9	15.00	20.00	10.00	20.00

DBR10
SUSAN BUNNYKINS
WILDLIFE SPOTTING™

Designer:	Unknown
Modeller:	Unknown
Height:	2 ¾", 7.0 cm
Colour:	White dress with blue flowers, brown basket
Issued:	1996 - 1997

Doulton Number	Price			
	U.S. $	Can. $	U.K. £	Aust. $
DBR10	15.00	20.00	10.00	20.00

DBR11
SUSAN AND HARRY BUNNYKINS
MINDING THE BABY BROTHER™

Designer:	Unknown
Modeller:	Unknown
Height:	2 ½", 6.4 cm
Colour:	Susan - white dress with blue flowers
	Harry - pale blue pyjamas, multi-coloured toys
Issued:	1996 - 1997

Doulton Number	Price			
	U.S. $	Can. $	U.K. £	Aust. $
DBR11	30.00	45.00	17.00	45.00

DBR12
FATHER BUNNYKINS AND HARRY
DECORATING THE TREE™

Designer:	Unknown
Modeller:	Unknown
Height:	4", 10.1 cm
Colour:	Father - blue trousers, white shirt and red pullover
	Harry - white pyjamas, green tree
Issued:	1996 - 1997

Doulton Number	Price			
	U.S. $	Can. $	U.K. £	Aust. $
DBR12	30.00	45.00	20.00	45.00

DBR13
MRS. BUNNYKINS AND WILLIAM THE BIRTHDAY CAKE™

Designer: Unknown
Modeller: Unknown
Height: 3 ¼", 8.3 cm
Colour: White dress with blue flowers, light yellow apron, red jacket, white shirt and brown trousers
Issued: 1996 - 1997

Doulton Number	Price			
	U.S. $	Can. $	U.K. £	Aust. $
DBR13	30.00	40.00	17.00	40.00

DBR14
HAPPY CHRISTMAS FROM THE BUNNYKINS FAMILY™

Designer: Unknown
Modeller: Unknown
Height: 6", 15.0 cm
Colour: Multi-coloured
Issued: 1996 - 1997
Series: Music Box

Doulton Number	Price			
	U.S. $	Can. $	U.K. £	Aust. $
DBR14	110.00	150.00	75.00	150.00

Note: This musical piece plays "We Wish You A Merry Christmas."

DBR15
PICNIC TIME WITH THE BUNNYKINS FAMILY™

Designer: Unknown
Modeller: Unknown
Height: 5", 12.7 cm
Colour: Multi-coloured
Issued: 1996 - 1997
Series: Music Box

Doulton Number	Price			
	U.S. $	Can. $	U.K. £	Aust. $
DBR15	90.00	150.00	75.00	150.00

Note: This musical piece plays "Here We Go Round the Mulberry Bush."

DBR16
BIRTHDAY GIRL™

Designer:	Unknown
Modeller:	Unknown
Height:	1 ½", 4 cm
Colour:	Pink and white dress
Issued:	1997 - 1997

Royal Doulton
Bunnykins
Birthday Girl
DBR16/ 874
©1996 Royal Doulton
Made In China

Doulton Number	Price			
	U.S. $	Can. $	U.K. £	Aust. $
DBR16	15.00	20.00	10.00	20.00

DBR17
BIRTHDAY BOY™

Designer:	Unknown
Modeller:	Unknown
Height:	1 ½", 4 cm
Colour:	Blue pyjamas, white bib
Issued:	1997 - 1997

Royal Doulton
Bunnykins
Birthday Boy
DBR17/ 1456
©1996 Royal Doulton
Made In China

Doulton Number	Price			
	U.S. $	Can. $	U.K. £	Aust. $
DBR17	15.00	20.00	10.00	20.00

DBR18
THE NEW BABY™

Designer:	Unknown
Modeller:	Unknown
Height:	3 ½", 8.9 cm
Colour:	Mother - white, lilac and rose
	Baby - light blue
Issued:	1997 - 1997

Royal Doulton
Bunnykins
The New Baby
DBR18/ 101
©1996 Royal Doulton
Made In China

Doulton Number	Price			
	U.S. $	Can. $	U.K. £	Aust. $
DBR18	20.00	30.00	15.00	30.00

DBR19
THE ROCKING HORSE™

Designer:	Unknown
Modeller:	Unknown
Height:	2 ¾", 7.0 cm
Colour:	Brown bunny, red and white dress, white horse
Issued:	1997 - 1997

Doulton	Price			
Number	U.S. $	Can. $	U.K. £	Aust. $
DBR19	15.00	20.00	10.00	20.00

DBR20
PHOTOGRAPH FRAME - GIRL

Designer:	Unknown
Modeller:	Unknown
Height:	5 ¼", 14 cm
Colour:	Cream and brown bunny dressed in pink
Issued:	1997 - 1997

Doulton	Price			
Number	U.S. $	Can. $	U.K. £	Aust. $
DBR20	30.00	45.00	15.00	45.00

DBR21
PHOTOGRAPH FRAME - BOY

Designer:	Unknown
Modeller:	Unknown
Height:	5 ¼", 14 cm
Colour:	Cream and brown bunny dressed in blue
Issued:	1997 - 1997

Doulton	Price			
Number	U.S. $	Can. $	U.K. £	Aust. $
DBR21	30.00	45.00	15.00	45.00

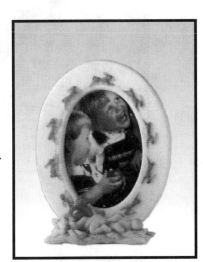

INDICES

ALPHABETICAL INDEX TO BUNNYKINS TABLEWARE

A

A Scene (CT96) 13
ABC Scene (CT95) 13
ABCDEF Scene (CT94) 13
Aerobics 14
Aeroplane 14
Afternoon Tea (HW116) 15
Airmail Delivery (LFa) 16
Apple Picking (SF25) 16
Art Class (LF107) 17
Artist (HW1) 17
Asleep in a Sleeping Bag (36) 42
Asleep in the Open Air (HW10) 18

B

Baby in Crib with Father Looking On (CT76) 36
Baby in Crib (CT78) 36
Baking Cakes with Mother (7) 22
Baking (SF19) 21
Bath Night (LF7) 23
Bathtime
  Style One (SF18) 23, 37
  Style Two, First Variation (CT21) 24
  Style Two, Second Variation (CT24) 24
  Style Three (22) 26
Beating Carpet (20) 158
Bedtime in Bunks
  Style One (SF3) 28
  Style Two (13) 27
Bedtime Story (SF130) 28, 37
Bedtime with Dollies (EC125) 29
Beware of the Bull (LF108) 29
Birthday Inscription (CT61) 92
Blowing and Bursting Bubbles (23) 26
Blowing Bubbles and Sailing Boat (24) 26
Bonfire (LF128) 30
Breakfast Time 30
Broken Umbrella (HW27R) 177
Bugler with Toy Donkey (HW26R) 62
Building Sand Castles (HW138) 31
Building Snowman (59) 155
Bunnies in the Bath
  First Version (CT25) 24
  Second Version (CT34) 25
Bunny on Rocking Horse (CT29) 118
Bunny on Swing (54) 128
Bunny on Trike (CT23) 148
Bunny with Bag (27) 146
Bunny with Cake Plate (CT88) 20
Bunny with Mirror (CT35) 119
Bunnykins 60th Anniversary Inscription (CT93) 38
Bunnykins Build a Snowman (PN198) 32
Bunnykins Celebrate Australia's Bicentenary 1788-1988 32
Bunnykins Celebrate Their Golden Jubilee
  Birthday Cake (SF140) 33
  Chicken Pulling a Cart (SF141) 33

Bunnykins Celebrate your Christening,
  Style One, First Version (SF139) 34
  Style One, Second Version (HW142) 34
  Style Two, Variation Variation (CT38) 35
  Style Two, Second Variation (CT41) 35
Bunnykins Celebrate Your
Bunnykins Help Santa (PN175) 37
Bunnykins Teaching Clock 40

C

Cake Stall (CT12) 122
Camp Site (SF113) 37, 41
Campfire (35) 42
Camping (34) 42
Carol Singer Bunnykins (CT70) 43
Carrying Letter (30) 130
Carrying Net (6) 78
Carrying Plates (45) 58
Carving the Chicken (LFc) 43
Chicken Pulling a Cart (SF8) 44
Christening Inscription
  (CT42) 35
  (CT65) 35
  (CT77) 36
  (CT79) 36
  (HW142R) 34
Christmas 1991 (CT69) 144
Christmas 1992 (CT71) 43
Christmas 1994 (CT81) 166
Christmas Inscription (CT44) 111
Christmas Ornaments
  1991 Santa Bunnykins (CT68) 144
  1992 Carol Singer Bunnykins (CT70) 43
  1994 Trimming the Tree 166
  1995 Fun in the Snow (CT80) 83
  1996 Christmas Morn 45
Christmas Party (LF9) 45
Christmas Tree (LF16) 46
Classroom Scene
  Style One (SF138) 39
  Style Two, First Version (CT36) 39, 47
  Style Two, Second Version (CT16) 47
Cleaning Bike (48) 54
Coconut Shy (32) 69
Commemorate Leaf Border (CT85) 19
Commemorative Ware 48, 49
Conducting the Orchestra (LF5) 50
Convalescing (SF5) 50
Cook and Bunny (CT31) 147
Counting Motif (CT8) 136
Cowboy on Rocking Horse (HW140R) 51
Cowboys and Indians (HW140) 51
Cricket Game (LF12) 52
Cricketer (HW22R) 175
Cuddling Under a Mushroom (HW4) 52
Cycle Ride (46) 54
Cycling (HW15R) 53

D

Daisy Chains (HW25)   55
Dancing in the Moonlight
    First Version (LFb)   56
    Second Version, First Variation (CT91)   38
    Second Version, Second Variation (CT92)   38
Dancing Round the Barrel Organ (HW139)   57
Dancing with Doll (HW115R)   127
Decorating the Cake (9)   22
Disturbing Sleeping Father (HW118)   59
Dodgem Cars (LF4)   60
Dog Carriage (LFe)   60
Doll's House, The (HW120)   61
Dress Making (HW26)   62
Dressing Up
    First Version (SF22)   63
    Second Version   63
Drummer and Bugler (EC126)   64
Drummer (EC2)   64
Duet, The (LF13)   65
Dunce (HW1R)   66
Dusting (19)   158

E

Easter Inscription (CT63)   93
Eating Apples (3)   151
Embracing at a Window (HW5)   67
Engine Pulling a Carriage (HW17)   68

F

Family at Breakfast (HW12)   70
Family Cycling (LF11)   71
Family Going out on Washing Day (HW8)   72
Family Group with Father Kneeling (CT98)   116
Family Group with Father Standing (CT97)   116
Family in the Garden (SF135)   37, 73
Family Photograph (LF15)   73
Family with Pram
    Style One (HW15)   74
    Style Two (CT14)   75
Father Asleep (CT90)   20
Father Bunnykins with Fishing Rod (CT27)   98
Feeding the Baby (HW13)   76
Fishing at the Pond (4)   78
Fishing in the Goldfish Bowl (HW3R)   79
Fishing on the Pier (LF3)   79
Fixing Braces (HW3)   80
Flying Kites (SF133)   37, 80
Footballer (HW13R)   81
Frightening Spider (SF4)   82

G

Game of Golf (SF11)   83
Gardener with Wheelbarrow (HW9R)   85
Gardening
    Style One (HW9)   86
    Style Two (55)   87

Geography Lesson (LF17)   88
Getting Dressed (LF2)   88
Going Shopping (SF10)   89
Golfer (HW4R)   90
Greetings (HW7)   90

H

Happy Birthday from Bunnykins
    Style One (SF136)   91
    Style Two, First Version (CT37)   92
    Style Two, Second Variation (CT60)   92
Happy Birthday from Bunnykins Inscription (CT64)   92
Happy Birthday Inscription   91
Happy Easter from Bunnykins Inscription (CT67)   93
Happy Easter from Bunnykins
    First Version (CT40)   93
    Second Version (CT62)   93
Hat Shop (HW28)   94
Haymaking (HW29)   95
Hiker Resting with Ice Cream (HW23R)   101
Hikers (EC124)   96
Hobby Horse
    Style One (HW24R)   141
    Style Two (EC121)   96
Holding Hat and Coat (EC4)   97
Home Decorating (SF131)   37, 97
Home from Fishing
    First Variation (C T18)   98
    Second Variation (CT26)   98
Hoopla (LF129)   99

I

Ice Cream on the Bench (HW136R)   135
Ice Cream Seller
    First Variation (CT5)   100
    Second Variation (CT11)   100
Ice Cream Vendor (HW23)   101
Ice Skating (SF24)   102

J

Jack and Jill Nursery Rhyme (CT10)   102
Jack and Jill (CT9)   102
Jogging   14
Juggling (LF127)   103

K

Kissing Under the Mistletoe (HW11R)   104

L

Lambeth Walk (HW16)   105, 106
Lasso Games (HW117)   107
Lassoing (HW117R)   107
Leapfrog (HW12R)   107
Letter Box (29)   130
Letterbox (SF13)   108
Lunch Break (HW29R)   95

M

Maths Lesson (25) — 146
Medicine Time (SF1) — 109
Member of Bunnykins Club — 37

Merry Christmas from Bunnykins
    Style One (SF137) — 110
    Style Two, First Variation (CT39) — 111
    Style Two, Second Variation (CT43) — 111
Merry Christmas from Bunnykins,
    Family Christmas Scene, First Variation (CT72) — 112
    Family Christmas Scene, Second Version (CT74) — 112

Merry Christmas Inscription (SF137R) — 110
Merry Christmas from Bunnykins Inscription
    (CT66) — 111
    (CT73) — 112
    (CT75) — 112
Mr. Pigglys Store (SF14) — 113
Mrs. Moppets Tea Room (LF6) — 114

N

Netting a Cricket (HW6) — 115
New Arrival Inscription (CT99) — 116
Nipped by a Crab (HW21R) — 143
Nursery, First Version (CT19) — 118
Nursery, Second Version (CT28) — 118

O

Orange Vendor (SF12) — 120

P

Pea Shooter (HW118R) — 59
Petrol in the Sports Car (37) — 84
Picking Daisies (CT4) — 122
Picnic and Cake Stall (CT2) — 122
Picnic Scene (CT87) — 20
Picnic Scene with Hamper (CT89) — 20
Picnic with Kangaroo and Koala
    First Variation (CT84) — 19
    Second Variation (CT86) — 19
Picnic (16) — 123
Picnic
    Style One, First Version — 121
    Style One, Second Version (LF10) — 121
Pillow Fight
    Style One (SF7) — 124
    Style Two (14) — 27
Playing and Reading (15) — 27
Playing Badminton (17) — 123
Playing in Tree House (56) — 87
Playing on the River (SF16) — 125
Playing with Ball (42) — 117
Playing with Balloons (33) — 69
Playing with Cup and Spoon (EC6) — 126
Playing with Doll and Pram (EC123) — 126
Playing with Doll and Teddy (HW120R) — 61
Playing with Dolls and Prams (HW115) — 127

Portrait Painter (SF20) — 129
Posting Letters (28) — 130
Postman Delivering Letters (HW19) — 131
Preparing Dinner (43) — 58
Pressing Trousers (HW14) — 132
Proposal (HW11) — 133
Pulling on Trousers (HW2) — 134
Pumping Tyre (38) — 84
Pumping Water (11) — 77
Punch and Judy Show (HW136) — 135
Pushing Pram (41) — 117
Pushing Swing (53) — 128
Pushing Wheelbarrow (CT3) — 176

Q

Queen of the May
    First Variation (CT7) — 136
    Second Variation (CT13) — 136

R

Raft (SF111) — 137
Raising Hat
    Style One (HW16R) — 138
    Style Two (EC7) — 139
Reading the Times (HW2R) — 140
Reading (EC122) — 139
Rest by Pond (5) — 78
Resting in Wheelbarrow (57) — 87
Resting (18) — 123
Resting (21) — 158
Resting (47) — 54
Ring-a-Ring o'Roses (SF21) — 140
Rocking Horse (HW24) — 141
Roller Skating Arm in Arm (HW137R) — 142
Roller Skating Race (HW137) — 142
Row Boat (HW21) — 143

S

Sailing Boats (HW138R) — 31
Santa Bunnykins (CT68) — 144

Santa Claus (SF9) — 145
School Dinner
    First Variation (CT17) — 147
    Second Variation (CT30) — 147
School Gates
    First Variation (CT20) — 148
    Second Variation (CT22) — 148
See-saw
    Style One (SF17) — 149
    Style Two (52) — 128
Serving Dinner (44) — 58
Serving Tea (HW116R) — 15
Sheltering Under an Umbrella (EC3) — 150
Shopping (1) — 151
Showing Baby at Window (40) — 117
Sitting on Oil Drum (39) — 84
Sitting on Suitcase (51) — 165
Skipping Game (HW139R) — 57
Skipping (HW20R) — 160

Sledging
    Style One (HW141)   152
    Style Two (60)   155
Sleeping in a Rocking Chair (EC1)   153
Smelling Flowers (HW25R)   55
Smoking in the Doorway (SF2)   154
Snow Scenes (58)   155
Snowball Fight (HW141R)   152
Soldier Marching (HW18R)   156
Soldiers Marching to the Music (HW18)   156
Space Rocket Launch (SF132)   37, 157
Splashing at Sink (CT33)   172
Spring Cleaning (LF14)   157
Standing by Pram (CT6)   75
Storytime (SF110)   159
Swinging Boats (31)   69
Swinging (HW20)   160

T

Taking Cake from Oven (8)   22
Teacher Scolding (26)   146
Television Time (SF112)   37, 161
Tennis   161
Ticket Office (50)   165
Ticket Queue (SF109)   162
To Celebrate the Marriage of the Prince Andrew
    with Miss Sarah Ferguson   48
To Celebrate the Birth of the First Child of T.R.H.
    the Prince and Princess of Wales 1982   48
To TRH the Prince and Princess of Wales A Second
    Child 1984 in Joyful Celebration   49
To the Station (HW17R)   68
Toast for Tea Today (SF23)   162
Top Hat (HW14R)   163
Toppling the Fruit Cart (SF134)   37, 163
Toy Shop (SF114)   164
Trimming the Tree (CT80)   166

Trumpeter (EC5)   167
Trying on Hat (12)   77
Trying on Hats (HW28R)   94
Trying on Knitting (HW119R)   168
Tug of War (LF1)   167

U

Unravelling Knitting (HW119)   168

V

Vegetable Stall (2)   151
Visiting the Cottage
    Style One (SF6a)   169
    Style Two (SF6b)   169

W

Waiting for Train (49)   165
Washing Day (HW8R)   170
Washing in the Open Air (HW10R)   171
Washing the Fire Engine (10)   77
Washing Up
    First Variation (CT15)   172
    Second Variation (CT32)   172
Watering the Flowers (SF15)   173
Wedding (LFd)   174
Wheelbarrow Race
    Style One (HW22)   175
    Style Two (CT1)   176
Windy Day (HW27)   177
Winning Post (LF106)   178
Writing Letters (HW19R)   131

X

Xmas Menu (LF8)   178

DESIGNS NOT ISSUED

Boating (CT47)
Boating (CT48)
Boating (CT54)
Christmas Tree Ornament (CT59)
Decorating the Tree (CT55)
In the Park (CT45)
In the Park (CT46)

In the Park (CT52)
Model Yachting (CT49)
Model Yachting (CT50)
Model Yacthing (CT53)
Santa Claus (CT58)
Showing the Baby the Tree (CT57)
Sorting the Decorations (CT56)
Train (CT51)

NUMERICAL INDEX TO BUNNYKINS TABLEWARE

Design No.	Name	Page No.
1	Shopping	151
2	Vegetable Stall	151
3	Eating Apples	151
4	Fishing at the Pond	78
5	Rest by Pond	78
6	Carrying Net	78
7	Baking Cakes with Mother	22
8	Taking Cake from Oven	22
9	Decorating the Cake	22
10	Washing the Fire Engine	77
11	Pumping Water	77
12	Trying on Hat	77
13	Bedtime in Bunks	27
14	Pillow Fight	27
15	Playing and Reading	27
16	Picnic, Style Two	123
17	Playing Badminton	123
18	Resting	123
19	Dusting	158
20	Beating Carpet	158
21	Resting	158
22	Bathtime, Style Three	26
23	Blowing and Bursting Bubbles	26
24	Blowing Bubbles and Sailing Boat	26
25	Maths Lesson	146
26	Teacher Scolding	146
27	Bunny with Bag	146
28	Posting Letters	130
29	Letter Box	130
30	Carrying Letter	130
31	Swinging Boats	69
32	Coconut Shy	69
33	Playing with Balloons	69
34	Camping	42
35	Campfire	42
36	Asleep in a Sleeping Bag	42
37	Petrol in the Sports Car	84
38	Pumping Tyre	84
39	Sitting on Oil Drum	84
40	Showing Baby at Window	117
41	Pushing Pram	117
42	Playing with Ball	117
43	Preparing Dinner	58
44	Serving Dinner	58
45	Carrying Plates	58
46	Cycle Ride	54
47	Resting	54
48	Cleaning Bike	54
49	Waiting for Train	165
50	Ticket Office	165
51	Sitting on Suitcase	165
52	See-saw, Style Two	128
53	Pushing Swing	128
54	Bunny on Swing	128
55	Gardening, Style Two	87
56	Playing in Tree House	87
57	Resting in Wheelbarrow	87

Design No.	Name	Page No.
58	Snow Scene	155
59	Building Snowman	155
60	Sledging, Style Two	155
CT1	Wheelbarrow Race, Style Two	176
CT2	Picnic and Cake Stall	122
CT3	Pushing Wheelbarrow	176
CT4	Picking Daisies	122
CT5	Ice Cream Seller, First Variation	100
CT6	Standing by Pram	75
CT7	Queen of the May, First Variation	136
CT8	Counting Motif	136
CT9	Jack and Jill	102
CT10	Jack and Jill Nursery Rhyme	102
CT11	Ice Cream Seller, Second Variation	100
CT12	Cake Stall	122
CT13	Queen of the May, Second Variation	136
CT14	Family with Pram, Style Two	75
CT15	Washing Up, First Variation	172
CT16	Classroom Scene, Style Two, Second Version	47
CT17	School Dinner, First Variation	147
CT18	Home from Fishing, First Variation	98
CT19	Nursery, First Version	118
CT20	School Gates, First Variation	148
CT21	Bathtime, Style Two, First Variation	24
CT22	School Gates, Second Variation	148
CT23	Bunny on Trike	148
CT24	Bathtime, Style Two, Second Variation	24
CT25	Bunnies in the Bath, First Version	24
CT26	Home from Fishing, Second Variation	98
CT27	Father Bunnykins with Fishing Rod	98
CT28	Nursery, Second Version	118
CT29	Bunny on Rocking Horse	118
CT30	School Dinner, Second Variation	147
CT31	Cook and Bunny	147
CT32	Washing Up, Second Variation	172
CT33	Splashing at Sink	172
CT34	Bunnies in the Bath, Second Version	25
CT35	Bunny with Mirror	119
CT36	Classroom Scene, Style Two, First Version	39
CT37	Happy Birthday from Bunnykins Style Two, First Version	92
CT38	Bunnykins Celebrate your Christening Style Two, First Variation	35
CT39	Merry Christmas from Bunnykins Style Two, First Variation	111
CT40	Happy Easter from Bunnykins, Second Version	93
CT41	Bunnykins Celebrate your Christening Style Two, Second Variation	35
CT42	Christening Inscription	35
CT43	Merry Christmas from Bunnykins Style Two, Second Variation	111
CT44	Christmas Inscription	111
CT45	In the Park	Not issued
CT46	In the Park	Not issued
CT47	Boating	Not issued
CT48	Boating	Not issued

Design No.	Name	Page No.
CT49	Model Yachting	Not issued
CT50	Model Yachting	Not Issued
CT51	Train	Not issued
CT52	In the Park	Not issued
CT53	Model Yachting	Not issued
CT54	Boating	Not issued
CT55	Decorating the Tree	Not issued
CT56	Sorting the Decorations	Not issued
CT57	Showing the Baby the Tree	Not issued
CT58	Santa Claus	Not issued
CT59	Christmas Tree Ornament	Not issued
CT60	Happy Birthday from Bunnykins Style Two, Second Version	92
CT61	Birthday Inscription	92
CT62	Happy Easter from Bunnykins Second Version	93
CT63	Easter Inscription	95
CT64	Happy Birthday from Bunnykins Inscription	92
CT65	Bunnykins Celebrate your Christening Inscription	35
CT66	Merry Christmas from Bunnykins Inscription	111
CT67	Happy Easter from Bunnykins Inscription	93
CT68	Santa Bunnykins	144
CT69	Christmas 1991	144
CT70	Carol Singer Bunnykins	43
CT71	Christmas 1992	43
CT72	Merry Christmas from Bunnykins Family Scene, First Version	112
CT73	Merry Christmas from Bunnykins Inscription	112
CT74	Merry Christmas from Bunnykins Family Scene, Second Version	112
CT75	Merry Christmas from Bunnykins Inscription	112
CT76	Bunnykins Celebrate Your Christening Baby in Crib with Father Looking On	36
CT77	Bunnykins Celebrate Your Christening Inscription	36
CT78	Baby in Crib	36
CT79	Christening Inscription	36
CT80	Trimming the Tree	166
CT81	Christmas 1994	166
CT84	Picnic with Kangaroo and Koala First Variation	19
CT85	Commemorate Leaf Border	19
CT86	Picnic with Kangaroo and Koala Second Variation	19
CT87	Picnic Scene	20
CT88	Bunny with Cake Plate	20
CT89	Picnic Scene with Hamper	20
CT90	Father Asleep	20
CT91	Dancing in the Moonlight, Second Version, First Variation	38
CT92	Dancing in the Moonlight Second Version, Second Variation	38
CT93	Bunnykins 60th Anniversary Inscription	38
CT94	ABCDEF Scene	13
CT95	ABC Scene	13
CT96	A Scene	13
CT97	Family Group with Father Standing	116
CT98	Family Group with Father Kneeling	116
CT99	New Arrival Inscription	116
EC1	Sleeping in a Rocking Chair	153
EC2	Drummer	64
EC3	Sheltering Under an Umbrella	150
EC4	Holding Hat and Coat	97
EC5	Trumpeter	167
EC6	Playing with Cup and Spoon	126
EC7	Raising Hat, Style Two	139
EC121	Hobby Horse	96
EC122	Reading	139
EC123	Playing with Doll and Pram	126
EC124	Hikers	96
EC125	Bedtime with Dollies	29
EC126	Drummer and Bugler	64
HW1	Artist	17
HW1R	Dunce	66
HW2	Pulling on Trousers	134
HW2R	Reading the Times	140
HW3	Fixing Braces	80
HW3R	Fishing in the Goldfish Bowl	79
HW4	Cuddling Under a Mushroom	52
HW4R	Golfer	90
HW5	Embracing at a Window	67
HW6	Netting a Cricket	115
HW7	Greetings	90
HW8	Family Going out on Washing Day	72
HW8R	Washing Day	170
HW9	Gardening, Style One	86
HW9R	Gardener with Wheelbarrow	85
HW10	Asleep in the Open Air	18
HW10R	Washing in the Open Air	171
HW11	Proposal	133
HW11R	Kissing Under the Mistletoe	104
HW12	Family at Breakfast	70
HW12R	Leapfrog	107
HW13	Feeding the Baby	76
HW13R	Footballer	81
HW14	Pressing Trousers	132
HW14R	Top Hat	163
HW15	Family with Pram, Style One	74
HW15R	Cycling	53
HW16	Lambeth Walk	105, 106
HW16R	Raising Hat, Style Two	138
HW17	Engine Pulling a Carriage	68
HW17R	To the Station	68
HW18	Soldiers Marching to the Music	156
HW18R	Soldier Marching	156
HW19	Postman Delivering Letters	131
HW19R	Writing Letters	131
HW20	Swinging	160
HW20R	Skipping	160
HW21	Row Boat	143
HW21R	Nipped by a Crab	143
HW22	Wheelbarrow Race, Style One	175
HW22R	Cricketer	175
HW23	Ice Cream Vendor	101
HW23R	Hiker Resting with Ice Cream	101
HW24	Rocking Horse	141
HW24R	Hobby Horse	141

Design No.	Name	Page No.
HW25	Daisy Chains	55
HW25R	Smelling Flowers	55
HW26	Dress Making	62
HW26R	Bugler with Toy Donkey	62
HW27	Windy Day	177
HW27R	Broken Umbrella	177
HW28	Hat Shop	94
HW28R	Trying on Hats	94
HW29	Haymaking	95
HW29R	Lunch Break	95
HW115	Playing with Dolls and Prams	127
HW115R	Dancing with Doll	127
HW116	Afternoon Tea	15
HW116R	Serving Tea	15
HW117	Lasso Games	107
HW117R	Lassoing	107
HW118	Disturbing Sleeping Father	59
HW118R	Pea Shooter	59
HW119	Unravelling Knitting	168
HW119R	Trying on Knitting	168
HW120	The Dolls House	61
HW120R	Playing with Doll and Teddy	61
HW136	Punch and Judy Show	135
HW136R	Ice Cream on the Bench	135
HW137	Roller Skating Race	142
HW137R	Roller Skating Arm in Arm	142
HW138	Building Sand Castles	31
HW138R	Sailing Boats	31
HW139	Dancing Round the Barrel Organ	57
HW139R	Skipping Game	57
HW140	Cowboys and Indians	51
HW140R	Cowboy on Rocking Horse	51
HW141	Sledging, Style One	152
HW141R	Snowball Fight	152
HW142	Bunnykins Celebrate Your Christening Style One, Second Version	34
HW142R	Christening Inscription	34
LFa	Airmail Delivery	16
LFb	Dancing in the Moonlight, First Version	56
LFc	Carving the Chicken	43
LFd	Wedding	174
LFe	Dog Carriage	60
LF1	Tug of War	167
LF2	Getting Dressed	88
LF3	Fishing on the Pier	79
LF4	Dodgem Cars	60
LF5	Conducting the Orchestra	50
LF6	Mrs. Moppets Tea Room	114
LF7	Bath Night	23
LF8	Xmas Menu	178
LF9	Christmas Party	45
LF10	Picnic, Style One, Second Version	121
LF11	Family Cycling	71
LF12	Cricket Game	52
LF13	The Duet	65
LF14	Spring Cleaning	157
LF15	Family Photograph	73
LF16	Christmas Tree	46

Design No.	Name	Page No.
LF17	Geography Lesson	88
LF106	Winning Post	178
LF107	Art Class	17
LF108	Beware of the Bull	29
LF127	Juggling	103
LF128	Bonfire	30
LF129	Hoopla	99
PN175	Bunnykins Help Santa	37
PN198	Bunnykins Build a Snowman	32
SF1	Medicine Time	109
SF2	Smoking in the Doorway	154
SF3	Bedtime in Bunks	28
SF4	Frightening Spider	82
SF5	Convalescing	50
SF6a	Visiting the Cottage, Style One	169
SF6b	Visiting the Cottage, Style Two	169
SF7	Pillow Fight	124
SF8	Chicken Pulling a Cart	44
SF9	Santa Claus	145
SF10	Going Shopping	89
SF11	Game of Golf	83
SF12	Orange Vendor	120
SF13	Letterbox	108
SF14	Mr. Pigglys Store	113
SF15	Watering the Flowers	173
SF16	Playing on the River	125
SF17	See-saw, Style One	149
SF18	Bathtime, Style One	23, 37
SF19	Baking	21
SF20	Portrait Painter	129
SF21	Ring-a-Ring o'Roses	140
SF22	Dressing Up, First Version	63
SF23	Toast for Tea Today	162
SF24	Ice Skating	102
SF25	Apple Picking	16
SF109	Ticket Queue	162
SF110	Storytime	159
SF111	Raft	137
SF112	Television Time	161
SF113	Camp Site	41
SF114	Toy Shop	164
SF130	Bedtime Story	28
SF131	Home Decorating	97
SF132	Space Rocket Launch	157
SF133	Flying Kites	80
SF134	Toppling the Fruit Cart	163
SF135	Family in the Garden	73
SF136	Happy Birthday from Bunnykins Style One	91
SF137	Merry Christmas from Bunnykins Style One	110
SF138	Classroom Scene, Style One	39
SF139	Bunnykins Celebrate your Christening Style One, First Version	34
SF140	Bunnykins Celebrate Their Golden Jubilee, Birthday Cake	33
SF141	Bunnykins Celebrate Their Golden Jubilee, Chicken Pulling a Cart	33

ALPHABETICAL INDEX TO
BUNNYKINS EARTHENWARE FIGURINES

A

Ace Bunnykins	DB42	214
Aerobic Bunnykins	DB40	213
Artist Bunnykins	DB13	203
Astro Bunnykins Rocket Man	DB20	205
Music Box	DB35	211
Aussie Surfer Bunnykins	DB133	242
Australian Bunnykins	DB58	219

B

Ballerina Bunnykins	DB176	255
Banjo Player Bunnykins	DB182	257
Bathtime Bunnykins	DB148	246
Batsman Bunnykins	DB144	245
Be Prepared Bunnykins	DB56	218
Bedtime Bunnykins		
First Variation	DB55	218
Second Variation	DB63	220
Third Variation	DB79	226
Fourth Variation	DB103	234
Beefeater Bunnykins	DB163	251
Billie and Buntie Bunnykins Sleigh Ride		
First Variation	DB4	200
Second Variation	DB81	227
Billie Bunnykins Cooling Off	DB3	199
Billy Bunnykins	D6001	197
Bogey Bunnykins	DB32	210
Bowler Bunnykins	DB145	245
Boy Skater Bunnykins		
First Variation	DB152	247
Second Variation	DB187	259
Bride Bunnykins	DB101	233
Bridesmaid Bunnykins	DB173	254
Brownie Bunnykins	DB61	220
Bunnybank	D6615	184
Buntie Bunnykins Helping Mother	DB2	199
Busy Needles Bunnykins	DB10	202

C

Carol Singer Bunnykins	DB104	234
Music Box	DB53	217
Cavalier Bunnykins	DB179	256
Cheerleader Bunnykins		
First Variation	DB142	244
Second Variation	DB143	244
Christmas Surprise Bunnykins	DB146	245
Clarinet Bunnykins	DB184	258
Clown Bunnykins		
First Variation	DB128	241
Second Variation	DB129	241
Collector Bunnykins	DB54	217
Cook Bunnykins	DB85	228
Cymbals Bunnykins		
First Variation	DB25	207
Second Variation	DB88	229
Third Variation	DB107	235

D

Daisie Bunnykins Spring Time	DB7	201
Doctor Bunnykins	DB181	257
Dollie Bunnykins Playtime		
First Variation	DB8	201
Second Variation	DB80	226
Double Bass Player Bunnykins	DB185	258
Downhill Bunnykins	DB31	210
Drum-major Bunnykins		
First Variation	DB27	208
Second Variation	DB90	230
Third Variation	DB109	236
Drummer Bunnykins		
First Variation	DB26A	207
Second Variation	DB26B	207
Third Variation	DB89	229
Fourth Variation	DB108	236

E

Easter Greetings Bunnykins	DB149	246

F

Family Photograph Bunnykins		
First Variation	DB1	199
Second Variation	DB67	222
Farmer Bunnykins	D6003	197
Father Bunnykins	DB154	248
Father, Mother and Victoria Bunnykins	DB68	222
Fireman Bunnykins		
First Variation	DB75	225
Second Variation	DB183	258
Fisherman Bunnykins		
Style One	DB84	228
Style Two	DB170	253
Footballer Bunnykins		
First Variation	DB117	237
Second Variation	DB119	238
Third Variation	DB121	238
Fourth Variation	DB123	239
Freddie Bunnykins	D6024	198
Freefall Bunnykins	DB41	213

G

Gardener Bunnykins	DB156	249
Girl Skater Bunnykins	DB153	248
Goalkeeper Bunnykins		
First Variation	DB116	237
Second Variation	DB118	237
Third Variation	DB120	238
Fourth Variation	DB122	239
Goodnight Bunnykins	DB157	249
Grandpa's Story Bunnykins	DB14	203
Groom Bunnykins	DB102	234
Guardsman Bunnykins	DB127	240

H

Halloween Bunnykins	DB132	242
Happy Birthday Bunnykins	DB21	205
Music Box	DB36	212
Harry the Herald		
First Variation	DB49	216
Second Variation	DB95	231
Third Variation	DB115	236
Home Run Bunnykins	DB43	214

I

Ice Cream Bunnykins	DB82	227
Irishman Bunnykins	DB178	256

J

Jester Bunnykins	DB161	250
Jockey Bunnykins	DB169	253
Jogging Bunnykins	DB22	206
Music Box	DB37	212
John Bull Bunnykins	DB134	243
Joker Bunnykins	DB171	254
Judge Bunnykins	DB188	259
Juggler Bunnykins	DB164	251

K

King John		
First Variation	DB45	214
Second Variation	DB91	230
Knockout Bunnykins	DB30	209

L

Lollipopman Bunnykins	DB65	221

M

Magician Bunnykins		
First Variation	DB126	240
Second Variation	DB159	250
Mary Bunnykins	D6002	197
Master Potter Bunnykins	DB131	242
Milkman Bunnykins	DB125	240
Mother and Baby Bunnykins	DB167	252
Mother Bunnykin	D6004	198
Mother Bunnykins	DB189	260
Mother's Day Bunnykins	DB155	248
Mountie Bunnykins	DB135	243
Mr. Bunnybeat Strumming	DB16	204
Music Box	DB38	212
Mr Bunnykins at the Easter Parade		
First Variation	DB18	204
Second Variation	DB51	216
Mr. Bunnykins Autumn Days	DB5	200
Mrs Bunnykins at the Easter Parade		
First Variation	DB19	205
Second Variation	DB52	217
Music Box	DB39	213
Mrs. Bunnykins Clean Sweep	DB6	200

N

New Baby Bunnykins	DB158	249
Nurse Bunnykins		
First Variation	DB74A	224
Second Variation	DB74B	224

O

Olympic Bunnykins		
First Variation	DB28A	208
Second Variation	DB28B	208
Out For a Duck Bunnykins	DB160	250

P

Paperboy Bunnykins	DB77	225
Partners in Collecting	DB151	247
Piper Bunnykins	DB191	260
Policeman Bunnykins	DB64	221
Polly Bunnykins	DB71	223
Postman Bunnykins	DB76	225
Prince Frederick		
First Variation	DB48	215
Second Variation	DB94	231
Princess Beatrice		
First Variation	DB47	215
Second Variation	DB93	231

Q

Queen Sophie		
First Variation	DB46	215
Second Variation	DB92	230

R

Rainy Day Bunnykins	DB147	246
Reggie Bunnykins	D6025	198
Ringmaster Bunnykins	DB165	252
Rise and Shine Bunnykins	DB11	202
Rock and Roll Bunnykins	DB124	239

S

Sailor Bunnykins	DB166	252
Santa Bunnykins Happy Christmas	DB17	204
Christmas Tree Ornament	DB62	220
Music Box	DB34	211
Saxaphone Player Bunnykins	DB186	259
School Days Bunnykins	DB57	218
Schoolboy Bunnykins	DB66	221
Schoolmaster Bunnykins	DB60	219
Scotsman Bunnykins	DB180	257
Seaside Bunnykins	DB177	256
Sergeant Mountie Bunnykins	DB136	243
60th Anniversary Bunnykins	DB137	244
Sleepytime Bunnykins	DB15	203
Soccer Player Bunnykins	DB123	239
Sousaphone Bunnykins		
First Variation	DB23	206
Second Variation	DB86	228
Third Variation	DB105	235
Statue of Liberty Bunnykins	DB198	261

Storytime Bunnykins
    First Variation   DB9   201
    Second Variation   DB59   219
Susan Bunnykins   DB70   223
Susan Bunnykins as Queen of the May   DB83   227
Sweetheart Bunnykins
    First Variation   DB130   241
    Second Variation   DB174   255
Sydney Bunnykins   DB195   261

T

Tally Ho! Bunnykins
    First Variation   DB12   202
    Second Variation   DB78   226
    Music Box
        First Variation   DB33A   210
        Second Variation   DB33B   211
Tom Bunnykins   DB72   223
Touchdown Bunnykins
    First Variation   DB29A   209
    Second Variation (Boston)   DB29B   209
    Third Variation (Ohio)   DB96   232
    Fourth Variation (Michigan)   DB97   232

Fifth Variation (Cincinnati)   DB98   232
Sixth Variation (Notre Dame)   DB99   233
Seventh Variation (Indiana)   DB100   233
Tourist Bunnykins   DB190   260
Trick or Treat Bunnykins   DB162   251
Trumpeter Bunnykins
    First Variation   DB24   206
    Second Variation   DB87   229
    Third Variation   DB106   235

U

Uncle Sam Bunnykins
    First Variation   DB50   216
    Second Variation   DB175   255

W

Welsh Lady Bunnykins   DB172   254
Wicketkeeper Bunnykins   DB150   247
William Bunnykins   DB69   222
William Bunnykins a Bunny in a Hurry DBR9   267
William Bunnykins Asleep in the Sun   DBR5   266
Wizard Bunnykins   DB168   253

ALPHABETICAL INDEX TO
BUNNYKINS RESIN FIGURINES

Birthday Boy   DBR17   270
Birthday Girl   DBR16   270
Father Bunnykins Home From Work DBR8   267
Father Bunnykins and Harry
    Decorating the Tree   DBR12   268
Happy Christmas   DBR14   269
    From the Bunnykins Family
Harry Bunnykins
Harry Bunnykins 'A Little Boy at Play' DBR1   265
Harry Bunnykins Playtime   DBR2   265
Lady Ratley Her Ladyship Explains DBR6   266
Mrs Bunnykins a Busy Morning Shopping DBR7   267
Mrs Bunnykins and William   DBR13   269
    The Birthday Cake

New Baby (The)   DBR18   270
Photograph Frames
    Boy   DBR20   271
    Girl   DBR21   271
Picnic Time with the Bunnykins Family DBR15   269
Reggie Bunnykins
Reginald Ratley Up To No Good   DBR3   265
Rocking Horse (The)   DBR19   271
Susan and Harry Bunnykins   DBR11   268
    Minding the Baby Brother
Susan Bunnykins the Helper   DBR4   266
Susan Bunnykins Wildlife Spotting DBR10   268
William Bunnykins A Bunny in a Hurry DBR9   267
William Bunnykins Asleep in the Sun   DBR5   266

NUMERICAL INDEX TO BUNNYKINS
EARTHENWARE FIGURINES

Model No.	Name	Page No.
D6001	Billy Bunnykin	197
D6002	Mary Bunnykin	197
D6003	Farmer Bunnykin	197
D6004	Mother Bunnykin	198
D6024	Freddie Bunnykin	198
D6025	Reggie Bunnykin	198
D6615A	Bunnybank, First Variation	184
D6615B	Bunnybank, Second Variation	184
D6966A	London City Gent Bunnykins Teapot	187
D6966B	U.S.A. President Bunnykins Teapot	187
D7027	Aussie Explorer Bunnykins Teapot	188
D7126	Japanese Bunnykins Teapot Geisha Girl	188
DB1	Family Photograph Bunnykins, First Variation	199
DB2	Buntie Bunnykins Helping Mother	199
DB3	Billie Bunnykins Cooling Off	199
DB4	Billie And Buntie Bunnykins Sleigh Ride First Variation	200
DB5	Mr. Bunnykins Autumn Days	200
DB6	Mrs. Bunnykins Clean Sweep	200
DB7	Daisie Bunnykins Spring Time	201
DB8	Dollie Bunnykins Playtime	201
DB9	Storytime Bunnykins, First Variation	201
DB10	Busy Needles Bunnykins	202
DB11	Rise and Shine Bunnykins	202
DB12	Tally Ho! Bunnykins, First Variation	202
DB13	The Artist Bunnykins	203
DB14	Grandpa's Story Bunnykins	203
DB15	Sleepytime Bunnykins	203
DB16	Mr. Bunnybeat Strumming	204
DB17	Santa Bunnykins Happy Christmas	204
DB18	Mr Bunnykins at the Easter Parade First Variation	204
DB19	Mrs Bunnykins at the Easter Parade First Variation	205
DB20	Astro Bunnykins Rocket Man	205
DB21	Happy Birthday Bunnykins	205
DB22	Jogging Bunnykins	206
DB23	Sousaphone Bunnykins, First Variation	206
DB24	Trumpeter Bunnykins, First Variation	206
DB25	Cymbals Bunnykins, First Variation	207
DB26A	Drummer Bunnykins, First Variation	207
DB26B	Drummer Bunnykins, Second Variation	207
DB27	Drum-major Bunnykins, First Variation	208
DB28A	Olympic Bunnykins, First Variation	208
DB28B	Olympic Bunnykins, Second Variation	208
DB29A	Touchdown Bunnykins, First Variation	209
DB29B	Touchdown Bunnykins, Second Variation	209
DB30	Knockout Bunnykins	209
DB31	Downhill Bunnykins	210
DB32	Bogey Bunnykins	210
DB33A	Tally Ho! Music Box, First Variation	210
DB33B	Tally Ho! Music Box, Second Variation	211
DB34	Santa Bunnykins Music Box	211
DB35	Astro Bunnykins Rocket Man Music Box	211
DB36	Happy Birthday Bunnykins Music Box	212

Model No.	Name	Page No.
DB37	Jogging Bunnykins Music Box	212
DB38	Mr. Bunnybeat Strumming Music Box	212
DB39	Mrs. Bunnykins at the Easter Parade Music Box	213
DB40	Aerobic Bunnykins	213
DB41	Freefall Bunnykins	213
DB42	Ace Bunnykins	214
DB43	Home Run Bunnykins	214
DB44	Not Issued	
DB45	King John, First Variation	214
DB46	Queen Sophie, First Variation	215
DB47	Princess Beatrice, First Variation	215
DB48	Prince Frederick, First Variation	215
DB49	Harry the Herald, First Variation	216
DB50	Uncle Sam Bunnykins, First Variation	216
DB51	Mr. Bunnykins at the Easter Parade, Second Variation	216
DB52	Mrs. Bunnykins at the Easter Parade, Second Variation	217
DB53	Carol Singer Music Box	217
DB54	Collector Bunnykins	217
DB55	Bedtime Bunnykins, First Variation	218
DB56	Be Prepared Bunnykins	218
DB57	School Days Bunnykins	218
DB58	Australian Bunnykins	219
DB59	Storytime Bunnykins, Second Variation	219
DB60	Schoolmaster Bunnykins	219
DB61	Brownie Bunnykins	220
DB62	Santa Bunnykins Happy Christmas Christmas Tree Ornament	220
DB63	Bedtime Bunnykins, Second Variation	220
DB64	Policeman Bunnykins	221
DB65	Lollipopman Bunnykins	221
DB66	Schoolboy Bunnykins	221
DB67	Family Photograph Bunnykins, Second Variation	222
DB68	Father, Mother and Victoria Bunnykins	222
DB69	William Bunnykins	222
DB70	Susan Bunnykins	223
DB71	Polly Bunnykins	223
DB72	Tom Bunnykins	223
DB73	Harry Bunnykins	224
DB74A	Nurse Bunnykins, First Variation	224
DB74B	Nurse Bunnykins, Second Variation	224
DB75	Fireman Bunnykins	225
DB76	Postman Bunnykins	225
DB77	Paperboy Bunnykins	225
DB78	Tally Ho! Bunnykins, Second Variation	226
DB79	Bedtime Bunnykins, Third Variation	226
DB80	Dollie Bunnykins Playtime, Second Variation	226
DB81	Billie and Buntie Bunnykins Sleigh Ride, Second Variation	227
DB82	Ice Cream Bunnykins	227
DB83	Susan Bunnykins as Queen of the May	227
DB84	Fisherman Bunnykins, Style One	228
DB85	Cook Bunnykins	228

Model No.	Name	Page No.
DB86	Sousaphone Bunnykins, Second Variation	228
DB87	Trumpeter Bunnykins, Second Variation	229
DB88	Cymbals Bunnykins, Second Variation	229
DB89	Drummer Bunnykins, Third Variation	229
DB90	Drum-major Bunnykins, Second Variation	230
DB91	King John, Second Variation	230
DB92	Queen Sophie, Second Variation	230
DB93	Princess Beatrice, Second Variation	231
DB94	Prince Frederick, Second Variation	231
DB95	Harry the Herald, Second Variation	231
DB96	Touchdown Bunnykins, Third Variation	232
DB97	Touchdown Bunnykins, Fourth Variation	232
DB98	Touchdown Bunnykins, Fifth Variation	232
DB99	Touchdown Bunnykins, Sixth Variation	233
DB100	Touchdown Bunnykins, Seventh Variation	233
DB101	Bride Bunnykins	233
DB102	Groom Bunnykins	234
DB103	Bedtime Bunnykins, Fourth Variation	234
DB104	Carol Singer Bunnykins	234
DB105	Sousaphone Bunnykins, Third Variation	235
DB106	Trumpeter Bunnykins, Third Variation	235
DB107	Cymbals Bunnykins, Third Variation	235
DB108	Drummer Bunnykins, Fourth Variation	236
DB109	Drum-major Bunnykins, Third Variation	236
DB110 to DB114 Not issued		
DB115	Harry the Herald, Third Variation	236
DB116	Goalkeeper Bunnykins, First Variation	237
DB117	Footballer Bunnykins, First Variation	237
DB118	Goalkeeper Bunnykins, Second Variation	237
DB119	Footballer Bunnykins, Second Variation	238
DB120	Goalkeeper Bunnykins, Third Variation	238
DB121	Footballer Bunnykins, Third Variation	238
DB122	Goalkeeper Bunnykins (4th Variation	239
DB123	Soccer Player Bunnykins	239
DB124	Rock and Roll Bunnykins	239
DB125	Milkman Bunnykins	240
DB126	Magician Bunnykins	240
DB127	Guardsman Bunnykins	240
DB128	Clown Bunnykins, First Variation	241
DB129	Clown Bunnykins, Second Variation	241
DB130	Sweetheart Bunnykins, First Variation	241
DB131	Master Potter Bunnykins	242
DB132	Halloween Bunnykins	242
DB133	Aussie Surfer Bunnykins	242
DB134	John Bull Bunnykins	243
DB135	Mountie Bunnykins	243
DB136	Sergeant Mountie Bunnykins	243
DB137	60th Anniversary Bunnykins	244
DB142	Cheerleader Bunnykins, First Variation	244
DB143	Cheerleader Bunnykins, Second Variation	244

Model No.	Name	Page No.
DB144	Batsman Bunnykins	245
DB145	Bowler Bunnykins	245
DB146	Christmas Surprise Bunnykins	245
DB147	Rainy Day Bunnykins	246
DB148	Bathtime Bunnykins	246
DB149	Easter Greetings Bunnykins	246
DB150	Wicketkeeper Bunnykins	247
DB151	Partners in Collecting	247
DB152	Boy Skater Bunnykins, First Variation	247
DB153	Girl Skater Bunnykins	248
DB154	Father Bunnykins	248
DB155	Mother's Day Bunnykins	248
DB156	Gardener Bunnykins	249
DB157	Goodnight Bunnykins	249
DB158	New Baby Bunnykins	249
DB159	Magician Bunnykins	250
DB160	Out For a Duck	250
DB161	Jester Bunnykins	250
DB162	Trick or Treat Bunnykins	251
DB163	Beefeater Bunnykins	251
DB164	Juggler Bunnykins	251
DB165	Ringmaster Bunnykins	252
DB166	Sailor Bunnykins	252
DB167	Mother and Baby Bunnykins	252
DB168	Wizard Bunnykins	253
DB169	Jockey Bunnykins	253
DB170	Fisherman Bunnykins, Style Two	253
DB171	Joker Bunnykins	254
DB172	Welsh Lady Bunnykins	254
DB173	Bridesmaid Bunnykins	254
DB174	Sweetheart Bunnykins, Second Variation	255
DB175	Uncle Sam Bunnykins, Second Variation	255
DB176	Ballerina Bunnykins	255
DB177	Seaside Bunnykins	256
DB178	Irishman Bunnykins	256
DB179	Cavalier Bunnykins	256
DB180	Scotsman Bunnykins	257
DB181	Doctor Bunnykins	257
DB182	Banjo Bunnykins	257
DB183	Fireman Bunnykins, Second Variation	258
DB184	Clarinet Player Bunnykins	258
DB185	Double Bass Player Bunnykins	258
DB186	Saxaphone Player Bunnykins	259
DB187	Boy Skater Bunnykins, Second Variation	259
DB188	Judge Bunnykins	259
DB189	Mother Bunnykins	260
DB190	Tourist Bunnykins	260
DB191	Piper Bunnykins	260
DB195	Sydney Bunnykins	261
DB198	Statue of Liberty Bunnykins	261

NUMERICAL INDEX TO
BUNNYKINS RESIN SERIES

Model No.		Page No.
DBR1	Harry Bunnykins A Little Bunny At Play	265
DBR2	Harry Bunnykins Playtime	265
DBR3	Reginald Ratley Up To No Good	265
DBR4	Susan Bunnykins The Helper	266
DBR5	William Bunnykins Asleep In The Sun	266
DBR6	Lady Ratley Her Ladyship Explains	266
DBR7	Mrs. Bunnykins A Busy Morning Shopping	267
DBR8	Father Bunnykins Home From Work	267
DBR9	William Bunnykins A Bunny In A Hurry	267
DBR10	Susan Bunnykins Wildlife Spotting	268
DBR11	Susan and Harry Bunnykins Minding The Baby Brother	268
DBR12	Father Bunnykins and Harry Decorating The Tree	268

Model No.		Page No.
DBR13	Mrs. Bunnykins and William The Birthday Cake	269
DBR14	Happy Christmas From the Bunnykins Family	269
DBR15	Picnic Time With the Bunnykins Family	269
DBR16	Birthday Girl	270
DBR17	Birthday Boy	270
DBR18	The New Baby	270
DBR19	The Rocking Horse	271
DBR20	Photograph Frame - Girl	271
DBR21	Photograph Frame - Boy	271

290

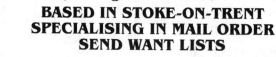